A BIOGRAPHY OF THE SEA

A BIOGRAPHY
OF THE SEA

*The story of the world ocean,
its animal and plant populations, and
its influence on human history*

Richard Carrington

BASIC BOOKS, INC.
New York

FOR PANTHER

CONTENTS

CONTENTS

PART III: MAN AND THE SEA

PLATES

ix

PLATES

DRAWINGS,
MAPS AND DIAGRAMS

xiii

PREFACE

I HAVE tried in this book to tell the reader something of the life story of the most majestic and challenging physical phenomenon on the earth's surface. The sea, although not literally 'alive', is a dynamic entity, and I therefore hope that the use of the term 'biography' in the title will not seem too much out of place. I have anyway interpreted it in the widest possible sense, and have included not only a summary of the history of the sea and the evolution of marine life through geological time, but also a good deal of general information concerning the sea as a physical feature of the earth, and the way it has influenced the lives of men.

The result is necessarily a work of synthesis, and no pretensions are made to originality of subject matter; nor, in such a vast field, can there be any attempt at completeness. The book is mainly a straightforward record of what I felt to be the most interesting, significant and exciting facts. But its existence will only be justified if, in presenting these facts, I have managed to convey to the reader something of my own feeling for the mystery and wonder of the sea.

A word must be said about documentation. I have listed the main sources of my facts in the bibliography, which appears between pages 263 and 276, and numbered quotations and any statement requiring authoritative support in square brackets in the text. These numbers refer to the key to biliographical references on pages 261-2, where I have followed the standard international practice of simply giving the author's name, the date of the work referred to and, where appropriate, a page reference. The full name of the book or paper can then be found by reference to the bibliography. It is hoped that this plan will enable specialists to follow up any point that particularly interests them, while allowing the layman to read the book straight through without distraction. I have not attempted to eliminate scientific names and terms where these are necessary to a proper understanding of the story, for I believe that no intelligent person would wish to be condescended to in this way. On the other hand, where a popular name exists, it is always given as well as its scientific equivalent, and technical terms are never used without explanation.

As in the past, I am extremely grateful to the authorities who have read the whole or part of the manuscript and helped me to make the information as reliable as possible. These are: Dr Angus Bellairs, Reader in Anatomy at St Mary's Hospital Medical School, London; Mr Ronald Currie of the National Institute of Oceanography at Wormley; Dr F. C. Fraser, Keeper of Zoology at the British Museum (Natural History); Mr N. A. Holme of the Marine Biological Association of the United Kingdom at Plymouth; Mr N. B. Marshall of the Department of Zoology, British Museum (Natural History); Dr L. Harrison Matthews, Scientific Director of the Zoological Society of London; Dr W. E. Swinton, Deputy Keeper of Palaeontology at the British Museum (Natural History); and Dr H. Gwynne Vevers, Curator of the Aquarium, Zoological Society of London. For any blunders that have escaped the scrutiny of these experts, I only am to blame.

My thanks are also due to Mr Maurice Wilson for undertaking most of the original line drawings and for his excellent reconstructions of some of the sea animals of the past, and to Mr Denys Baker, who drew or adapted many of the maps and diagrams. Acknowledgements for photographs are made to the following: Mt Everest Foundation, Plate 1a; Camera Press Ltd, Plates 1b, 4a, 4b, 15a; National Institute of Oceanography, Plates 2a, 2b, 3a, 3b, 5b, 10a, 18b, 28b, 29b; Australian High Commissioner, Plate 5a; Frank Lane, Plates 6a, 6b, 8a, 15b, 17b, 18a, 19a, 19b, 23a, 27a, 27b; Paul Popper, Plates 7a, 7b, 8b, 10b, 10c, 11a, 11b, 11c, 14a, 14b, 17a, 22b, 23b, 29a; Musée de Monaco, Plates 9a, 9b; Trustees of the National Maritime Museum, Plates 24b, 26a, 28a; National Maritime Museum, Greenwich Hospital Collection, Plates 24a, 24d; Radio Times Hulton Picture Library, Plates 24c, 30a, 30b, 31a, 31b; U.S. Navy Electronics Laboratory, San Diego, Plate 26b; Trustees of the British Museum, Plate 32a; Trustees of the National Gallery, London, Plate 32b.

The manuscript was typed by Mary Eden, the only person, including the author, who could decipher it. For this, and everything else she does, I am deeply grateful.   R. C.

London, 1960

PART I
THE WORLD OCEAN

Chapter One

EARTH AND SEA

A TRAVELLER from the outer universe, approaching our globe for the first time, might well halt his space ship for a while some thousands of miles from his goal to see what he could learn by observation of the new territory ahead of him. From behind the plate-glass window of his cabin, he would watch and wonder while the rotating earth revealed to him the complex patterns of her face. If he had happened to pause on the plane of the equator he would see the majestic procession of continents and oceans passing across the surface of the sphere. If he then moved his ship towards the extremities of the earth's axis he would discern, through gaps in the clouds, the radiance of the polar ice-caps. And when, sated with the splendour of these spectacles, he gave the order to make a closer approach, his wonder would soon be reawakened by the grandly sculptured relief of the continental masses and the rhythmic movements of the waves on the surface of the sea.

The lay-out of the world ocean, as well as its emotional appeal, can best be appreciated from the viewpoint of such a cosmic observer. As land animals, we are too apt to think of the physical features of the earth in the narrow context of our own environment. Our maps encourage us in this conceit, as can be seen by turning the pages of the atlas and noting the relative importance attached to sea and land. Yet the sea is not only far vaster than the land, and supports a far greater number of living organisms, but can even claim to be the source of life itself. If it were not for the watery covering of the earth, and the complicated processes that have taken place in it during more than 1,000 million years of evolution, neither you nor I nor any other living thing would ever have existed.

A few statistics may help us understand something of the sea's immensity. The surface of the earth is about 197 million square miles in extent. Of this area no less than 139 million square miles, or about 71 per cent, is covered by water. The volume of the sea defies comprehension, being some 330 million cubic

3

miles; the volume of all the land above sea level is about fifteen times less, being only 23 million cubic miles. If the water of all the oceans were poured into gigantic cube-shaped vessels measuring a mile in each direction, these vessels, if laid end to end, would span the distance between the earth and the sun nearly four times. The land above sea level, cut into cubes of equal size, would only reach one-quarter of the distance to the sun.

Naturally the ocean basins containing this enormous quantity of water must be of correspondingly vast proportions, but here there is a discrepancy between average and maximum depth and height when the sea is compared with the land. At the time of writing, the greatest known depth of the ocean, which occurs in the Marianas Trench in the Pacific Ocean, is 37,800 feet, or about 7 miles. This is not so very much more than the height of the world's highest mountain, Mount Everest, which is 29,002 feet high, or about 5½ miles. When the over-all average is considered, however, the sea is an easy winner. The average depth of the ocean basins is about 12,600 feet, whereas the average height of the land is only 2,300 feet. As these figures show, if all the exposed land were sliced off at sea level and crammed into the ocean basins, the floors of the sea would still be covered by water to an average depth of nearly two miles.

But although the sea is far vaster than the exposed surface of the land, and occupies a much larger area of the earth's surface, its proportions are insignificant when compared with the bulk of the earth itself. The greatest depth of the ocean is only a fraction of the thickness of the earth's solid crust, which extends to a depth of some seventy miles. Even the huge volume of the sea is negligible in comparison with the volume of the earth, which is no less than 260 thousand million cubic miles. From a geological point of view, therefore, the earth's liquid mantle represents no more than a thin film of moisture clinging to the surface of a football.

This liquid mantle is known to geophysicists as the 'hydrosphere', and is one of the four great natural zones, into which our earth is divided. The others are the gaseous envelope surrounding the earth, known as the atmosphere; the solid rocks of the crust, known as the lithosphere; and the inaccessible regions of the interior, known as the centrosphere. Strictly speaking the hydrosphere includes the lakes and rivers as well as the sea, but here we are only concerned with that part of it which comprises the great ocean basins and their offshoots. Before going further we must look at the lay-out of these features rather more closely.

One of the facts that must immediately strike us when we study a map of the earth is that the arrangement of land and sea follows a distinctive and intriguing pattern. Broadly speaking, the great land masses are confined to the northern hemisphere, whereas the southern hemisphere is mainly occupied by sea. The land in the southern hemisphere consists principally of the Antarctic continent, and three offshoots of the northern land mass which project southward as gigantic peninsulas. Two of these peninsulas, South America and South Africa, are continuous with the northern land mass, even though the connections are tenuous. The third, which ends at the southern tip of Tasmania, is not a true peninsula, for it is intersected in places by sea; it is nevertheless comparable to the others in forming a demarcation line between two of the earth's major oceans.

The number of oceans on the earth's surface is variously given as from three to seven by different writers. This underlines the fact that the boundaries between the oceans are largely artificial, and the sea must be thought of as a continuous whole. Nevertheless, certain dividing lines, however arbitrary, must be recognized if it is to be intelligibly described.

It is now time to return to our cosmic observer, and see how the oceans would look to him from his special point of vantage. As the earth rotated beneath his gaze his attention would probably first be drawn by the ocean we know as the Pacific, which is the largest continuous expanse of water on the earth's surface. With his space ship on the plane of the equator, and hovering midway between the East Indies and the coast of Ecuador, he would observe that the greater part of this side of the globe is covered by water. With the exception of Australia, the fringes of the Asiatic, North American and Antarctic continents, and a few scattered islands, no land would be visible to alter the general impression of a water hemisphere.

But waiting until the planet had rotated some 120 degrees, the prospect before him would be very different. Towards the

5

north pole, the earth's surface would consist entirely of land; in the opposite, or southerly, direction there would be a great gulf, enclosed on three sides, but stretching away on the fourth to the borders of Antarctica. The waters of this gulf would be what we know as the Indian Ocean.

After rotating another 100 degrees, the earth would reveal yet another facet of her ocean mantle. Our observer would see an ocean running north and south between the great land masses of America on the one side, and Europe and Africa on the other. It would be bounded in the north by the shores of Greenland, and in the south by the ice fringing the Antarctic continent, it would be compressed in the middle between Cape de São Roque in Brazil, and Cape Verde on the western coast of Africa. This wasp-waisted ocean would be the Atlantic, the second largest expanse of water in the world.

These three great oceans – the Atlantic, the Pacific and the Indian – together comprise the greater part of the earth's liquid covering. But to complete the picture we must also mention the Arctic Ocean, which covers the north pole, and much of which is permanently frozen, and the Antarctic, or Southern Ocean which washes the ice-bound shores of Antarctica. Incidentally, the former is sometimes regarded simply as an extension of the Atlantic, and the latter as an extension of the Atlantic, Pacific and Indian Oceans. The reader may decide for himself where he is going to draw the line, for, as I have said, the open sea knows no exact geographical boundaries. My own view is that it is simplest to regard the waters of the earth as being divided into five main oceans, each possessing certain limited extensions in the form of bays, gulfs and seas.

Now what of the aspect of the earth's crust in those mysterious regions lying beneath the surface of the universal sea? Here the reader might suspect that we should be figuratively, as well as literally, in deep water, for even the most ardent of underwater explorers has not so far succeeded in penetrating to the sea bed either to a sufficient depth or for sufficiently long to learn much by visual observation. But fortunately the resources of science have come to our aid in the matter, and it is really remarkable to what extent the sea bed is now known, at least where its relief is concerned.

Before I describe some of the techniques by which these discoveries are made, let us imagine ourselves equipped with a super-submarine, such as that commanded by Captain Nemo in Jules Verne's *Twenty Thousand Leagues under the Sea*, and make a preliminary tour of the ocean floor. Leaving the shore behind us, and heading for the open ocean, we should first of all follow that part of the sea bed known as the 'continental shelf'. This extends outwards from all the lands of the earth for an average distance of 30 miles. If our voyage had begun on a coast backed by broad lowlands the shelf might extend much further than this, its width running into several hundreds of miles, whereas if we had started from a mountainous coast, there might be only a very narrow shelf, or even no shelf at all. In north-western Europe, for example, the shelf would be fairly broad, for here it not only supports the whole of the British Isles and the North Sea, but extends some 200 miles westward from Land's End; off western South America, on the other hand, it would be practically non-existent, for in this region the steep slopes of the Andes range plunge directly into the Pacific to a depth of 20,000 feet. This last phenomenon is extremely rare, however, and off the majority of coasts we should find the shelf sloped so gradually (about 1 in 500) that the angle of decline was scarcely perceptible. Its surface, we should observe, was generally smooth, although certain irregularities might occur, such as hills and depressions, or terraces lying for the most part at right angles to the path of our advancing craft.

After some time there would be an abrupt change in the character of the land beneath us. In most regions, this would occur when we had reached a depth of between 500 and 700 feet. The gentle incline of the shelf would here suddenly increase, and we should find ourselves poised on the brink of a steep slope dropping away into the depths below.

The name of this feature of the sea bed is the 'continental slope', and it occupies an area about three times as great as the continental shelf. Although the angle of descent is at first extremely abrupt, it becomes less so as the sea bottom is approached. To give an example, the average incline of the continental slope off the eastern seaboard of North America is about 1 in 10. This represents a very gentle slope near the floor of the sea, but a slope of 1 in 6, or even more, towards the top. The slope itself is in general less regular than the shelf, and may be gashed by canyons as rugged and dramatic as anything to be seen on the surface of the earth above sea level.

Beyond the base of the continental slopes we should begin to traverse the sombre landscape of the abyss. No sunlight penetrates to these gloomy regions, and the only bright objects we should see would be the bodies of luminescent animals.

It was once thought that these deepest floors of the sea were largely flat, but this view has had to be revised. Soundings made in the oceans of the world, and particularly the Atlantic, where much work has been done in connection with submarine telegraph cables, show that the sea bed varies greatly in depth from place to place. Yet the topography of the abyss bears little resemblance to that of the exposed surface of the continents. Although in most regions it is too far from the coasts to be affected by the rocky sediments carried by rivers and off-shore currents, which seldom travel further than the continental slopes, much of the bottom is concealed beneath a carpet of organic oozes. These are composed of the remains of tiny marine plants and animals which live near the surface of the sea and sink when they die to the ocean floor. The ooze-covered slopes of the abyss do not have the sharply sculptured outlines of the mountain ranges on dry land. Even where the oceans vary greatly in depth, the slopes between the different levels are so gradual that the eye would hardly discern them. There are exceptions to this rule, however, such as submarine volcanoes, which sometimes rear their cone-like shapes from the sea bed at an angle of 35 degrees. Some of these reach nearly to the surface, where they form dangerous shoals; others actually project above the waves as islands. Bermuda in the Atlantic, Christmas Island in the Indian Ocean, and Hawaii in the Pacific are all examples of islands formed by submarine volcanoes.

Apart from these abrupt and dramatic elevations, the abyss has many other large-scale topographical features. One example is the submarine ridge, corresponding to a mountain range, which runs down the centre of the Atlantic and divides it into two gigantic basins; others are the trenches, between five and seven miles deep, which lie off the coasts of Japan, the Philippines and Puerto Rico.

But even if the sun's rays could penetrate to the sea bottom and illuminate the landscape outside the portholes of our super-submarine, we should not be particularly impressed by what we saw. The slimy ooze, or the accumulated skeletons of larger marine animals, would cover everything as with a shroud, and the gentler slopes would offer little variety of shape or texture to divert the eye. We should find that the general configuration of the ocean floor could not be so easily grasped on the spot as from a diagram, such as that shown in the figure below. This represents a 'profile' of the South Atlantic ocean bed between the South Shetlands and Bouvet Island, based on the results of over 1,300 soundings. An actual voyage along this segment of the sea bottom would not give us nearly such a

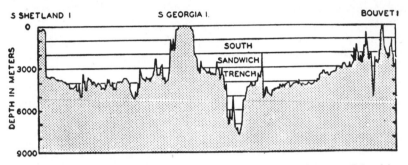

Profile of the ocean bed between the South Shetlands and Bouvet Island in the South Atlantic. *After Sverdrup, Johnson and Fleming* (1942), *p.* 18.

clear idea of its contours. In a diagram, the horizontal scale can be so compressed in relation to the vertical that differences of relief which would be hardly noticeable on the spot become easy to appreciate.

The technique of sounding the ocean bed has now evolved into an exact science, but this is a fairly recent development. The first clear reference to deep sounding in the literature of the sea occurs in a note in the log book of Magellan's voyage round the earth in 1519–21. This tells how the navigator tried to measure the depth of the Pacific between the islands of St Paul and Tiburones with six ordinary sounding lines tied together; he did not strike bottom, and therefore rather rashly concluded that he had discovered the deepest spot in the ocean.

Magellan's sounding lines were probably made of hempen rope, marked in fathoms, with a metal weight attached to the end. Lines of this type were the main ones used up to the beginning of the nineteenth century, when the United States navy began using thinner lines made of twine. The twine was not sufficiently strong to lift a weight to the surface, so when the sinker hit bottom the line was cut; the depth was then determined by subtracting the length of the twine left on the drum from the known total length of the whole line. In 1854 an improvement was introduced by an American midshipman named Brooke, who devised a method for detaching the weight from the end of the twine, so that the whole line could be recovered. Still another improvement was made by the British physicist Lord Kelvin, who substituted piano wire for the twine, and this was used to sound depths down to 34,000 feet.

The modern method of sounding is by means of a sonic depth-finder, which dispenses with the need for reeling in and out long lengths of twine and wire altogether. A signal is sent out from the bottom of the ship, and its echo from the ocean bed is recorded by a sensitive receiving apparatus. As the speed of sound in water is known, the depth of the sea below the ship can be simply calculated from the time elapsing between the emission of the signal and the reception of its echo.

The reader may feel that, before concluding this chapter, I should say something about the nature of the rocks composing the sea bed. Unfortunately, little is known of this subject, the main reason being the immense difficulty of obtaining specimens. A machine has to be devised that will extract a sample of solid rock at depths of anything up to six miles; the surface of the rock will probably also be blanketed with the thick layer of slimy organic ooze mentioned above. The expense of producing a specialized machine of this kind, and then mounting an expedition to use it, would be sufficient to daunt even the most enthusiastic devotee of science. Nevertheless an approach has been made to the problem in recent years, and dredging operations off the British coast and off southern California have not been unsuccessful. As long ago as 1929 the French geologist Dangeard demonstrated the presence of rocks dating from the Age of the Dinosaurs on the bed of the Bristol Channel, while in 1948 W. B. R. King made similar discoveries off the Isle of Wight.

Recent operations conducted from *Discovery II* and other

research ships have succeeded in obtaining specimens from much deeper waters, and we may hope that improved techniques will eventually allow scientists to build up a representative collection of rock specimens from many different parts of the abyss.

Chapter Two

THE ORIGIN OF THE
OCEAN BASINS

IN the previous chapter I tried to give the reader a general picture of the arrangement of the earth's continents and oceans, and of what scientists have deduced about the nature of the sea bed. At this point it would be possible to go straight on to a more detailed consideration of the sea itself, but this would be to omit one important problem. Why are the continents and ocean basins arranged as they are?

This is a very awkward question, and the simple answer to it is that we do not know. On the other hand, like all mysteries, it has stimulated several intriguing theories, and inspired at least one of the great poetic hypotheses of earth science. To appreciate the relative value of these explanations it will be necessary to make a brief excursion into cosmology.

I have summarized in my book *A Guide to Earth History* (Chapter 2) some of the suggestions that men have made to account for the earth's origin and present form. Here it will only be necessary to consider how certain assumptions of these hypotheses could have affected the dynamic behaviour of the crust.

The most popular hypothesis assumes that the earth began as a large mass of incandescent star material, which gradually cooled and shrunk until it reached a partly solid state. The source of this material is variously regarded as the sun or some other star, but such considerations are irrelevant here. The important point is that the hypothesis requires us to regard the behaviour of the earth's crust as largely due to the stresses and strains set up by the cooling and shrinking of the interior. In other words, the earth can be compared to a gradually desiccating orange, whose skin has become wrinkled as its centre has slowly shrunk.

The main alternative theory, put forward in the early years of this century by two American scientists, T. C. Chamberlin and F. R. Moulton, suggests that the earth was originally a bolt of gas ejected from the face of the sun by tidal forces. Smaller whisps of gas were released at the same time, and these rapidly condensed into solid bodies known as planetesimals. The earth-bolt attracted the planetesimals by its larger gravitational force, and, far from being a shrinking body, our planet reached its present size by a process of accretion.

It is obvious that these two different concepts must lead to different interpretations of the origin of the continents and the ocean basins. We will deal first with the planetesimal hypothesis which, although now discredited, was the inspiration of quite an intriguing theory of how such major features of the earth's crust were formed.

We must picture, first, the earth-nucleus orbiting through space, collecting planetesimals on the way. These would have come in at different angles, some striking the earth in the direction of its rotation, thus imparting extra momentum to it, others in the reverse direction, thus acting as a brake. It is possible, of course, that the effects of these impacts might always have been so evenly balanced that they would have cancelled out; but Chamberlin thought it reasonable to assume that this would not have been the case, and that the incoming planetesimals would therefore have sometimes accelerated and sometimes retarded the speed of the earth's rotation. As a result of this oscillation in speed there would have been a tendency for the earth to undergo a corresponding change in shape. During periods of fast rotation the polar regions would have become more flattened and the equatorial regions would have showed an increased bulge. During periods of slow rotation this effect would have been diminished. The result of such tendencies would have been to set up lines of stress in the earth-body, just as the body of an athlete is subjected to different stresses and strains according to the energy, speed and direction of his movements. These lines of stress were called by Chamberlin 'yield-tracts' and, as the name implies, they were the places where the earth would tend to give, or 'yield', as a result of changes in its rotational speed.

Now the response of bodies to stress obeys certain laws, and Chamberlin knew that the behaviour of a rotating sphere under such conditions would be roughly predictable. A common response would be for the sphere to crack along three lines radiating from the poles at angles of approximately 120 degrees. These lines would run to the zone of least stress, called by Chamberlin the 'fulcrum-zone', which occurs about two-thirds of the way to the equatorial circumference in each hemisphere. Further stress lines would link the northern and southern zones, so that the sphere could be divided into a number of stable quadrilateral shapes separated by yield tracts. Without going into further complications, it was found that when these principles were applied to the earth, the yield tracts coincided to a remarkable extent with the pattern formed by the continents and ocean basins. It seemed at least possible, therefore, that these great terrestial features were the result of earth movements along the yield tracts in the early stages of our planet's history.

This theory of the origin of the ocean basins may strike the modern reader as more ingenious than plausible, but it caused a great stir at the time and is therefore historically important. Today the various hypotheses based on the conception of a cooling and shrinking earth have found greater favour, and the more important of these must now be summarized.

Nearly all the hypotheses are broadly agreed that the ocean basins appeared as the result of two main causes. The first was the 'sorting out' of rocks of different densities which occurred during the solidification of the earth's crust. The second was the interplay of forces in the interior of the shrinking earth, which caused revolutionary changes in the relief.

To explain this further, let us begin by imagining our earth in the very earliest stages of its history, some four thousand million years ago. Torn from its parent, whether this was the sun or some other star, by a great cosmic force, it would have begun circling in its orbit as a brilliant ball of incandescent gas. As cooling occurred, the gaseous earth would first have become molten, and then, after a comparatively short period, the solid crust would have begun to form. This would not have appeared in a single sheet like ice on a pond, for the molten interior was composed of many different substances, and these would have solidified into rock at different rates. There would have been a tendency for the lighter rocks to float to the surface, and the heavier ones to sink down towards the core.

When we reach the point where the crust was not only complete over the whole surface of the sphere, but had also solidified to a depth of several miles, we should expect to find that the different rocks had separated into layers, with the lighter ones on top and the denser ones below. This, in fact, is what occurred. On the earth today, the lighter rocks, consisting mainly of granite and granodiorite, are superimposed on a much thicker layer of heavy rocks, such as basalt. Beneath the basalt again is a layer of peridotite, which has a greater density still. The lighter rocks at the surface are known as 'sial', the heavier rocks below, both basalt and peridotite, as 'sima'. The two words were coined by the great Austrian geologist Suess, the first representing Si for silicon and Al for aluminium, the second Si for silicon and Ma for magnesium, these being the commonest elements believed to exist in the layers.

Thus, our picture of the earth shortly after the formation of the crust is of a very hot molten mass enclosed in a uniform double skin of sial and sima. Why did this skin not remain uniform, instead of becoming corrugated into continental plateaux and ocean basins? Here the supporters of the hot earth theory invoke the second of the two influences mentioned above. The corrugations, they say, were the result of the contraction of the cooling sphere. As the molten material below the crust grew smaller in volume with loss of heat, great stresses were set up in the crust itself. These caused it to warp, buckle and subside on a grand terrestial scale. The parts that buckled upwards formed the continents, those that were depressed became the ocean basins.

It seems likely that some such-process must have occurred, but its actual mechanism remains obscure, and the picture is additionally complicated by certain geological facts. The most important is that sial and sima are not distributed today in anything like equal proportions over the face of the earth. In fact, we find, very significantly, that the sial layer either becomes very attenuated, or else ceases altogether, at a point roughly corresponding with the fringes of the continents, and that the ocean floors consist very largely of sima.*

* This, incidentally, is not known by direct sampling of the floors themselves, owing to the difficulties referred to in the previous chapter; it is deduced from such evidence as the behaviour of earthquake waves and the nature of the extrusions from submarine and coastal volcanoes.

Numerous theories have been put forward to explain this interesting fact, but I shall only have space here to mention very few of them. One of the most interesting is that proposed by the Dutch geologist J. H. F. Umbgrove. Umbgrove suggested that, due to the action of forces inside the earth, the original uniform layer of sial was crowded together and piled up on one side to form primeval continents. The underlying sima was thus exposed over vast tracts of the earth's surface, particularly in the region now covered by the Pacific Ocean, where there is no sialic layer at all. The continents were at first arranged asymetrically, but drifted at an early stage into their present more balanced positions. In doing so parts of them became stretched, and thus left behind the thin layer of sial now known to cover parts of the floor of the Indian and Atlantic Oceans.

The great exposure of sima on the floor of the Pacific has led to some intriguing theories of the origin of this ocean basin. It has even been suggested that it represents a gigantic scar left in the crust by the breaking away of matter to form the moon. This attractive hypothesis was first put forward in the eighties of the last century by Professor George Darwin of Cambridge. The cause of the event cannot be properly understood without the use of mathematical technicalities, but, briefly, it is believed that a tidal wave was formed on the surface of the molten earth by a combination of the magnetic attraction of the sun and the free oscillation of the earth's body; this wave eventually rose so high that its crest broke away altogether and began circling the earth as a satellite. This satellite, which we know as the moon, was composed mainly of the earth's surface material; in other words it contained a large proportion of sial. Conversely, the crater left behind on the crust was denuded of sial, a condition which the floor of the Pacific is now known to fulfil.

Investigation of the materials of the moon has confirmed the prediction that it must be largely composed of sial. But not every authority will accept this, or the other supporting evidence that has come to light, as being conclusive. Umbgrove in particular has suggested reasons why the theory may not be true. He has pointed out that the origin of the moon from a tide of this kind could not have occurred unless the surface of the earth was still in a fairly free-flowing condition. That it actually was so is confirmed by the spherical outline of the moon, for unless its material had been fully molten at the time of its origin, its gravity would have been insufficient to pull it into this regular shape. This being so, it is difficult to see why the sial remnants on the earth should have kept their form as steep-sided continental blocks. One would have expected that the far stronger gravitational force of the earth would soon have flattened out the irregularities, and drawn the remaining sial over the Pacific scar to create a new, uniform mantle.

The most poetic theory of the origin of continents and oceans is mainly associated with the name of the Austrian geologist Alfred Lothar Wegener, although the American Frank B. Taylor and the South African Alexander Du Toit also played an important part in its development. It is known as 'the dis-placement theory', or, more popularly, as 'continental drift'. In recent years the theory has been much criticized, and it is now certain that many of its details will have to be modified. Nevertheless it remains the most imaginative approach made to the problem during the present century.

Wegener observed that there was a remarkable conformity between the margins of several of the continents, almost as though, if pushed together, they would interlock like the pieces of a jig-saw puzzle. The most obvious example was the eastern coast of the Americas and the western coast of Africa. If we look at a globe (this is better than an atlas, where the world is often shown on Mercator's projection, which introduces mis-leading distortions) we cannot fail to notice that the easterly bulge of South America fits into the Gulf of Guinea, and that the curved eastern seaboard of the United States corresponds very well with the coast of north-west Africa and western Europe. In the South Atlantic it can even be noticed that the bays and projections on one side of the ocean correspond almost exactly with the projections and bays on the other.

These facts led Wegener to believe that the two continents had once directly adjoined one another, or perhaps even formed a single global land mass, and had later drifted apart. Going on this assumption, he began to consider how the other land masses of the earth might have fitted into the same great continental block. The result was the series of maps overleaf, which are reproduced from his book *The Origin of Continents*

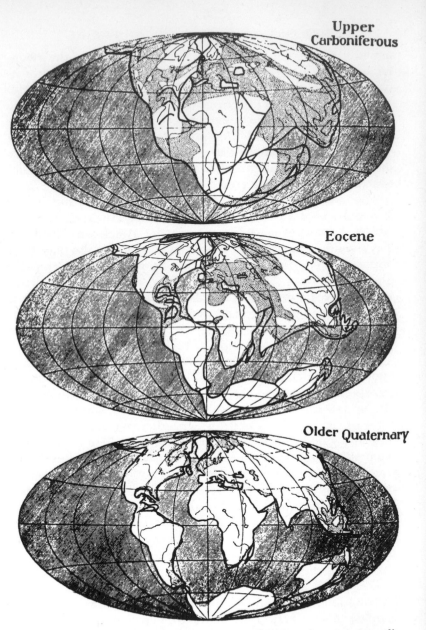

Upper Carboniferous

Eocene

Older Quaternary

Three stages in the origin of the modern continents and oceans, according to A. L. Wegener's displacement theory. The upper map shows the possible geography of the earth some 230 million years ago, the others some 60 million and one million years ago respectively. *Reproduced by permission of Messrs. Methuen & Co. Ltd.*

and Oceans. The first shows the ancestral continent, which Wegener called Pangaea, as it might have looked some 230 million years ago. The two lower maps show it in process of disintegration, the continental fragments slowly drifting towards the positions they occupy today.

Wegener believed, like Umbgrove, that at some point in the earth's history its uniform sialic layer had become crowded up on one side. This was the origin of Pangaea. He suggested that this mass of sial floated on the denser sima below, rather as a piece of cardboard would float on treacle. When it disintegrated, the horizontal movement of the fragments caused their forward edges to buckle. This was the origin of such high coastal ranges as the Andes and the Rocky Mountains.

The theory has a grand and poetic simplicity which in itself almost persuades us that it must be true. It is open, however, to several serious objections. Only one of these need be mentioned here. Wegener believed that the drift had begun in quite recent times (geologically speaking 230 million years is not a particularly long period) and was still continuing. During the period of drift, therefore, the crust of the earth must have been fully solidified. Now, even if we assume, as Wegener did, a considerable plasticity in the underlying earth materials (which would have been necessary for drifting to occur at all), the resistance to horizontal movement on the suggested scale must have been enormous. There is no known force that would have been capable of causing such large-scale movements in the given conditions.

Many other theories have been put forward to account for the origin of the ocean basins, but none is any more satisfactory than the foregoing. We can sum up by saying that the Pacific basin is probably the oldest, being perhaps a primeval scar on the earth's crust, and that the others could have come into existence at a somewhat later period through the disintegration of an ancestral continental block. Further than that we cannot go. No episode in the biography of the sea is more mysterious than the origin of the depressions in which it lies.

Chapter Three

THE CHANGING PATTERNS
OF SEA AND LAND

ALTHOUGH the origin of the ocean basins is still a mystery, the way they came to be filled with water, and to evolve through the geological past of the earth, can be more exactly determined. To follow this history we will begin by imagining ourselves transported in a kind of Wellsian time machine to that remote epoch when our planet's crust was still in process of formation. This would be a very long journey indeed, and to achieve it in a reasonable length of time our craft would have to be capable of speeds far surpassing anything we can imagine. Let us suppose, for example, that it could traverse a time-distance of a thousand centuries an hour. If we regard the age of the earth as some 4,000 million years – a decidedly conservative estimate – it would still take us well over four years to reach our destination.

Hovering at a discreet distance from the spinning sphere below, we should behold through our telescopes a majestic spectacle. The surface would glow with dazzling brightness like a star, and the white-hot masses of sial would heave and bubble like molten metal in a gigantic blast furnace. Putting our time machine into reverse, and coasting slowly back towards the present at a few millenia an hour, we should see the major structural features of our earth slowly form themselves before our eyes. The molten crust would gradually solidify, and the rocks would glow with diminishing brightness. At length the earth would be encased in an opaque envelope, studded with innumerable volcanoes, their craters extruding fiery streams of lava in continual eruptions. Occasionally an explosion would blow off whole sections of the crust, revealing the fires still raging within, or fissures would snake across the smoking land from horizon to horizon. But gradually, as the crust was reinforced from within by solidifying basalt, the landscape would grow more stable. It is possible that even in these early times we would be able to recognize the broad pattern of the ocean basins, some, such as the Pacific, being very much as we know them today. On the raised continental blocks between them we would also see the outlines of the first mountain ranges and the broad expanse of the primeval plains. But these would not be the plains or mountains we know now, for such features of our planet's crust are comparatively ephemeral, and many generations of mountains had still to be upraised and worn down before the earth's face began to assume the familiar contours of today.

Once the crust was completely formed its surface cooled very rapidly. This was because it now began to lose heat far more quickly by radiation into space than it could receive it by conduction from within. The region surrounding the earth at this time was filled with the gases thrown off from it when it was still incandescent. Among these gases there was a great deal of water vapour, which was for a long time kept in suspension by the great heat. But as the cooling continued, this vapour formed a thick blanket of cloud covering the whole face of the earth. Eventually the temperature dropped to a point where the cloud blanket was forced to precipitate its moisture, and so the first rains began to fall.

It was these rains, falling for century after century on the face of the earth, that were the source of most of the water in the ocean basins. The sea was thus the child of the atmosphere, which in turn was the gaseous emanation of the primeval earth. But not all the water on the earth was produced in this way. Further quanitites, much smaller in amount, but by no means insignificant, were added from the interior – a process that has continued ever since the crust was formed. Molten rock and water mix in all proportions, and a great deal of water is still present inside the earth. Every time a volcano erupts, this water comes to the surface, and is released in great clouds of steam. Throughout the ages the earth's watery covering has been constantly augmented from this source.

As soon as water began to fall from the sky to fill the ocean basins an important dynamic process was introduced into the terrestial scene. This process was erosion, which, coupled with local crustal movements, has had a profound effect on the evolution of earth and sea. Although it seems likely that some of the major ocean basins are fairly permanent features of the earth's crust, or at least were defined by the drifting of the continents many millions of years ago, this is by no means true of their adjacent seas. These have fluctuated greatly in outline, and the margins of the oceans themselves have also undergone considerable changes. As a result of erosion and earth movements, new seas have often been created, and old seas upraised to become dry land. These processes are so interesting that we must now briefly consider the principles that govern them.

When the universal deluge was first washing the face of our planet it is obvious that the rain fell in regions of widely varying altitude. That which fell in the deepest hollows in the ocean basins remained there, gradually filling them up, and then extended from these centres over the surrounding regions. But that which fell in the shallower parts of the basins, or on the continental blocks between them, tried to find the lowest level, and so streams and rivers were formed, all flowing towards the most low-lying parts of the earth. As the streams and rivers passed over the earth's crust they picked up particles of rock from its surface and carried them down towards the sea. The heavier particles were carried only a short distance, but the lighter ones remained in suspension until the river waters had flowed some distance into the ocean. But here these too were let fall, so that a layer of sediment began to collect on the sea bed. The sediments naturally varied with the kind of rock particles brought down, and so the different sedimentary rocks of the earth were gradually brought into being. Most geologists also believe that the deposition of these sediments was one of the main causes of the continental shelf which fringes nearly all the world's coastlines.

Now it is obvious that the erosive force of water, bringing down these rock particles to the ocean bed (assisted, incidentally, by wind and other agencies which attack the earth's face), was gradually causing the land to become lower and the seas shallower. If this had been the only force at work it would not have taken many millions of years for the land to disappear altogether beneath the surface of the sea. Fortunately for us, however, there is another terrestial agency which constantly tends to counteract the wasting effects of erosion. This is the force already alluded to which is responsible for building mountains and raising whole regions of the earth's surface above their former level. It is the result of stresses and strains produced in the earth's crust by the shrinking of the core. As the molten interior grows smaller through gradual loss of heat, it tends to shrink away from the underside of the crust, which is thereby laterally compressed. The tremendous pressures set up eventually cause something to give. Mountain ranges are folded up in regions of crustal weakness, while in other areas the land subsides. These earth movements are nearly always very gradual, and may take many millions of years to complete. Only during earthquakes are the movements sudden, but on a terrestial scale the results of these are so small as to be almost negligible.

Large-scale earth movements generally occur in cycles, as if there were a gradual build-up of pressure over a long period, followed by a period of release. Erosion, on the other hand, proceeds all the time. The effect of these counteracting forces on the shorelines of the world's oceans therefore follows a fairly regular pattern. The cycle begins with high continental masses and deep seas; these differences are then gradually ironed out by the forces of erosion. But before the land can be covered entirely by the oceans, the shrinking of the earth initiates a new period of uplift, and the cycle begins all over again.

The effect of these recurring cycles is to alter the outlines of the great ocean basins to a considerable extent, even though their global distribution remains approximately the same. Smaller seas may be entirely metamorphosed, some becoming larger and deeper, while others disappear altogether. In the geological past of the earth such changes have sometimes been so great that the beds of seas have been upraised to form high mountain ranges. The most spectacular example is the Himalayan range in Asia, the highest piece of land on the earth's surface. Examination of the rocks of this range proves beyond any doubt that some of them, at heights of 20,000 feet or more, once formed part of the sea bed (see Plate 1a).

Apart from such grand transformations, less spectacular changes are constantly taking place in the patterns of sea and land. The evolution of shore-lines is a most interesting subject, which can be studied by any visitor to the seaside. But it is too complicated to consider here, and we must content ourselves with saying that waves, tides, and the action of rivers all play a part in the process, which can change the entire aspect of a coast well within one man's lifetime.

A study of the principles governing changes in the contours of the earth's crust enables us to draw a tentative picture of the outline of ancient seas. This study belongs to the science of palaeogeography, which uses geological evidence to establish what the surface of our planet may have looked like at different periods of the remote past. In order to appreciate some of its findings a word must first be said about the divisions of geological time.

The history of our earth is divided by geologists into four great eras. These are known as the Archaean, the Palaeozoic, the Mesozoic, and the Cenozoic, and their approximate duration is shown on the chart on the opposite page. The ancestral ocean basins were formed sometime during the Archaean and, as we shall see later on, the first living organisms appeared in the seas towards the end of this era. In the Palaeozoic era life increased enormously in variety and complexity, and the first living creatures forsook the sea for the land. The Mesozoic era, popularly called the Age of Reptiles, saw the domination of the famous extinct reptilian group known as the dinosaurs on land, and the origin of the first mammals. In the Cenozic era these last enjoyed a tremendous evolutionary flowering, so that this era (which is the one in which we still live) is sometimes called the Age of Mammals. Both the Mesozoic and the Cenozoic saw the return of several groups of reptiles and mammals to their ancestral environment, the sea, and this interesting story will be dealt with in its place. Meanwhile, what do we know of the geography of the earth in these far-off times, and particularly of the lay-out of the ocean basins?

A further glance at the chart will show that each great era of earth history is divided into a number of subsidiary periods and epochs. These subdivisions represent the era's successive phases, and each is characterized by different types of fossil remains buried in the rocks. By a careful study of these rocks and their fossil content, palaeogeographers can now tell us a great deal about the arrangement of former continents and oceans. As an example, on page 26 is reproduced a palaeogeographic map, to show how the oceans of just one of those periods can be very roughly reconstructed.

Era	Period	Epoch	Years ago in Millions
Cenozoic	Tertiary	Pliocene	12
		Miocene	26
		Oligocene	34
		Eocene	58
		Palaeocene	63
Mesozoic	Cretaceous		125
	Jurassic		168
	Triassic		200
Palaeozoic	Permian		220
	Carboniferous		270
	Devonian		312
	Silurian		360
	Ordovician		426
	Cambrian		500
Archaean	Pre-Cambrian		3,000
	Origin of Earth's Crust		4,500

Chart of the geological eras, periods and epochs in our earth's past. The Archaean era consists of an Azoic (lifeless) and a Proterozoic (first life) phase but to simplify the presentation these are omitted from the chart. The two parallel lines at the top represent the Pleistocene and Holocene epochs, or Quaternary period. None of the divisions is strictly to scale. *After Oakley and Muir-Wood* (1959), *p.* 62, *and Carrington* (1956), *p.* 41.

25

GEOGRAPHY OF THE CAMBRIAN PERIOD

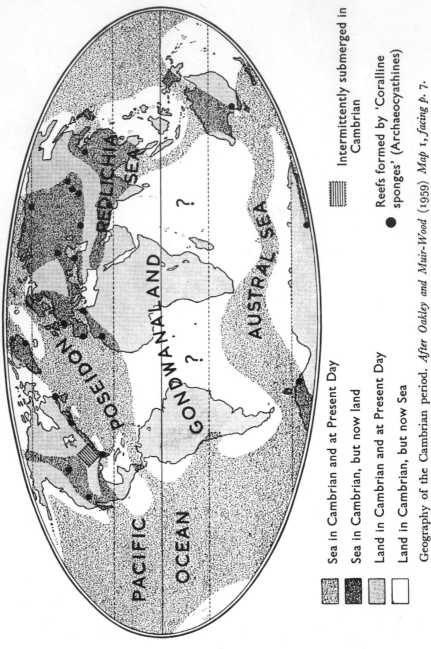

Sea in Cambrian and at Present Day

Sea in Cambrian, but now land

Land in Cambrian and at Present Day

Land in Cambrian, but now Sea

Intermittently submerged in Cambrian

Reefs formed by 'Coralline sponges' (Archaeocyathines)

Geography of the Cambrian period. *After Oakley and Muir-Wood* (1959) *Map* 1, *facing p.* 7.
Reproduced by permission of the Trustees of the British Museum.

26

The period chosen is the Cambrian, which is the first division of the Palaeozoic era, and therefore some 500 million years away from us in time. We can see from the map that the lay-out of the world ocean in the Cambrian was strikingly different from what it is today. The Pacific, which, as we have seen, may possibly be a permanent scar on the earth's crust, occupied much the same position, but the other oceans encroached to a large extent on regions that are now land. For instance, we can tell from the presence of reefs of 'coralline sponges' (Archaeocyathines) in the regions marked with a dot, that the ancestral North Atlantic (which palaeogeographers call Poseidon) spread over much of western Europe, and extended across northern Russia into the very heart of Siberia. Conversely it seems possible that a large fragment of the original crowded up sialic layer of the earth persisted in the region lying eastward between the present western coast of South America and the westernmost extremity of Australia. This fragment is known to palaeogeographers as Gondwanaland, and its partial subsidence in later ages may have produced the South Atlantic and Indian Oceans as we know them today. Further differences in the distribution of sea and land will be apparent from a study of the map.

Of course, this map, like the others produced by palaeogeographers, is extremely tentative. The various data on which it is based are difficult to come by, and still more difficult to interpret. Many different explanations can be provided for the available evidence, and the map redrawn accordingly. Nevertheless it is valuable to look at such maps from time to time. They are reminders of the impermanence of even the mightiest terrestial features, and that constant change is as much a law of the physical universe as it is of the world of living things.

Chapter Four

SEA WATER

W E have seen in an earlier chapter that there is a huge quantity of sea water lying on the face of our planet. The figure mentioned, which may be taken as approximately correct, was 330 million cubic miles. Even the youngest child would not need an oceanographer to tell him that all this sea water has at least one universal and readily detectable quality: it is extremely salt. We take this fact for granted, and the saltiness of the sea is popularly regarded as its most characteristic attribute. This is justifiable enough, for the average salt content of a single cubic mile of sea water is no less than 166 million tons. The figures for the world ocean as a whole reach astronomical proportions (about 55 quadrillion tons), and are thus quite beyond the grasp of the human imagination. To simplify the concept, and make it manageable, it has been calculated that if all the salt in the sea could be dried and piled up on the continents it would cover the entire land surface of the globe to a depth of 500 feet.[1]

The nature and source of all this salt, as well as of the other substances dissolved in the sea, must now be considered. First of all, what do we mean by 'salt'? The salty matter dissolved in sea water is far from being a single substance. Its main constituent is sodium chloride, which accounts for some 85 per cent of the total, but at least six other dissolved solids are present in measurable proportions. These are magnesium chloride, magnesium sulphate, calcium sulphate, potassium sulphate, calcium carbonate and magnesium bromide. [2] Many other substances also exist in the sea, and it seems likely that it contains a certain amount of every known terrestial element, as well as possibly some less familiar air-borne materials blown in from interplanetary space. However, most of these exist in such minute proportions that they can only be measured with extreme difficulty, and mainly come to light when concentrated in the bodies of marine animals. Thus vanadium has been found in the blood of ascidians and holothurians, nickel in molluscs, and cobalt in lobsters and mussels.[3] As these substances can only have been acquired from the creatures' environment, we must conclude that they exist dissolved in the sea even though they are not easily detected in sea water itself.

The main source of all these substances is, of course, the earth's rocky mantle, but the way they came to exist in the oceans in their present proportions is still mysterious. It might be thought that the world's rivers, flowing across the crust for many millions of years, would have been the main agency by which salt was deposited in the sea. Rivers certainly contribute each year to the sea's salinity by bringing down a variety of dissolved solids, but if we regard them as the only source of the sea's salt we run into difficulties. The salts in rivers are found in different proportions from those in the sea, and it is quite wrong to suppose that sea salt is simply river salt at a higher concentration. As we have seen, the main salts dissolved in the sea are chlorides, and especially chloride of sodium; in rivers, on the other hand, carbonates predominate, especially carbonate of lime, or calcium.

A number of explanations have been put forward to explain this fact. The first is that, when the primeval seas began to collect in the hollow places of the earth, they acquired most of their salt from the rocky floor of their basins, and that the effect of rivers since then has been almost negligible. This is not so unlikely as it appears to be, for much of the salt brought down by rivers is thrown out of solution by precipitation. The river salt may therefore be only just sufficient to redress the balance of losses in other directions, leaving none over to change the chemical composition of the sea. But a more likely explanation is based on the functioning of marine organisms. The seas may originally have had the same chemical balance as the rivers, but as sea creatures multiplied they must have begun to use up ever larger quantities of carbonates to make their shells and skeletons of silica and lime. The effect of this would have been to leave behind a higher and higher proportion of chlorides. This explanation, combined with the effects of submarine volcanism, may perhaps be sufficient to account for the difference between river salts and sea salts today.

But if rivers have not necessarily altered the chemical

balance of the sea, it is difficult to agree, as some writers assert, that they have not added to the actual amount of sea salt. Compared with the vast quantity of salt already dissolved in the oceans, the contribution from the rivers is admittedly very small – not more than a two millionth part each year according to one estimate.[4] But we must not forget that the geological time scale allows us a very long period to play with, and that the effect of even such a small contribution sustained over several hundreds of millions of years, could be very considerable. Even when we allow for wastage due to such causes as the upraising of parts of former sea beds to become dry land, it seems likely that the sea is now very much more salt than when the ocean basins first began to fill up over 2,000 million years ago.

In general, the proportions of the different salts do not vary to any great extent from place to place. This is due to the constant mixing effect of waves, winds and currents. The salinity, or concentration of salt, on the other hand, is very different in different parts of the ocean, both horizontally and vertically. There are three main factors governing salinity. The first, and most obvious, is the nearness of a supply of fresh water. At the mouths of great rivers, in regions of heavy rainfall, and along the fringes of melting ice-sheets, the salinity of the surface water is normally low. In regions remote from such influences it is normally high. I say 'normally', for a second influence may modify the position considerably. This is the rate of evaporation, which is the most important single factor affecting the salinity of the oceans.

It is a matter of common knowledge that vast quantities of moisture are continually being evaporated from the surface of the sea by the action of sun and wind. These are then transported to other regions of the earth's surface, where much of the moisture is precipitated as rain, snow or hail. When this happens the salts are, of course, left behind in the sea. Now it is obvious that in areas where the evaporation rate is fast there will be a tendency for the proportion of residual salt to be greater than in areas where it is slow. Hence in areas of quick evaporation the seas usually have a high salinity.

There are, however, complicating factors. To take only one example, we might expect as a result of the above line of argument that salinity would be greatest at the equator and diminish as one travelled towards the poles. But in the event this assumption proves to be mistaken. The greatest concentration of salt is not found at the equator, but in two belts running approximately along the lines of the tropics of Cancer and Capricorn. It decreases on either side of these towards both the equator and the poles.

The solution of the mystery is quite simple. The blazing sun and clear skies of the Cancer-Capricorn belts encourage a fast rate of evaporation, and the air-borne vapour is carried away by the trade winds to fall in other regions. A high degree of salinity is thereby encouraged. The decrease north from Cancer and south from Capricorn is also logical enough, for lower temperatures and increased cloud reduce the evaporation rate. But we must remember that over the equator also there is often a thick cloud belt which shields the surface from the sun's rays. This is also the region of torrential tropical rains, which dilute the waters of the oceans. Both these factors play a part in keeping the salt content comparatively low in equatorial regions.

The third influence determining salinity is the rate at which seas with a high salt content mix with others where the content is lower. In the open oceans winds and currents are constantly moving the water so that the salinity tends to even up. But this is not the case in partially enclosed or inland seas, where the salinity is affected entirely, or almost entirely, by local conditions. For example, both the Mediterranean and the Red Sea are exceptionally salt, whereas the Baltic is little more than brackish. To quote the actual figures, the salt content of the Red Sea is no less than 40 parts per thousand, whereas that of the Baltic is only 7·2 parts per thousand. The reason for this wide discrepancy is that the evaporation rate in the Red Sea and, to a lesser extent, the Mediterranean, is exceptionally high, and very little mixing can occur owing to the narrow connections with the open ocean at the straits of Bab el Mandeb and Gibraltar; in the Baltic, on the other hand, which is likewise largely cut off from the open ocean, there is a low evaporation rate and much dilution by rain and rivers.

The reader may next be interested to learn something about the techniques by which the saltiness of the sea is measured. The principal method is that known to chemists as 'titration'.

It consists of adding to the sample a certain amount of silver nitrate, which combines with the chloride in the sea water to form a precipitate of silver chloride. This is then measured, and as the proportion of chloride to the other dissolved substances is constant, the salinity can be fairly simply determined mathematically. Other techniques depend on measurements of the refractive index, the density, or the electrical conductivity of the sample, all three of which depend on the salinity.

The samples themselves are not always so easily obtained as might be imagined, especially at great depths, or when a series of different samples are required from different levels. They are collected in a container known as a 'water-bottle', which, in spite of its homely name, is quite an elaborate piece of equipment. It consists of a metal cylinder, open at both ends, so that when it is lowered on a length of rope or wire the water passes freely through it. When the time comes to close the bottle, a cylindrical weight, known as a 'messenger', is sent down the line; this either turns a rotating valve, or actuates a pair of stoppers which close the bottle at either end. When a series of bottles are suspended on a single line at different depths, the messenger, after closing the first bottle, automatically releases another messenger which passes down the next section of line to close the second, and so on. To obtain a series of samples in this way requires much care on the part of the operators, and is one of the most important, if humdrum, aspects of the routine of oceanography.

Marine organisms have a considerable effect on the chemical composition of sea water in different regions. They use nearly all the substances dissolved in the sea for their nourishment, but in very different proportions. Thus in thickly populated regions the supply of substances in heavy demand, such as phosphates and nitrogenous compounds, may be reduced to a somewhat lower level. Conversely the death, followed by the sinking and decomposition, of surface-living animals and plants transfers a certain amount of organic substance from one region to another. The release of this substance into the sea is another factor that may alter the local chemical balance. The influence of living things on sea water must therefore cause us to modify at times the general rule that the proportion of sea salts in different regions remains constant.

One of the main influences affecting the chemical cycle in the seas is the vast population of drifting organisms known as plankton, which I shall talk about more fully in the second part of this book. These organisms live at or near the surface and, when they die, their bodies fall towards the ocean bed as a perpetual organic rain. Most of them are either microscopic or extremely small, and their bodies thus have a very big surface area compared with their volume. Owing to the resistance of the water this causes them to fall very slowly. Even a fairly large planktonic crustacean such as a copepod would take about a minute to fall two feet, and might not reach the bottom for several days. The smaller organisms, which vastly predominate, would take even longer.

Many of the slowly falling bodies of the plankton are devoured by scavenging animals before decomposition, but it seems that others are actually dissolved into the sea water before reaching the ocean floor. The amount of dissolved organic matter which accumulates in this way is surprisingly large. According to a recent estimate it exceeds the amount of living matter at any one time by as much as three hundred times. Put another way, the dissolved organic substances in the Atlantic Ocean alone are equal to about twenty thousand times the world's wheat harvest for one year.[5]

The use of this dissolved organic matter by other organisms has been the subject of much speculation. Some authorities have suggested that it is taken in through the gills of marine animals, who thereby obtain a portion of their food by direct absorption [6]; others that it may be very largely wasted. There is certainly little chance that organic solutions in the depths of the sea ever return to the surface, for the effects of currents are hardly felt there, and the amount of water diffused upwards is thought to be insignificant.[7] On the other hand, it is possible that the dissolved substances are used as nourishment by bottom-living bacteria.

Apart from salts and organic substances the sea also contains dissolved gas. We do not normally think of the sea as being full of gas, but this must obviously be the case, or marine animals would not be able to breathe. The three most common gases of the atmosphere are present in large quantities in sea water. These are oxygen, nitrogen and carbon dioxide. Part of this gas is derived from submarine sources or the life activities of animals and plants. Thus carbon dioxide is released by volcanic springs on the sea bed, or by putrefaction [8]; nitrogen is produced by the action of marine bacteria on the bodies of sea animals; and the process, known as photosynthesis, by which seaweeds and other plants use the sun's rays to make their food, releases a considerable amount of oxygen. But the greater part of the gas is derived not from such sources as these, but from direct contact with the atmosphere. Along the surface of the sea there is a constant mingling of the two elements. Moisture is sucked up by the air and carried away on the sea winds; gases are absorbed from the atmosphere and dissolved in the body of the ocean.

The quantity of a particular gas that can be absorbed by water depends on three factors: the temperature, the partial pressure of the gas in the atmospheric mixture, and its chemical constitution. For practical purposes, the last two factors can be regarded as constant for each gas, and therefore in practice the most powerful influence determining the interchange is temperature. If the sea is cold, more gas will be absorbed than if it is warm; a rise in temperature will liberate gases from the surface just as steam is released from liquid heated in a saucepan. Strong winds increase the rate of interchange by bringing a stream of air in contact with the sea surface, and the contact is increased by breaking waves and spray which, in effect, greatly increase the surface area of the water. Standing on the bow of a ship watching the majestic progress of a foam-capped wave, our wonder may well be increased by reflecting on the great physical processes thus eternally controlling the interplay of sea and air.

No chapter on sea water would be complete without a reference to its colour. To begin with, let us consider the question with which Awful Children habitually baffle their parents at the sea-side: 'Mummy, why is the sea blue?' Those who only know the waters round our own islands might well be tempted to counter this quite simply by saying: 'It isn't, dear; just take a look!' But this would be to beg the question. Although the appearance of the sea varies greatly in different regions and under different conditions, blue is the colour habitually associated with it. The accuracy of the association can be amply confirmed by observation, especially in middle and lower latitudes, on the open ocean.

The main cause of the blueness of the sea is the same as that which causes the blueness of the sky. It is simply a result of the behaviour of light. As every schoolboy is alleged to know (at least until examination time comes round), pure white light is composed of a spectrum of colours of different wave-lengths, ranging from ultra-violet to infra-red. When these pass through sea water, the blue rays, being of very short wave-length, are scattered laterally by minute particles in suspension. This imparts a blue tinge to the surface waters.

There are, however, other factors involved. The most obvious of these is the composition of the light falling on the surface. If the blue rays are absent it is evident that no blue tinge can appear in the water. A visitor to the Mediterranean, if not otherwise engaged in such a romantic setting, can give himself an instructive object-lesson in optics by watching at sunset how the brilliant blue waters of the sea turn slowly to gold. The effect is due to the setting sun being at a tangential instead of a near-vertical angle to the point of observation, so that its rays must pass through a greater thickness of the earth's atmosphere; this causes the blue rays to be largely filtered out before they meet the sea surface. Similar effects can be studied off our own shores, where the colour of the sea often changes from minute to minute due to the filtering effect of different clouds passing across the face of the sun.

The least obvious and in many ways the most interesting cause of the sea's colour is the presence of objects in suspension in the water itself. All the more unusual variations of colour spring from this cause. The objects may be organic or inorganic, but the principle governing the effect is the same. Thus the green colour of much sea water is due to the presence of plankton, and a wide range of colour variations can occur when finely suspended mineral particles are carried into the sea after heavy rains. Such effects can sometimes be so remarkable and characteristic that seas have been named after them. The Red Sea, where the presence of an alga with the rather forbidding name of *Trichodesmium erythraeum* turns the water reddish-brown, is one example: another is the Vermilion Sea in the Gulf of California.

Much more could be said on the chemistry and physics of sea water, but, considered on their own, such details are apt to be dull. They will be introduced later as they become relevant in a wider context. Meanwhile, our next step must be to look at some of the principles governing the behaviour of tides and currents, so that the whole vast picture can be set in motion.

Chapter Five

THE SEA IN MOTION

THE main movements of the sea are controlled by cosmic or major terrestrial processes: the tides by the attraction of the sun and moon; the ocean currents by heat, wind, and the spinning of the earth. The other factors involved are purely local, and in any case depend on the same great fundamental forces.

Since Newton's first experience in an orchard, when the fall of an apple suggested to him the concept of gravity, we have been generally aware that an attraction exists between the various congregations of atoms which we know as physical bodies. This attraction may be large or small, but it is in direct proportion to the distance between the bodies, and their mass. Here, also, it is important to emphasize a fact that is not always appreciated: the force works both ways. The earth, it is obvious, attracts the falling apple; what is less obvious, but equally true, is that the apple also attracts the earth.

Applying Newton's principles to the solar system, it is apparent that the sun and its satellites, the planets, must exert an attraction on each other. But the sun, being bigger, exerts the more powerful force, and thus dominates the planets by causing them to revolve around it. The same principles operate in the outer universe, for a mutual attraction exists between the sun and its satellites on the one hand, and all the other heavenly bodies on the other. But this vaster concept need not concern us here, for the effects are small and difficult to measure. In discussing the behaviour of the tides we can safely restrict ourselves to the relative forces operating within the solar system itself.

Just as there is an attraction between the sun and the earth, so there is an attraction between the earth and the moon. But in this latter relationship the earth's pull is the stronger, and therefore causes the moon to revolve around it. The dominance of the earth in this respect may cause us to underestimate the moon's strength, but we should not forget that our satellite exercises a force that greatly influences our lives.

37

Earth and moon moving round one another like a pair of dancers have, through the force of gravity, a tendency to mutual disruption. The tides are caused by the moon's constant attempt to disrupt the surface of the earth. It lacks the strength to affect the rigid materials of the crust (although delicate instruments show that even these are disturbed to some extent); but what it can do is to modify the shape of the hydrosphere. The moon's attractive powers lift the waters of the ocean towards it. These waters are pulled away from the crust and pile up in the direction of the moon. But the pull decreases with distance, and thus the waters on the far side of the earth are less affected than those round the centre. This makes them more susceptible to the force, known as centrifugal force, which counteracts gravity and is constantly attempting to make things fly off the surface of rotating bodies. The result is a second piling up of water on the side of the earth facing away from the moon.

As the earth rotates once in every twenty-four hours, the masses of piled-up water are raised along the earth's shorelines approximately twice a day. These are the high tides. Conversely, the low tides occur in the regions at right angles to these piled-up masses, where the water is lowest. In the southern seas, where there are no southward projecting land masses to check the flow, the two great tidal bulges pass continually round the earth in majestic procession. But further north, where the Atlantic, Pacific and Indian Oceans are flanked on either side by continental blocks, and thus form great bays, another pattern is imposed. Here the waters tend to revolve round nodal areas in each basin, where the level does not fluctuate to nearly such a great extent as on the circumference. A similar effect can be seen when water is rocked in a saucer so as to rotate about a central region where rise and fall does not occur.

A complicating factor is introduced by the sun. Although the sun is so much larger than the moon, its immense comparative distance (93 million as against 239 thousand miles) causes its attractive power to have much less effect on the earth's tides. The sun's pull on the earth's surface is, in fact, estimated as being only some four-ninths that of the moon's. Now when the earth, sun, and moon are in line (the condition known rather pleasingly, as 'syzygy'), the combined attraction of sun and moon, pulling in the same direction, causes the difference between the earth's tides to be exceptionally great. When, on the other hand, the sun and the moon as seen from the earth are at right angles to one another, the difference between the tides is exceptionally low. Tides with a maximum rise and fall are known as spring tides, those where the difference is least as neap tides. This cycle repeats itself once every fortnight, the spring tides occurring when the moon is approximately new or full, the neap tides at the half-moons. Other factors, such as the moon's distance from the earth at different parts of its orbit, and seasonal variations of the earth's distance from the sun, also affect the tides, but these matters are too technical to be gone into here.

Apart from the tides, the greatest movement of the hydrosphere is that imparted to it by the ocean currents. The currents behave as they do partly because of differences in the temperature and salinity of the sea, and partly because of the direction of the prevailing winds. They are also locally affected by the action of the tides. Before we investigate some of these movements more closely we must briefly state where the main currents flow.

The map on the next page gives a very much simplified picture of the surface currents of the world's oceans. Other well-defined currents flow beneath the surface at different depths, but these cannot be discussed in detail here. In the Atlantic it will be seen that there are two great oceanic eddies, one in the northern hemisphere and one in the southern. The northern eddy consists of the North Equatorial Current, the Gulf Stream, and the Canaries Current. The southern eddy consists of the South Equatorial Current, the Brazil Current, the West Wind Drift, and the Benguela Current. In the Pacific the pattern is roughly repeated, although it is less clearly defined in the southern hemisphere. In the southern part of the Indian Ocean the same eddying movement occurs, but northwards the circulation is complicated by the monsoons, and the currents do not remain constant throughout the year.

How do the two main influences I have mentioned contribute to this large-scale circulation of the earth's surface waters? First we will take the influence of temperature and salinity. In equatorial regions considerable heating of the water

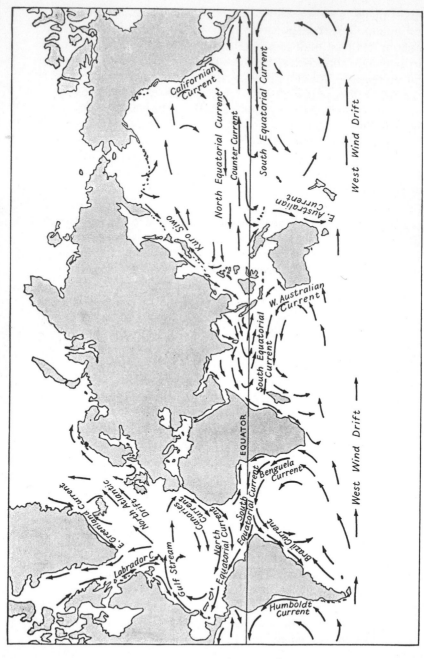

Ocean currents. *N.B.* The Indian Ocean currents are shown as they flow during the north-east monsoon; during the south-west monsoon the pattern changes.

takes place. This has a twofold effect: first, it causes the water to expand, and thereby to become less dense; second, it evaporates part of it into the atmosphere, causing the residue to become more saline. Because an increase in salinity causes an increase in density, this effect counteracts the first one. But the first effect outweighs the second, and, on balance, surface water at the equator is constantly being rendered less dense by the sun's heat.

We must now pause for a moment to see what is happening towards the poles. Here cold air is constantly tending to keep the temperature of the water at a low level, thereby making it more dense. At the same time, salinity is being increased by freezing. This occurs because, when sea water freezes, a large proportion of the salts are left behind (in fact, sea ice is very nearly fresh); thus the salinity of the water is increased, and it becomes denser from this cause as well.

Putting these two processes together, what happens? As the equatorial water expands, it tends to raise the sea level in those regions. At the same time the high density of the cold temperate and polar waters causes them to sink towards the bottom. The net result is that the surface water at the equator is constantly tending to stream away 'down hill' towards the poles.

The direction of the prevailing winds, which is the second factor affecting the oceanic circulation, has a far more potent influence on currents than the salinity and temperature of the sea itself. Considerable friction occurs even when so comparatively diffuse a substance as air passes over the surface of the oceans. If the flow of air is consistent in direction, and sustained for a sufficiently long period, it will carry vast masses of the surface water with it.

To the lay eye a wind map of the earth is simply a bewildering jumble of colours and arrows. Nevertheless, the winds conform to a logical pattern, and their behaviour can be explained by reference to two main causes: atmospheric pressure and the spinning of the earth. Atmospheric pressure is closely bound up with temperature. The heating effect of the sun at the equator causes the air to expand. Therefore over any given unit of the earth's equatorial surface there is usually less air than in the regions to north and south, and in this way a belt of 'low pressure' is formed. Conversely at the poles, where the heating effect of the sun is least, the air does not expand to the same extent, and a zone of high pressure is formed.

Now, as air flows from regions of high pressure to regions of low pressure, it might be thought that the earth's main winds would blow steadily in a straight line from the poles to the equator. There are two complicating factors, however. The first is that, for reasons too technical to go into here, the polar winds tend to break up into eddies soon after setting out on their journey. The centres of these eddies form pockets of lower atmospheric pressure, and the presence of many of these in two belts, one round each pole, produces a general low-pressure effect in these latitudes similar to that found in the belt round the equator. As a result, the air between the equatorial and the polar belts in each hemisphere is at comparatively high pressure, and therefore tends to flow away, either outwards towards its own hemisphere's eddy belt, or inwards towards the equator. The normal line of flow would, of course, be due north and south, but here our second complicating factor comes in. The winds are deflected by the spinning of the earth, and so blow along a line running south-west and north-east in the northern hemisphere, and south-east and north-west in the southern hemisphere.

The arrangement of the earth's main wind belts is illustrated in the diagram on the opposite page. In reality the picture is much more complicated than this, for there are wide local variations, especially in the monsoon regions of southern Asia. Also, the presence of large land masses in the northern hemisphere causes winds to behave somewhat differently north and south of the equator. But on the whole the diagram gives an accurate picture of the general pattern of atmospheric circulation.

The movement of the earth's winds as shown in the diagram will go a long way towards explaining the behaviour of the major ocean currents, and especially the great eddy systems operating in the Atlantic and Pacific Oceans. The latter find their main cause in the two belts of 'Trade Winds' which converge at the equator and tend to blow the equatorial waters towards the west. When these waters reach the eastern seaboards of the continents they divide into two streams, one flowing away towards the north and the other towards the south. Passing through the calm high-pressure zones in each hemisphere, they then reach the second pair of wind belts lying to the north and south. But here the winds are blowing in the opposite direction to the Trades, and the streams of water are still further encouraged on their way. I shall not have space to consider the more complicated aspects of the behaviour of these oceanic eddies, nor the interaction between the effects of wind and the other influences described above. But the

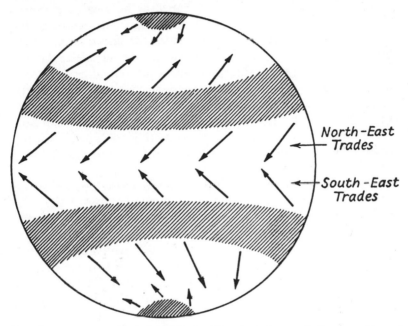

North-East Trades

South-East Trades

Some of the earth's main wind belts. The shaded areas indicate regions of high pressure. *Simplified from Lake* (1952), *p.* 25.

reader will already have gathered, even from the single example given, how closely the oceanic circulation is related to the other major physical processes operating on the surface of the earth.

One interesting aspect of currents which I have not yet touched upon is their velocity. We all know that certain inshore currents may run sufficiently fast to be a danger to bathers, especially when reinforced by the action of tides, but we do not normally think of the currents of the open ocean as moving at any appreciable speed. It is certainly true that many currents are slow, and do not travel at more than a few miles a day. There are, however, come notable exceptions to this rule. For example, the Gulf Stream travels at a steady three to five miles an hour, and off Chesapeake Bay is estimated to move water at the rate of between 74 and 93 million cubic metres per second.[9] The Kuro Siwo, which flows past the coast of Japan, is another current whose speed is comparable with that of a fairly swift-flowing river.

The speed of surface currents can now be measured from a ship at anchor by a wide range of complex instruments, but for amateur oceanographers a float on the end of a line is still one of the most practical and accurate devices. The float is made by cutting out a thin piece of wood shaped as a sector of a circle. This is then weighted with lead along the curved edge so that it floats upright in the water, and allowed to drift with the current away from the ship at the end of a piece of light twine marked at every ten feet. By noting the amount of line paid out in a given time the speed of the current can be easily deduced.

A more elaborate piece of apparatus is needed for measuring the speed of currents beneath the surface. One of the most satisfactory gadgets is the Ekman current meter, which consists essentially of a propeller geared to a number of recording instruments. These are contained in a box which is lowered to the required depth and then orientated by a vane so that the propeller receives the full force of the current. The velocity is calculated from the number of times the propeller turns in a measured length of time.

Another use of the Ekman meter is in finding the direction of sub-surface currents. This is very cleverly contrived. A compass with an exceptionally heavy needle is mounted beneath the propeller. The two arms of the compass needle are inclined downward, and one of them has a deep groove running down it from centre to point. In the box above the compass is a store of small shot, and one shot is released with each turn of the propeller. This falls on the centre of the compass needle, passes down the groove, and drops into one of a number of compartments arranged round the circumference of the compass card. When the apparatus is hauled to the surface the compartment containing the shot will indicate the direction from which the current was flowing.

44

The tides and currents represent the grand terrestial movements of the sea, but even more fascinating from a visual point of view are those perturbations of its surface we know as waves. It is only necessary to imagine for a moment how monotonous the sea surface would be if it were perpetually flat to realize what an enormous contribution the waves make to its aesthetic appeal. From the scientific angle also they are exceptionally interesting, if only because many aspects of their behaviour, even after centuries of investigation, are still only imperfectly understood.

There are many kinds of sea waves, and these have been classified in various ways by different authorities. The most important type are those formed by the action of the wind. Let us imagine ourselves looking down on a perfectly still, deep water surface, in a perfectly calm atmosphere. Gradually a wind begins to get up, moving parallel to the surface of the water. If the winds were perfectly steady no waves would appear, for there would be no force to act on one part of the water surface more than another. But natural winds do not blow steadily, even when they appear to do so. They fluctuate slightly in speed, and even the most imperceptible eddy will affect the amount of friction at the surface, and slightly deform the surface of the water. The first visible effect will be the formation of small ripples, which will gradually increase in size as the wind continues to blow. This is because, once ripples have been formed, the wind acts more strongly on the sides of the undulation nearest to it than on the sides facing the sheltered depressions beyond. As the wind force increases, the waves will get larger and larger, moving across the face of the water in regular procession.

One important thing to realize about such waves is that the water itself is not carried bodily forward, but that each particle rotates round a focal point and returns to its original position. This can be proved by watching the movements of a cork floating on the surface of a pond. As a wave approaches, the cork is lifted by the front slope, carried forward as it reaches the crest, lowered again by the rear slope, and carried backward when it comes to the trough. If any movement occurs other than this cylindrical one (a drift towards one shore for example) it is not due to the wave, but to the action of a current

45

or, more likely, the pressure of the wind on the cork itself. Moreover, however large the wave, it has practically no effect on the water lying a short way beneath the surface. A certain movement of water particles does go on here as a result of the surface waves, but at a depth equal to the distance between the crests of two waves this is five hundred times less than in the agitated water above.

The reader may now ask what causes the crests of waves to break, thus creating the foaming 'white horses' which add so much to the beauty of the sea. In deep water this only occurs when the wind has attained a certain strength. As the wind velocity increases it tends to speed up the forward motion of the water particles in the crest of the wave relative to the backward motion in the trough. The result is a steepening of the face of the wave, so that the water particles at the crest tend to topple forward out of their orbital path. If the wind is sufficiently strong, this is in fact what occurs, and the detached water particles are blown forward into the adjacent trough as foam and spray.

A similar process can be studied in the breaking of waves on the seashore, but here the effect is due to the decreasing depth of the water. As a result of changes in the orbiting behaviour of the water particles, and perhaps partly because of the friction of the sea bed, waves move more slowly in shallow water than they do in the deep sea. Now, when a wave advances up a beach the front is obviously in shallower water than the back, and this part of the wave is therefore moving relatively more slowly. The back of the wave gradually overtakes the front, and the leading face becomes steeper and steeper. Eventually the slope is almost vertical, and at this point the forward movement of the water particles at the top of the wave causes the crest to fall forward. It is rather as if a man ran into a layer of sand, which so retarded his footsteps in comparison with the forward movement of his head, that he fell flat on his face.

One curious fact that must have struck every visitor to the seaside is that, whatever the direction of the waves in the deeper water off shore, the breakers always seem to come in roughly parallel with the beach. This is likewise due to the slower speed of waves in shallow water, and can best be ex-

plained with the aid of the accompanying figure. The waves
are seen to be approaching the beach at an angle of roughly
45 degrees. Now if we take the dotted line as representing
the point where the water becomes sufficiently shallow to slow
them up, we can clearly see that not the whole of each wave
is affected at the same time. The shoreward end is progressively
slowed up as the water becomes shallower, but the seaward end

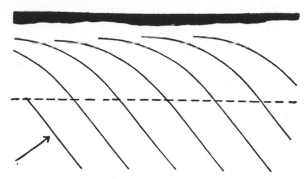

Waves approaching a shore. *Simplified from Lake* (1952), *p.* 170.

races on at its original speed until it too begins to be influenced
by the shallows. The result is that the wave turns gradually
to the left, so that it ends up nearly parallel with the shore-
line (see also Plate 4*b*).

The sport of surf-riding is only made possible by the characteristic behaviour of waves upon gently sloping beaches. I hope
that those who have enjoyed this activity, and can perhaps
practice it with the skill shown on Plate 5*a*, will not think me
too prosaic if I describe some of the scientific principles
on which it is based. For a successful surf-ride up a beach it is
essential that the board should travel at the same speed as the
advancing wave, and also be kept stable so that it resists the
tendency to broach to. The first of these requirements is met
by choosing a wave that is just beginning to break, so that the
forward movement of the water particles in the crest is almost
as great as the speed of the wave itself. The balance of speed
is made up by movement of the board through the water, this
being due to the fact that it is perpetually sliding 'downhill'.
The second requirement must be provided by the surf-rider.
As we have seen, the water particles in the crest are advancing

more rapidly than in any other part of the wave. Therefore the velocity of the front edge of the surf-board is higher relative to the water than the velocity of the back. This means that the slightest deviation in the direction of the board must cause it to slew round parallel to the advancing crest. It is the surf-rider's job to counteract any such tendency by moving the weight of his body to left or right as required. Surf-riding is thus seen to be a beautiful example of a most delicately balanced interplay of forces, relying for its main motive power on the tremendous vitality of the sea itself.

Breakers are quite different from deep sea waves in that it is not only the wave that is moving, but large masses of water are actually being given a powerful forward impetus. Waves breaking on a steep coast often cause tremendous destruction, which is not surprising when one learns that they can exert a pressure of over two tons per square foot. At such times water may be thrown to very great heights. One report from Urst in the Shetlands states that a door in the lighthouse was broken open 195 feet above the sea. It is possible in this case that it was the story and not the wave that was so exceptionally tall; but there are certainly well-authenticated cases of breaking waves throwing water to heights of over a hundred feet.

In the open sea, waves over 40 feet high are by no means uncommon, although there is a natural tendency to give exaggerated estimates. One of the highest waves ever reported was seen from the liner *Majestic* during an Atlantic crossing in February, 1923. This rose so high that the horizon was blotted out to observers on the bridge, 89 feet above the water-line. Allowing for the possibility that the pitching of the liner exaggerated the effect, it is still quite likely that this wave was some 75 feet high.[10]

Records have also been kept of the speed of giant waves, and their maximum distance from crest to crest. This distance (which is the same, of course, as the distance between any other two corresponding and identifiable spots on the surface of successive waves) is known as the wavelength. Big rollers often have a wavelength of 800 to 1,000 feet, and the longest ever recorded measured 3,700 feet from crest to crest. [11] Speed varies enormously, and in the open ocean depends entirely on wavelength (as we have already seen, in shallow water, it is

48

1*a* Panorama from Mount Everest. Much of the land now upraised to a height of over 20,000 feet in the Himalayan range once formed part of the sea bed

1*b* The onslaught of the sea is constantly changing the aspect of the world's coastlines

2*a* The frozen sea. Pack ice and bergs in the
Antarctic Ocean

2*b* A tabular berg 75 feet high between the
South Shetlands and the South Orkneys

3*a* A much-weathered berg in loose pack ice

3*b* The death of an iceberg: the last sculpted fragments
before final dissolution

THE MOODS OF THE SEA

4*a* The pattern of storm waves on a rocky coast,
Outer Hebrides

4*b* A tranquil shore. Note how the waves turn parallel
to the shore as the water grows shallower

5*a* Surf-riding at Bondi Beach, Sydney, Australia. The sport demonstrates a principle of wave mechanics (see p. 47)

5*b* The bed of the deep sea. Photograph taken at a depth of 5282 metres west of the Iberian abyssal plain. The track was made by an unknown animal

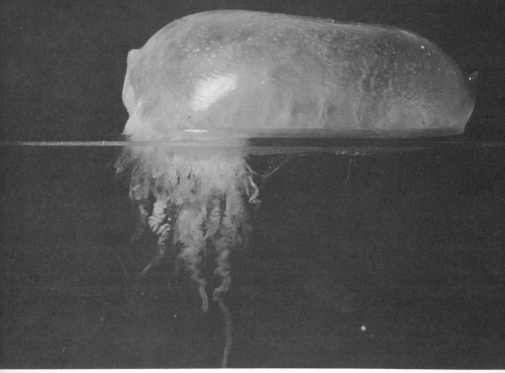

6*a* A Portuguese man-o'-war (*Physalia*) with tentacles retracted
6*b* Sea anemones, marine animals with a superficial
resemblance to plants

7*a* Sea-squirts

7*b* A group of feathery sea-worms, grotesque but beautiful animals of the sea

8a The colonial marine animal *Obelia*

8b The soft coral *Alcyonium digitatum* is popularly known as 'Dead Man's Fingers'

also affected by depth). The speed of a wave with a distance between crests of about a thousand feet would be well over forty miles an hour.

When the wind drops, or waves run out of a storm area, the waves gradually become more rounded in shape, and the troubled surface subsides into the low, regular undulations of a swell. Yet, as R. E. Coker has pointed out, the term swell is by no means employed in its slang meaning of superb, or delightful. A powerful swell, while appearing deceptively placid, may have such a big amplitude between crest and trough that it does tremendous damage when it breaks on an exposed coast. It is most eerie to stand on a shoreline where no breath of wind is blowing while a swell drags ships from their moorings and reduces quays and piers to twisted masses of steel and concrete. These damaging swells occur quite commonly along the coasts of the Pacific, and one which regularly visits Peru is sufficiently notorious to have its own name – the *mar brava*, or 'wild sea'.[12] Such swells have often travelled many hundreds, or even thousands, of miles from a storm centre on the far side of the ocean. To give an example, storms on the eastern American seaboard have been known on several occasions to cause swells that have damaged harbour works in western France.

So far we have only been dealing with waves caused directly by the action of the wind. These, I have said, are the most important, but waves of several other types exist in the ocean. For example, there are waves known as 'boundary waves', which occur at the plane of contact between liquids of different densities, and others known as 'standing waves', or 'seiches', where the water particles do not complete their orbit, but stop at a certain point and return along the same path. In a general survey these waves cannot be considered in any detail, and the interested reader is referred to the more technical books on waves listed in the bibliography. I shall here restrict myself to only one other group of waves: those commonly but inaccurately referred to as 'tidal waves', which have always appealed to the human imagination because of their immense size and capacity for destruction.

'Tidal' waves have nothing whatever to do with the tides, but are caused by earthquakes and underwater explosions. To avoid confusion they are therefore sometimes referred to by their Japanese name of 'tsunamis', but a more familiar, and therefore better, term is 'seismic' waves, and this will be used here. We are all familiar, by report if not by direct experience, of the havoc that can be wrought by large-scale earth movements on land. When similar events occur on the sea bed the destructive force is transferred to the water and may travel hundreds or even thousands of miles in the form of a wave before expending itself on some innocent and unsuspecting coastline.

Seismic waves are of several different kinds, but the reason for this and even the exact manner of their production is unknown. One type of wave takes the form of a quick oscillation which travels through the water with the same velocity as sound. Vessels affected by such waves suffer a short, sharp shock, and the mariners often think at first that their ship has run on to a rock. The charts of the old navigators are commonly marked with non-existent shoals which probably originated in some such experience. In extreme cases ships can be severely damaged by these waves, or even destroyed entirely, but in general they do not have any important visible effect at the surface.

A more spectacular type of seismic wave is that caused by major dislocations of the sea bed. If we suppose that uplift or subsidence suddenly occurs on a fairly wide scale, the effect is to cause a large dome or depression in the water at the surface of the sea. This generates a wave which begins to move across the ocean at enormous speed. At first very high, it quickly subsides, and in the open ocean its lowness, flatness and extreme length may cause it to be unnoticed by shipping. This quiescent phase is deceptive, however, for as the water grows shallower over the continental shelf, the wave begins to pile up to a tremendous height and eventually breaks on the shore with a vast quantity of boiling surf. The same behaviour characterizes waves generated by submarine eruptions. In this case the sea surface above the volcano is at first broken by small jets of water, and then becomes domed to a considerable height. Eventually thousands of tons of water may be hurled into the air by the pressure of the pent-up gases below the surface.

Seismic waves following such events sometimes travel at speeds comparable with those of the fastest modern aeroplanes.

There are records of their effects having been transmitted over a distance of 10,000 miles in a day, and the German oceanographer Otto Krümmel quotes one instance where a speed of 900 miles per hour was attained. Successive waves from the same centre of activity may have a length of anything between 100 and 600 miles from crest to crest, and pass a given point at intervals ranging from fifteen minutes to two hours.[13]

The effects of such gigantic waves breaking on a coastline can well be imagined. There are records of their destructiveness dating from as long ago as the fourth century, when seismic waves in the Mediterranean engulfed islands and deposited boats on the rooftops of Alexandria. Coming to more recent times we know that in August 1868 waves produced by an earthquake off the coast of Peru carried a United States warship a quarter of a mile inshore in Arica. The vessel remained high and dry for nine years, when a second wave, caused this time by the Iquique earthquake, carried it still further inland. The waves responsible for inflicting this indignity on the U.S. Navy were estimated to have varied in height from 20 to 80 feet. Even larger waves occurred after the famous explosion of Krakatoa in 1883. One of these carried a gunboat two miles inland on the southern coast of Sumatra, while another, breaking along the shallow shore at Merak in Java, reached the altogether fantastic height of 125 feet. This is about as high as a block of modern flats of twelve storeys.

Several other records could be quoted, but fortunately such catastrophic events have been rare in recent years. The only waves to approach the largest seismic waves in size since the war have been those caused by man-made atomic explosions in the southern Pacific. It is odd that our species can thus almost equal the destructive power of nature without being able to breathe life into one dead fish in the sea.

Chapter Six

THE SEA AND CLIMATE

To appreciate the beauty of wave mechanics or the slow evolution of a coastline one must perhaps be something of a scientist or a poet; but climate and weather are of direct practical interest to us all. Both these aspects of our environment manifest themselves through the atmosphere, the climate being dependent on the behaviour of the atmosphere over a wide region, the weather on its local eccentricities. Both are influenced to a great extent by the sea.

To understand the sea's effect on climate and weather we must first consider one or two of its physical characteristics which have not so far been described. The most important of these is its capacity to absorb and radiate heat, and the general effect this has on its temperature. We loosely think of 'heat' and 'temperature' as being the same thing, but this concept is most misleading. If a given amount of heat is applied to different substances their temperature will rise by different degrees. Thus if we place a vessel containing water to the weight of one pound over a gas flame, and find that its temperature is raised one degree centigrade in one minute, an equal weight of iron on the same flame will be raised no less than ten degrees in an equal length of time. From this fact we can deduce that different substances have different heat-storing capacities. The heat storage capacity of a substance is known as its 'specific heat', and this quality has great significance when we begin to examine the physical characteristics of sea and land and their influence on climate and weather.

Water, we have seen, has a high specific heat. In other words, it can absorb greater quantities of heat with less rise in temperature than many other substances. Conversely, it can lose larger amounts of heat without its temperature falling to any great extent. Now, where the majority of solid substances are concerned, the position is exactly reversed. These in general have a much larger specific heat than water, and therefore

52

cannot absorb or radiate heat to nearly the same extent without wide fluctuations in temperature.

Applying these general laws to the surface of the earth, what do we find? First let us assume that the rays of the sun are shining at the same strength on two equal areas, one consisting of sea, the other, land. Because of its higher specific heat, the sea will absorb much more heat than the land without any marked rise in temperature. Conversely, after the sun has set, the land will radiate its stored heat much more quickly than the sea, with a much more rapid fall in temperature.

Here already is a basic difference in the behaviour of land and sea when subjected to the heating effects of the sun. But this is not the whole of the story. Other factors tend to exaggerate the differences between the two types of substance. In the first place the earth's crust is not viscous, and therefore contains no convective currents. This means that heat falling on its surface is only stored by the very upper stratum of rocks, and by those immediately below to which a certain amount of heat is transferred by conduction. The sea, on the other hand, is constantly in motion. There is a perpetual interchange between the warm surface water and the cooler layers below, and heat applied at one place is constantly being moved horizontally by the action of currents. This constant mobility allows the available heat to be more widely dispersed, thus creating a greater thermal reservoir than would be possible on land.

Another factor intensifying the sea's capacity to store heat is evaporation. At the surface, at all ordinary temperatures, evaporation, or the change of water into gas, is constantly taking place. Now, evaporation always requires absorption of heat, and the scale of evaporation occurring at the surface of the sea involves heat storage of a prodigious kind. This can be better appreciated when one realizes that to turn one gram of water at its normal boiling point into steam requires as much heat as to increase the temperature of 539 grams of water by one degree centigrade. To express the fact even more graphically by thinking of heat in terms of energy, we can say that the evaporation occurring each year at the equator over a single square kilometre absorbs energy to the approximate amount of one million horsepower.

The general principle that the sea both absorbs and radiates heat very much more slowly than the land has a decisive influence on the world's climates. These can be broadly divided into two types, the 'continental' and the 'oceanic'. Generally speaking, continental climates are found in the middle of large land masses, oceanic climates wherever the land is bordered by wide oceans. The British Isles are a good example of an oceanic climate, whereas central Siberia is typical of a continental climate.

The detailed picture of both types of climate naturally depends on a wide range of factors, including the influence of the great terrestial wind belts and the proximity of high mountains, but the sea's effect is fundamental. As we in Great Britain know only too well, oceanic climates tend to produce cloud-covered skies and a fairly high rainfall for much of the year; continental climates are drier, and there is seldom a high proportion of cloud. Oceanic climates show comparatively little variation in temperature throughout the year, being characterized by only moderately warm summers and mild winters. This is because the sea acts as a thermostat, remaining cool in summer and warm in winter, and extending its influence over the nearby land. Continental climates show far greater extremes of temperature. Thus in the middle of the Asiatic land mass the winter temperature often falls many degrees below zero, and there is a permanent freeze-up for several months of the year; in the summer, on the other hand, hot sun and cloudless skies turn the same region into a sweltering dust bowl.

The sea's effect on global temperatures is the cause of some of the earth's great winds. Its influence is particularly well shown in southern Asia, where the seasonal fluctuation of temperature between the Indian Ocean and the continental block to the north is the cause of those famous winds known as the monsoons. The word 'monsoon' is derived from the Arabic *mausim*, meaning a set time or season, and the monsoons blow from the south-west between April and October, and from the north-east between October and April. The mechanism of these winds is most interesting. In the blazing summer of this part of the northern hemisphere both land and sea receive the full impact of the sun's rays; but, as we have seen, the sea only absorbs this heat slowly and the land therefore becomes the hotter. As a result the air above it becomes hot too, and begins to expand, thus creating a region of low pressure. Winds then rush in off the sea, where the comparatively low temperature produces a region of higher pressure. This is the south-west monsoon. Conversely, in winter the land radiates its stored heat much more quickly than the sea; the location of the regions of high and low pressure is reversed, and the winds begin to blow from the land to the sea as the north-east monsoon. The direction of the winds would, of course, normally be north and south, but they are deflected north-east and south-west by the spinning of the earth.

The effect of currents has already been briefly touched upon. But these do not only affect climate by increasing the total amount of heat stored by the sea; they also have a direct local effect on coastlines. This can be seen very clearly in the North Atlantic, where the climate of the bordering lands is largely controlled by the behaviour of three currents, one warm, two cold. The warm current is the Gulf Stream. This forms part of the great North Atlantic current eddy, and carries warm water from the equator up the eastern coast of North America and then across the whole breadth of the ocean to western Europe. The cold currents are the Labrador Current and the East Greenland Current, carrying the freezing water of the North Pole southwards along the west and east coasts of Greenland respectively.

When the Gulf Stream meets the two colder currents off Newfoundland its temperature is lowered some 10° to 15° F. This is not only due to actual mingling with the cold water, and to the melting of icebergs which drift into it, but to the bitter winds blowing from the cold to the warm water. Nevertheless its temperature remains sufficiently high for it to wash the western coasts of Europe with warmer water than that found anywhere else in the world at the same latitude. The whole coast above Gibraltar is affected, and the warm waters reach north to Spitzbergen and east to Novaya Zemlya on the Barents Sea. In the latter region they become overlain by colder waters, and lose their identity, but in Spitzbergen they greatly ameliorate the climate. It is an odd fact that the west coast of that island is kept largely free of ice throughout the year, whereas the port of Riga in the Baltic, nearly 30 degrees nearer the equator, is entirely frozen up.

I said above that, broadly speaking, continental climates are found in the middle of large land masses, and oceanic climates where the land is bordered by wide oceans. But there are important exceptions to this rule, especially in middle latitudes, where the general movement of the atmosphere is from west to east. Here east coasts are mainly influenced by air that has travelled across land, west coasts by air that has travelled across sea. Thus the east side of a land mass may sometimes have a strictly continental climate right up to the water's edge simply because it is primarily influenced by off-shore winds.

A good way of bringing out the difference in climate between east and west coasts in the westerly wind belt is to compare the climate of the Japanese city of Yokohama with that of San Francisco in California, both of which are nearly in the same latitude. In August in Yokohama the average temperature is 25·4°C. as against 3°C. for January. In San Francisco, on the other hand, the temperatures are 15·2°C. and 9·7°C. respectively. Subtracting the lower from the higher temperature in each case to get the range, we find that Yokohama has the very large range of 22·4°C. against 5·5°C. for San Francisco. The climate of San Francisco is oceanic, which is exactly what we should expect; but that of Yokohama is continental, although it stands at the very edge of the vast Pacific Ocean. In this case the ocean's influence on climate is entirely counteracted by westerly winds blowing from the heart of Asia.

And now, to conclude, how does the sea affect those local aspects of climate which we know as weather? When we begin to examine this problem in any detail we quickly become lost in a maze of technicalities. I shall therefore restrict myself to one very simple aspect of the subject, which the reader can experience for himself when he is next at the seaside: the behaviour of land and sea breezes.

We all know the delicious feeling of lying on a sunny beach while a cool breeze blows off the sea and prevents our bodies from becoming uncomfortably hot. We may also remember how, after the sun has set, the breeze drops, so that for some time there is complete calm. If we wait for long enough, however, we may next find that the breeze is beginning to get up again. Only this time, instead of blowing from sea to land, it has changed direction, and is blowing from land to sea.

Both on- and off-shore breezes are due to the relative capacity for heat storage of land and sea. In the daytime in warm weather the heat of the sun's rays causes the land temperature to rise higher than that of the sea, and so the air above the land is at relatively low pressure. This causes a breeze to blow in from the sea. In the evening the position is reversed, for the land radiates its heat more quickly. Eventually the air above the land is cooler, and therefore at a higher pressure, than the air over the sea, and an off-shore breeze develops.

Land and sea breezes can best be observed in calm sunny weather, for their behaviour depends on the quick heating effect of the sun, and is easily obliterated if other winds are blowing to any large extent. In Britain they seldom reach a speed of more than 10 m.p.h., but in the tropics, where the heat contrasts are greater, they may blow at more than double that rate. They are, in effect, little monsoons, having a twenty-four hour cycle depending on the alternation of night and day, instead of a yearly cycle depending on the alternation of summer and winter. Thus, when we experience them, we are not only seeing the effect of the ocean on local weather, but a tiny working model of one of the great wind systems of the earth. In this system, as in all other aspects of our climate, the world ocean exercises a decisive influence.

PART II
THE LIFE OF THE SEA

Chapter Seven

THE SEA AS A HOME
FOR LIVING THINGS

ACCORDING to the author of the first chapter of Genesis, God said: 'Let the waters bring forth abundantly the moving creature that hath life.' Modern science confirms the Hebrew poet's view, and it now seems probable that the intertidal beaches of the primeval seas were the cradle of life, the starting point of the majestic process we know as evolution.

To those of us who are stirred by the profounder poetry of earth science the idea of empty seas thundering up the slopes of barren continents for perhaps a thousand million years deeply affects the imagination. But it must be admitted that it is an austere concept. We find it disturbing to look down those long corridors of time, when not even the simplest forms of life stirred in the waters of the oceans; and we turn with relief to the warmer, more familiar, emotions inspired by the contemplation of sea plants and animals.

The story of life in the seas begins over a thousand million years ago and its opening chapters have still been only partially deciphered. The very first chapter is the most difficult of all. How did life begin in the world's first seas? Where did it come from? And what mysterious forces caused it to develop and increase?

Four main explanations have been put forward to account for the origin of life.[14] The first simply denies the validity of the question altogether, stating that the universe has existed for an infinite period, and has always contained living cells. As each star cooled to the point where it became habitable by living things it was colonized by tiny 'seeds' of life, or 'cosmozoans', originating on other heavenly bodies. These were transported from one body to the other by the radiation pressure of starlight.

There is a certain poetic quality about this concept which is very appealing, and it ties up well with the theories recently put forward by Hermann Bondi and Fred Hoyle of the continuous creation of matter. But at the same time we cannot help feeling that it is rather far-fetched. In any case, as it cannot yet be confirmed or disproved by observation or experiment nothing valuable can be said about it at the present time.

The second explanation goes even further in the direction of magic than the first. It simply states that life originated as the result of a supernatural event. The world's religions and mythologies are mainly based on this explanation, and it is surprising how many otherwise high-souled and imaginative men have been persuaded to support a view so lacking in grandeur. There is surely no longer any valid justification for the use of the word 'supernatural' by educated men. The operation of universal law is one of the most pleasing and beautiful qualities of the universe, and every phenomenon must be ultimately explicable in terms of natural processes, whether these be at the physical, mental or spiritual level. To deny this is to deny the majesty of the whole concept, and to plunge the human spirit back into the well of ignorance and superstition from which it seems only recently to be reluctantly emerging.

The third and fourth explanations are more worthy of consideration. The third suggests that life began as the result of some extremely improbable accident, which was nevertheless almost bound to occur given the presence of enough matter in a suitable state for a long enough period of time. Life, it is suggested, resulted from a chance combination of chemical elements which had a statistically possible, although unlikely, chance of being found together in the right place, under the right conditions, at the right time. To take an approximate parallel, if I repeatedly throw twenty dice on a table the degree of probability that I shall, after so many throws, be confronted by, say, twenty sixes, or twenty ones, is mathematically discoverable. The same thing applies to all the other numbers between one and six on the dice. Similarly with the origin of life. Given certain chemical elements known to behave in a certain way under certain conditions of temperature, pressure, and so on, then the chance of producing a 'living' organism (if this is recognized as an inherent possibility in the chemical elements at all) can be determined mathematically.

What the reader may have already detected in this explanation is that it, too, possesses its own particular brand of magic. A quality which I can best describe by the term 'cosmic energy' has been omitted. This is akin to the now discredited 'life-force' of the vitalists, but is extended to cover transformations of inorganic matter as well. The concept assumes that, after all, the changes occurring in the universe are not simply chance events, but have some discoverable direction. It has been popular in recent years to deny the existence of this direction, and to accept only the idea of change. Even today scientists of great eminence are prepared to state that change occurs in an entirely random fashion, and that evolution of either organic or (to broaden the use of the term 'evolution') inorganic matter is an essentially blind process. But if this is so, it is odd that the universe in general, and that aspect of it we call 'life' in particular, shows such a remarkably consistent trend. We accept as a matter of course that non-living matter should precede living matter, that animals are in some way 'higher' in the evolutionary scale than plants, that mammals are 'more advanced' than reptiles, and that man is 'superior' to all other creatures. Even among the ranks of our own species we recognize that spirituality, or 'goodness', is a higher quality than intelligence as such, and that intelligence is certainly superior to unbridled passion, ignorance or lust. If this does not represent an evolutionary hierarchy in which a purposeful progression of values is implicitly assumed, it would be difficult to say what does. It is this consistent trend in evolution that invalidates the suggestion that life was produced by the same blind chance that governs the throwing of a set of dice.

Now once we are convinced that a directional trend in evolution does occur, the need for our third explanation disappears. We are persuaded instead to accept the fourth view – that 'live' matter evolved as logically and inevitably from 'dead' matter as the mammals from the reptiles, the reptiles from the amphibians, and the amphibians from their vertebrate and invertebrate ancestors in the seas. There is, in fact, no real break between living and non-living matter at all. 'Living' matter is simply 'dead' matter at a higher level of organization.

I have gone into this subject at more length in *A Guide to Earth History*.[15] The only point that concerns us here is that this particular stage of evolution – the development of the living from the non-living – probably occurred along the borders of the primeval seas. Have we any idea how the process took place?

We must say at the outset that the subject is highly speculative. We cannot state what actually occurred; we can only suggest certain possibilities. Bearing this fact in mind, let us begin by considering some very odd organisms that live on the borderlines of life: the filter-passing viruses. These minute entities, too small to be detected by the optical microscope, but discernible with the electron microscope, possess some of the properties of both living and non-living matter. They are composed of the substances known as proteins which are strictly chemical in composition. Several kinds of virus, when considered in isolation, have no detectable qualities other than the chemical ones possessed by their constituent proteins. To all intents and purposes they are simply minute crystalline solids. Yet – and here is the important point – if placed in contact with living tissue these same viruses can literally come to life. A good example of this is the tobacco mosaic virus, which, when isolated, seems to be purely chemical in nature, but when injected into the leaves of the tobacco plant infects them with a fast-spreading disease. Alone, the virus is inanimate and incapable of reproduction; introduced into the plant, it multiplies rapidly like any other primitive organism.

It seems possible, therefore, that we must seek for the origin of life in the behaviour of proteins, or the constituents of proteins, under certain physical conditions. Proteins themselves are composed of amino-acids, substances whose chemical composition is known. (Incidentally it is interesting to note that amino-acids can now be artificially produced in the laboratory.) And it so happens that the chemicals found in amino-acids correspond very closely with those we believe to have existed along the shores of the primeval oceans.

It would be extremely rash in the present state of our knowledge to make any dogmatic assertions concerning the actual process by which life was first produced. But as we have already seen, even the earliest seas probably contained a high proportion of dissolved chemicals. Among these there would probably have been carbohydrates derived from carbon compounds in the earth's crust. The sea would also have absorbed such gases as carbon dioxide, chlorine and nitrogen from the atmosphere above. Under these conditions, combinations of the kind found in typical amino-acids could easily have occurred. These in turn may have been acted upon by a chemical agitator, such as phosphorus, so that a new type of chemical combination was produced. This new combination we may regard as a mutation, or 'evolutionary jump', of the kind which has long been familiar to students of the history of life.

Recently several alternative theories have been put forward to explain how the mechanism of the process may have worked. For instance, Dr S. L. Miller of Columbia University suggested in 1956 that lightning flashes may have played a part. At a joint meeting of the New York Academy of Sciences and the American Association for the Advancement of Science, he described some experiments in which powerful electric sparks were passed through a gaseous mixture, including water vapour and gases of the kind that were almost certainly present in the atmosphere of the primeval earth. After a week it was found that a number of organic compounds had been formed, including several different amino-acids.

Another theory put forward at the same meeting by Dr S. Granick of the Rockefeller Institute for Medical Research suggested that the process known as 'photosynthesis' by which plants use sunlight to combine water and carbon dioxide into organic substances, may have originated in a simpler reaction involving inorganic substances alone.[16] Whatever the truth of these, or several other theories that have been put forward, sea water was probably an important ingredient in the development of life.

In later chapters we shall describe some of the strange and beautiful creatures which from such shadowy beginnings spread throughout the waters of the world. But first we must speak in more general terms of the sea as a home for living things. It is one of the vastest and most varied biological environments on the surface of our planet, and its properties have played a vital part in shaping the whole course of evolution.

First, we may find it instructive to compare the relative composition of sea water with that of the body fluids of some of its inhabitants. These are found to be remarkably alike. And not only sea animals, but amphibians, and even the highest

65

land vertebrates, exhibit the same striking parallels. It may at first seem surprising that the liquids in the bodies of such animals as a simple invertebrate, a cod, a frog, and mankind so much resemble the sea in composition, but it becomes less so when we remember the aquatic origin of life. This evidence which we carry in our bodies of our debt to our universal mother, the sea, may also help us understand that the brotherhood of all living things is not just a sentimental conceit but one of the most indisputable facts of science.

The connection will be made clearer by a few figures. The table below gives a comparison between the composition of sea water and the body fluids of various organisms. The reader

COMPARISON BETWEEN THE COMPOSITION OF SEA WATER
AND THE BODY FLUIDS OF VARIOUS ORGANISMS
Adapted from Sverdrup, Johnson and Fleming (1942), p. 270

	Sodium	Potassium	Calcium	Magnesium	Chlorine	SO_4
Sea water ...	100	3·6	3·8	12·1	180	25·2
King crab ...	100	5·6	4·1	11·2	187	13·4
Lobster ...	100	3·7	4·9	1·7	171	6·7
Cod	100	9·5	3·93	1·41	149·7	—
Pollock ...	100	4·33	3·10	1·46	137·8	—
Frog... ...	100	11·8	3·17	0·79	135·6	—
Dog... ...	100	6·6	2·8	0·76	139·5	—

will see that nowhere are the proportions of the different salts very widely divergent, and in some instances (between the dog and the pollock for example) the congruity is quite remarkable.

Water is, of course, essential to the maintenance of all life, but is obtained, and retained, by the organism in different ways according to the environment. Land animals have devised means, such as their watertight skins, to conserve the supply of liquid in their bodies and land plants have roots and stiff-walled tubes, or 'arteries', which carry the moisture of the ground to all growing parts. Animals that have spent the whole of their evolutionary history in the sea have no need of such devices. Except in the coastal strip between the tide lines there is no danger of desiccation, and sea organisms do not require highly specialized means for the conservation or transport of water within their bodies. This difference, resulting directly

66

from the difference between the land and sea environment, is one of the most radical to be found on the surface of our planet.

Apart from its actual wetness, the sea has many distinctive qualities as an environment which strongly affect its inhabitants. One of these, which was referred to in Chapter 6, is its capacity for absorbing and losing large amounts of heat without a rapid or extreme change in temperature. This comparative 'thermal stability' of the sea, as we may call it, means that aquatic organisms are not in general required to make nearly such violent adjustments to temperature changes as those that live on land. Conversely, if a change in temperature does occur, the organisms are exceptionally sensitive to it, and a radical change may produce disastrous results. Disturbance of a regular current system is one of the main ways in which such changes manifest themselves. For example, off the coasts of Ecuador and Peru, which are normally washed by cold currents, a warm current known as El Nino sometimes appears. The result is a wholesale destruction of marine life, including not only fish and other animals that live in the sea itself, but also of sea birds which rely on marine organisms as a source of food.

The sensitivity of aquatic organisms to temperature means that the dividing line between two oceanic regions of different temperature will also represent a barrier between two quite different marine faunas. These will be separated as effectively as cattle are separated by an electrified fence across a field. Such a boundary line, or 'convergence' as it is technically called, occurs in many parts of the world, and especially between the great oceanic currents. For example, one great convergence runs round the earth at approximately 50° S. This is known as the 'antarctic convergence', and it occurs where the dilute but cold (and therefore dense) water of the West Wind Drift, meets the saltier but warm (and therefore lighter) water of the sub-antarctic seas. A ship sailing southwards at this point does not experience a gentle transition from warm to cold, but an abrupt and dramatic climatic change. Within a few hours the temperature of the sea falls between 2° and 5° C. and the clear sub-tropical sky is curtained by sombre grey clouds. The regions on either side of the convergence are entirely distinct biological habitats, with faunas as different from each other as, say, those of forest and plain on the land surface of the earth.

Other factors tending to divide the ocean into a number of distinct habitats are salinity, depth and pressure. As we have seen, the concentration of salt in the sea varies considerably between the dilute waters to be found off the mouths of rivers and the exceptionally saline waters to be found in such regions as the Red Sea. Although the toleration of marine organisms to salinity is remarkably high, the salt concentration does have a noticeable effect on the distribution of species. The effects of depth are still more important. The sun's rays naturally become weaker as they penetrate more deeply beneath the surface, and animals living at different depths must make different adjustments to this factor. This leads to different physical specializations, and also in some species to a daily cycle of vertical migration, depending on the varying light intensity at any given level as the sun rises and sets. At comparatively shallow depths, where the light has not yet been uniformly diffused by scattering in the water, the backs of fish are more fully lit from above than their sides or bellies, and many of them show a protective gradation of colour from dark above to light below. An extreme example of a natural zone of the ocean whose boundaries are entirely determined by light is the abyss, to which the sun's rays never penetrate. This region is of course entirely devoid of plant life, and many of its animal inhabitants have developed luminescent organs.

Pressure, like light intensity, is a factor which depends on depth. The pressure of sea water at different depths varies enormously, ranging from one atmosphere at the surface to nearly a thousand atmospheres in the abyss. Expressed in more familiar terms, this represents a pressure range of from 15 pounds to no less than $6\frac{1}{2}$ tons per square inch. Even at the comparatively moderate depth of five hundred fathoms (where there is a pressure of a little over a hundred atmospheres) a block of ordinary cork or timber can be reduced to half its volume by the squeezing out of the air normally contained in its cells, and in this compressed state it will sink instead of float. Examples have been cited where hollow brass cylinders, closed at both ends, have been squeezed flat, and glass instruments, even when protected by a stout copper case, have been crushed to pieces as a result of being lowered to a depth of 3,000 fathoms. The famous nineteenth-century oceanographer Sir Wyville Thomson used to refer aptly to such phenomena as 'implosions'.[17]

The idea that living things can exist under such extreme pressures strikes us at first as unthinkable, and indeed it was at one time believed that marine life was restricted to the upper waters. But then investigations made with deep-sea trawls, dredges, and plankton nets showed that far from the depths of the sea being barren they were inhabited by a wide variety of organisms. The explanation of this fact is that water is virtually incompressible, so that the environment does not expand or contract with pressure, and an equilibrium is achieved between the inner and outer forces affecting the body tissues. Thus an organism that habitually lives at a certain level is just as well adapted to its environment as we ourselves are to the far from inconsiderable pressure of the atmosphere. Only if it attempts to move rapidly upwards or downwards through a wide range of pressures does it run into trouble. Thus, if a deep sea fish strays accidentally above its normal habitat, the disproportionate expansion of air occurring in the part of its body known as the swim-bladder will make it so buoyant that it will be carried involuntarily upwards towards the surface. The diminishing pressure will cause distension of the body, and a severe disruption of the tissues. As Sir William Herdman has well expressed it, the animal dies a violent death 'from falling upwards'.[18]

It will be seen from the above that the sea is not just a single habitat whose occupants can wander about from place to place at will. It is composed of a number of biological zones, separated by boundaries quite as real as those represented by mountain ranges on the surface of the earth. The only difference is that the barriers in the sea are less obvious and tangible, being more like climatic barriers on land, which subtly but effectively determine the distribution of animal and plant populations. And, as on land, we should remember that certain organisms, less specialized than their fellows, are able to jump these barriers, and enjoy a more wide-ranging life. For example, squids and whales and certain kinds of fish are found over a far wider range of habitats than, say, oysters or sponges or even many free-moving creatures which are nevertheless tied to a narrow range of temperature, pressure or salinity.

So much for the natural factors operating in the sea, and determining its character as a home for living things. But to conclude this chapter we must briefly explain a few of the terms used by scientists to classify the sea into easily distinguishable zones. These are not based on the natural criteria described above, but are for the most part purely arbitrary. They are nevertheless a great convenience, and the reader will find them essential to a proper understanding of the chapters that follow.

The sea itself is one of the three great natural regions of the earth capable of supporting life. These regions are known as 'biocycles', and they collectively constitute the 'biosphere'. Apart from the oceanic biocycle, there is the land biocycle and the fresh-water biocycle. The reader may think that logically there should be an air biocycle as well, but this is really an extension of the other three, into which such animals as birds and insects make only temporary incursions.

The oceanic biocycle is by far the largest of the three, for not only do the seas cover a greater proportion of the earth's surface than the land, but they are habitable to a much greater depth. Land animals and plants can only exist beneath the surface for at most a few feet, but the sea is habitable in parts to a depth of over seven miles. The two main divisions of the oceanic biocycle are the 'pelagic' and the 'benthic'. The first term simply comes from the Greek word for 'sea', and comprises the whole mass of waters in the ocean. The second comes from the Greek for 'depth of the sea', and comprises the sea bottom from the high tide line to the lowest depths of the abyss. Both the pelagic and the benthic zones are themselves sub-divided as shown in the diagram opposite.

It will be seen from the diagram that the two main divisions of the pelagic zone are the neritic province and the oceanic province. The vertical division between these regions has been set somewhat arbitarily at two hundred metres, this figure representing the average depth at the edge of the continental shelf. Seaward of this boundary lies the oceanic province, shoreward the neritic province. Apart from the depth of the bottom in the two provinces, a second important factor dis-

tinguishes them. Two hundred metres not only represents the
vertical boundary separating the continental shelf from the
continental slope and the abyss, but also the approximate
horizontal boundary between the well lighted upper waters
above and the twilight zone and the regions of perpetual
darkness below. Thus, whereas the whole of the neritic province
is a world of light, this is only true of the upper part of the
oceanic province. Below the two hundred metre mark the light
quickly fades away, and there soon begins the dark immensity
of the deep sea.

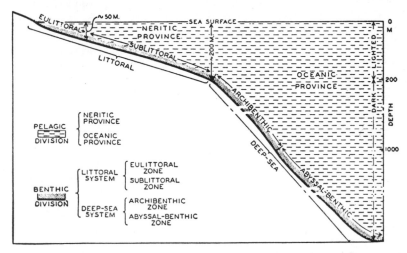

The main divisions of the marine environment. *From Sverdrup, Johnson and
Fleming* (1942), *p.* 275.

The benthic, or bottom, zone, is likewise divided into two
parts, corresponding with the divisions of the pelagic zone
above. Under the neritic province, where the bottom is continually illuminated by the rays of the sun, lies the 'littoral system';
under the oceanic province lies the 'deep sea system'. These two
regions we may also note in passing, are themselves subdivided:
the littoral into the 'eulittoral' and 'sublittoral'; the deep sea
into the 'archibenthic' and 'abyssal-benthic'. The dividing
line between the first two is drawn at the lowest depth occupied
by bottom-growing plants; that between the second pair is
vaguer, and is drawn at different depths according to the views

71

of different oceanographers. The criteria on which they base their decisions are the characters of the animal populations, but such niceties of classification need not concern us here.

The foregoing account has involved the use of a certain number of technical terms, and in the next chapter also, where we shall describe some of the main groups of sea organisms, the reader may feel he is being asked to work rather harder than he should. If such thoughts should occur to him I must ask for his indulgence, for I believe that when he comes to the more lively subject matter that follows he may feel that the effort has been worth while. The knowledge he will then have gained will help him to a far better appreciation of the rest of the story than would otherwise be possible. It will also, I hope, increase his wonder at the principles that govern the great drama of ocean life.

Chapter Eight

THE KINDS OF SEA ORGANISMS

THE organisms living in the sea are classified in two ways: by their habitat and by their family relationships. The earliest classification by habitat was proposed by the German biologist and philosopher Ernst Heinrich Haeckel (1834–1919). He divided all sea organisms, whether they were animals or plants, into two great groups which he called the 'nekton' and the 'benthos' respectively. The nekton (from a Greek word meaning 'swimming') comprised all the organisms of the pelagic zone, or open ocean; the benthos comprised the organisms of the benthic zone, or sea bottom. Later the German physiologist Viktor Hensen added a third vitally important group. This comprised those members of the nekton which were not strictly speaking free-swimming, but drifted helplessly with the tides and currents. Hensen called them by the now familiar name of 'plankton', from the Greek *planktos*, meaning 'wandering'.

The classification by natural family relationship is more complex, but will probably be familiar to readers who already have some knowledge of the biological sciences. The object of the classification is to group together animals and plants with certain anatomical affinities so that they can be considered in a number of convenient 'pigeon holes'. The two main groups into which all living things are divided are, of course, the animal and vegetable kingdoms. These in turn are split up into a number of subdivisions called 'phyla', from the Greek word *phulon*, meaning a 'tribe', or 'race'. In the animal kingdom the vertebrates, or animals with backbones, and a large number of groups of invertebrates are all recognized as phyla. In the vegetable kingdom different phyla contain the seaweeds, the mosses, the ferns, the flowering plants, and so on. The phyla are themselves subdivided into a number of smaller groups called classes, orders, families and genera. Finally come the individual kinds of animals and plants, properly known as

73

species. Here we shall only mention some of the main types of organisms found in the sea.

To begin with the plants, we find that there is a far narrower range of types than is met with on land. The great majority of sea plants belong to the group known as the algae. These are also found in fresh water, and even in damp environments on land, and they are fairly closely related to the fungi and lichens. The members of the group most familiar to us are referred to collectively, and rather inexactly, as 'seaweeds'. There are both fixed and drifting forms of marine algae, and some of the smaller species attach themselves to the bodies of other plants, or even animals. They can be broadly classified into five main groups, distinguished by structure, colour and habitat.

The first are the blue, or blue-green, algae (Cyanophyceae). These little plants commonly live at or near the surface, and are sometimes responsible for forming a slimy covering on the rocks just below high water mark, or even for sliming the whole surface of the sea. The description blue, or blue-green, although generally appropriate enough, is sometimes misleading. For instance, the free-floating form *Trichodesmium erythraeum* has a red accessory pigment, and, as mentioned in Chapter 4, is the organism responsible for tingeing the waters of the Red Sea.

The second group, the green algae proper (Chlorophyceae), are mainly freshwater plants. In the oceans they are normally found close inshore, particularly in the lower tidal zone of fairly warm waters. The commonest examples are *Ulva lactuca* and *Ulva latissima*, commonly known as 'sea-lettuce', which sometimes give the water a perceptibly greenish tinge.

Much more common than either of the foregoing are the brown algae, or Phaeophyceae. These hardly occur at all in fresh water, but their marine forms have a great range of size and structure. Some, such as *Ectocarpus*, are tiny, delicate, branching plants which can only be properly examined under the microscope. Others, such as *Nereocystis* and *Macrocystis* of the Pacific Ocean, are the giants of the alga group, and often measure several hundred feet in length. Between these extremes are several familiar seaweeds found on our own shores: the flat, crinkly *Laminaria saccharina*, for example, or the fronded *Fucus vesiculosus*, with its egg-shaped bladders which children love to pop near the ears of unsuspecting adults.

Seaweeds do not put down true roots into the sea bed as land plants do into the ground. They generally anchor themselves to a rock by a mass of strong root-like processes known as a 'hold-fast'. Often the movement of the sea, especially close inshore on stormy coasts, breaks these hold-fasts and some of the seaweeds become free-drifting organisms. To use the terms we

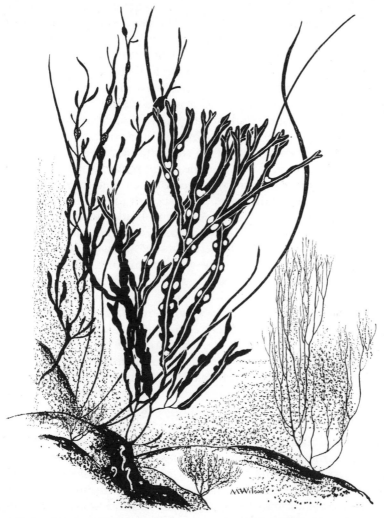

Some characteristic marine algae, including *Ascophyllum* (left), *Fucus vesiculosus* (centre) and *Stilophora* (right).

75

have just described, they cease to be members of the benthos, and join the ranks of the plankton.

Among the brown algae there are numerous planktonic weeds of this kind, some of considerable size. One of the most important groups, including several different species, is known as *Sargassum*, or 'gulf-weed'. The name comes from the Portuguese word *sarga*, meaning 'grape', after the grape-like bladders which give the plant buoyancy. In the great eddy of the North Atlantic known as the Sargasso Sea vast quantities of *Sargassum* have accumulated to form a carpet of weed on the surface of the ocean. This extends over an area between 20° and 40° N. and from about 30° W. to the American coast, and is the home of a huge community of planktonic animals.

The fourth group of algae are the so-called red algae, or Rhodophyceae. Like the brown algae, nearly all these are marine, but they are smaller in size, the largest species being about six feet long. They are the most remarkable of all the algae in appearance, both by reason of their colour and also, in some species, their iridescence. Their colour may range from red to violet, the most purely red forms living at the greatest depths. Apart from their beauty some are also commercially important as the source of the substance known as agar-agar, which is used as a substitute for size, for making culture media for certain moulds and bacteria, and (in a more homely context) as a laxative.

The last group of algae, the yellow-green algae, are in many ways the most interesting. They include a large number of microscopic organisms, notably the little drifting plants known as diatoms. These secrete membranes of translucent silica, infinitely beautiful in their variety of shape and colour. When the plants die, their shells sink to the sea bottom, where they form an important part of the oozes that cover so much of the ocean floor. Grouped with the diatoms are a number of other yellow-green algae that seem to behave to some extent like animals. Typical of these are the dinoflagellates, which are able to propel themselves through the water by a pair of whip-like processes. Many of these microscopic plant-animals are luminescent, and are sometimes present in such numbers as to impart a characteristic colour to the surface waters of the ocean.

Apart from the algae, which are comparatively primitive in

76

structure, some thirty species of higher plants are represented in the sea. These all belong to the phylum Angiospermophyta, which includes also the familiar flowering plants to be found on land. The most interesting sea angiosperm is the plant known as *Zostera marina*, or 'eel-grass'. This is not really a grass at all, but owes its popular name to its long, slender grass-like leaves. It lives from the lowest tide line down to fifty feet below the surface, putting down true roots into the sea bed. Its flowers are pollinated under water by the action of currents. Like all the marine angiosperms, the eel-grass did not originate in the sea, but reinvaded it from the land by way of fresh water. It thus corresponds in the vegetable kingdom to the whale and the seal among animals.

We should remember that all sea plants, like their cousins on land, depend on the rays of the sun for life. Their cells contain a green substance known as chlorophyll, which enables them to use light energy to combine the chemicals of their environment into food. This process is known as photosynthesis, and it is possessed only by plants. Animals cannot perform photosynthesis, but must rely on plants for their food. Even carnivores ultimately need plants for their existence, for their prey, or their prey's prey, turns out at some stage to be vegetarian in habit. This fact is of great significance in determining the pattern of life in the sea. It means, for example, that no sea plants can live below the depth to which the sun's rays penetrate, and that animals below that level must either be strictly carnivorous, or must depend on dead organic matter sinking down from the luminous regions above. The greatest depths from which plants have been taken with any likelihood that they have actually been growing on the bottom is 180 feet. But many floating plants, such as diatoms and dinoflagellates, can exist at much greater depths than this. As we said in the last chapter, the 'light barrier' in the oceans occurs at a depth of about two hundred metres.

Turning now from sea plants to sea animals, we must first say a few words about the way these are classified. Apart from the 'betwixt and between' organisms such as dinoflagellates, thirteen major phyla of animals are represented in the sea. First there is the huge phylum of single-celled, generally microscopic, animals known as the Protozoa. This group includes the

77

famous amoeba of the zoological textbooks, and such creatures as the foraminifera and radiolaria whose shells play an important part in the formation of organic oozes on the sea bed. The next group is the Porifera, or sponges, which includes some of the most primitive and extraordinary creatures existing in the sea. Next come the Coelenterata, including the familiar jellyfish; the Brachiopoda, or 'lamp shells'; the Bryozoa, or 'moss animals'; the Echinodermata, or starfish and starfish allies; the Arthropoda, or crustacean 'shellfish'; the Mollusca, or true shellfish; and four phyla of Vermes, or worms. Last, and also highest in the evolutionary scale, comes the phylum Chordata, consisting mainly of the vertebrates, or back-boned animals.

In the space at our disposal it would be quite impossible to give even the briefest review of the natural history of this vast assemblage of creatures. In any case, this book is intended to be a biography, not an annotated catalogue. But before proceeding, the reader should know at least a few of the characteristics of each group, so that he will recognize the different animals as they turn up.

The Protozoa will unfortunately make but little appeal to the person whose enthusiasm for animals increases in proportion to their size (a reprehensible but common trait even among naturalists). They are nevertheless extremely interesting. Most of the group are so small that they can only be identified under the microscope, and even the largest are no bigger than a pinhead.

A typical protozoan simply consists of a tiny speck of living jelly. This is technically known as protoplasm and is divided into two parts, a central nucleus and an enveloping body of different consistency known as cytoplasm. The organism functions very simply, for there are no special organs for feeding, digestion, reproduction, and so on. Food, which consists largely of plants, is absorbed into the body through a temporary rupture in the cell wall, and the waste products are expelled in the same way. Reproduction is even more primitive, being achieved by the simple expedient of dividing in two. Thus the individual protozoan is not condemned to inevitable death as are all the higher animals. It may die, it is true, by some accident, but in general the immortality of the parent is assured because it passes completely into the body of its two offspring. This is a fact worth pondering by philosophers.

The number of protozoans probably exceeds that of all other animals combined. The amoeba is the best-known form, but in the context of the sea the foraminifers (or 'forams' as they are popularly called) and the radiolarians are more interesting. They are found in all the world's oceans, and somewhat rarely in fresh water as well. Most of them live on the bottom or cling to the fronds of fixed algae, and are thus members of the benthos; but others (about twenty species) are planktonic, floating on or near the surface. Foraminifers are microscopic in size, and secrete a delicate shell, usually of calcium carbonate. This is pierced by a number of tiny holes through which the animal projects writhing whips of protoplasm to reach its food. Incidentally, these holes are the origin of the name foraminifer, which literally means 'hole-bearer'. Radiolarians are not unlike foraminifers, but instead of shells they have elaborate external skeletons, often of great delicacy and beauty.

Our second group, the Porifera, or sponges, are not single-celled animals like the protozoans, but are communities of cells which have already begun to show some degree of specialization. A typical sponge is shaped rather like a slender vase, and consists of a hollow space surrounded by a wall of living tissue. The wall is made up of three layers. The outer layer consists of protective cells, and is known as 'ectoderm'; the inner layer consists of feeding cells, and is known as 'endoderm'. Between these, like the filling of a sandwich, is a jelly-like substance called 'mesoglea'. Piercing the walls are a number of holes, or pores, through which the sponge draws in water by a mechanism of whip-like flagella inside its body cavity. It then ejects this through one end. Food particles in the water are absorbed by the endodermal cells, which act like a battery of individual protozoans. The ectodermal cells take no part in the food gathering, but simply take in what they want from the nearby endodermal cells. All sponges grow on the bottom, usually attaching themselves firmly in colonies to submarine rocks. The homely bath sponge is simply the skeleton of a particularly specialized member of the group which has been dried in the sun and put through a number of purifying processes.

The coelenterates resemble sponges in consisting essentially of a body wall surrounding an empty space (the name Coelenterata comes from two Greek words meaning 'hollow cavity').

But they represent a considerable advance on the Porifera in structure, and are also closer to the main evolutionary stream. For these reasons they must be regarded as very much higher animals. There are three main kinds of coelenterates; the hydroids, the coral polyps and sea-anemones, and the jellyfish. Superficially a vertical section through a typical hydroid suggests that it has close affinities with a sponge. The section reveals the same hollow interior and the same three-layered walls. But on closer examination several important differences become apparent. First, it is found to have muscular tissue which enables it to expand and contract and even to enjoy some degree of locomotion; a complex of muscles also controls a ring of tentacles round the mouth which assist it in capturing food. Second, glands on the inner layer of the body wall are found to secrete juices which help the digestion of food. Third, there are a number of stinging cells which enable it to paralyse animals that come in contact with its outer surface.

The closely-related coral polyps and sea-anemones have a family likeness to the hydroids, but are more complicated in structure. The coral polyps live in colonies in warm shallow seas. They secrete external skeletons of calcium carbonate, which build up over the years into the familiar coral reefs of tropical and sub-tropical seas. It is these skeletons, and not the polyps themselves, which are properly termed coral. They are often very brightly coloured, and in this respect resemble the bodies of their cousins, the sea-anemones. Visitors to the Zoo aquarium often mistake sea-anemones for plants, and indeed some species have a superficial likeness to chrysanthemums. A thick 'stalk' is surrounded at the top by a ring of tentacles with which the anemone draws its food into the central mouth cavity. The beauty of these simple animals is as appealing to the senses as anything in the flower gardens at Wisley or Kew (Plate 6b).

The best-known of the coelenterates round our own shores is the jellyfish. Few visitors to the seaside will have failed to notice these strange animals, which can often be seen stranded on the beach by the ebb tide, or slowly pulsating in the water. They have an umbrella-like shape, with a number of long tentacular 'lips' surrounding the mouth. They progress by opening and closing the umbrella, and the lips trail behind them as they move along. A related coelenterate is the 'Portuguese man-o'-war', scientifically known as *Physalia* (Plate 6*a*). This creature consists of an oval gas-filled bladder, bluish-pink in colour, with a notched pink-coloured crest. Each *Physalia* is not a single animal, but a colony of individuals specialized in different directions. A number of long tentacles trail beneath the bladder

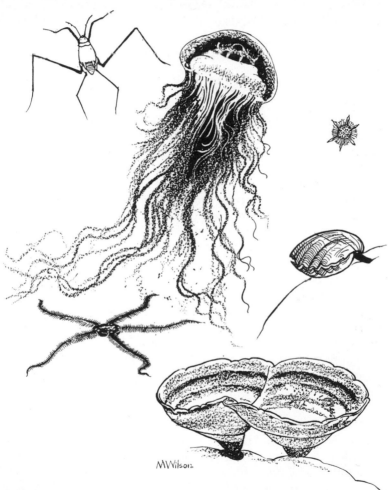

Some characteristic marine invertebrates. The marine insect *Halobates* (top left); the jellyfish *Cyanea* (top centre), a microscopic radiolarian (top right); a brachiopod (right centre), the brittle-star *Ophiocoma nigra* (bottom left); and the sponge *Axinella infundibuliformis* (bottom right).

to a depth of many feet. Even ordinary jellyfish can inflict a painful sting, and that of the Portuguese man-o'-war is exceptionally severe. When, as sometimes happens, it appears off our shores in large numbers it is customary for notices to be posted to tell bathers of the danger, and for a warning to be broadcast by the B.B.C.

Compared with the coelenterates, the brachiopods are an unspectacular phylum. They have a double hinged shell seldom measuring more than an inch across. At one end is a hole through which the animal projects a fleshy stalk, or 'peduncle', to attach itself to the sea bed. In the geological past of our earth the brachiopods were a very successful phylum, and their fossilized remains are found in strata at least 400 million years old. Even today more than two hundred species are recognized, including the little Australian brachiopod *Lingula*, which can claim to be one of the oldest 'living fossils' in the world.

Our next phylum, the bryozoans, are not unlike brachiopods in some respects, but are very small and always grow in colonies. They form simple external skeletons, tubular or box-like in shape, from which they can thrust out the fore-part of their bodies to feed. Their name comes from the Greek word *bryon*, meaning 'moss', which the colonial skeleton sometimes resembles when it spreads its encrustations over the intertidal rocks. But the skeletons vary greatly between the different species (of which there are over three thousand) and below low tide level the colonies often grow rigid and erect.

The three great phyla we must next consider are the most important among marine invertebrates. The echinoderms, or 'hedge-hog skins', are often characterized by a covering of spines, as their name suggests. The phylum consists of seven natural classes: the echinoids, or 'sea-urchins'; the crinoids, or 'sea-lilies'; the ophiuroids, or 'brittle-stars'; the holothurians, or 'sea-cucumbers'; the starfishes; the blastoids; and the cystoids. Of these, the last two classes are now extinct. I do not intend to weary the reader by describing each of these groups in detail. The familiar starfish and the sea-urchin will suffice to give a very good idea of what a typical echinoderm is like. Similarly it would be quite impossible to give an adequate description here of all the many subdivisions of the molluscs and arthropods. There are probably over fifty thousand living species of molluscs alone, not to mention the many extinct forms. Typical members of the group, such as the clams and marine gastropods, have hinged or spirally twisted shells, but others, such as the octopuses, are shell-less. The arthropods are distinguished by their jointed legs and a segmented external skeleton of chitin. The group includes lobsters, crabs, barnacles, copepods, sea-spiders, and one of the very few examples of a marine insect, the creature known as *Halobates*. Both the molluscs and the arthropods are well represented on land as well as at sea, the former by the snails and their kin and the latter by such creatures as insects and spiders.

Little need be said about the four phyla of worms, which are mainly of interest to specialists. But we may note in passing that by no means all the species of worms found in the sea are as uninspiring in appearance as the common earthworm. Many are beautifully coloured, and there is an infinite variety of structure and shape between the different species.

The last great natural group of animals represented in the sea is the phylum Chordata. This is almost entirely composed of vertebrates, although it also includes a few primitive creatures which have no true back-bone, but only the structure known as a 'notochord', which preceded the back-bone in the evolution of life. The most widely distributed marine vertebrates are the fish, but the group also includes the marine reptiles, and certain mammals, such as the whale, porpoise and seal which have returned from the land to their ancestral environment. Sea birds, although not marine vertebrates in the strictest sense, likewise form part of the pattern of ocean life – as, indeed, does man himself.

This, then, is the cast that plays out the great drama of life in the sea. It is a drama of which we on land are still scarcely conscious, although the development of underwater photography, and the studies of oceanographers and marine biologists, are bringing it increasingly before our minds. Many more life-times will have to be devoted to these studies before we can hope fully to understand the workings of marine organisms, or even to discover all the kinds of animals that live beneath the waves. In the following chapters the most we can do is to indicate some of the problems involved, and outline a few of the marvellous facts that have already been revealed.

Chapter Nine

THE OCEAN WANDERERS

THE plankton, or ocean wanderers, are the largest of all the populations of the sea, and are the basis of its economy; yet until the middle of the last century their significance had not even begun to be recognized. As we have already seen, the term plankton simply means 'wandering', but it now needs a more exact definition. The plants and animals of the plankton are not wanderers in the sense that a migrating fish is a wanderer. The fish, like the other larger animals of the sea, is a free swimmer, and can strike out its own line through the water. But the animals of the plankton are all minute, many of them microscopic. Such creatures do not have organs of locomotion of sufficient strength to make them independent of the major movements of the sea; they are doomed to drift helplessly at the mercy of the great ocean currents.

The distribution of plankton throughout the world ocean is clearly defined. Some areas are so rich in life that a liqueur glass of sea water will contain several thousand planktonic organisms. Other areas are almost barren. Moreover the concentration of planktonic life varies as much at different depths as it does in horizontal distribution. Each layer of the sea has its own population according to the different specializations of the organisms inhabiting it.

To a traveller on an ocean liner the distribution of the surface plankton will often be readily apparent, even if he does not know the cause of the phenomenon. One of the main indications, as we have seen, is the colour of the water. Deep green water indicates the presence of plankton in large numbers. Blue, on the other hand, is the colour of the deserts of the sea, where only very few drifting organisms occur. Other shades may indicate the presence of planktonic populations containing a higher proportion of this or that organism. This is very important to fishermen, for the nature of the plankton determines to a large extent the nature of the fish that come to feed in the region. A practised fisherman is capable of recognizing subtle

84

variations in hue which would be scarcely noticeable to the untrained eye. And according to whether he is fishing in 'green water', 'yellow water', or 'red water', he will often be able to predict with reasonable likelihood the nature and size of his catch.

At night the presence of plankton is indicated by the phenomenon we know as phosphorescence. This was for many centuries regarded as one of the great mysteries of the ocean. An early, and quite erroneous, hypothesis was that the sea stored up the sun's light by day and radiated it again at night; another, equally inaccurate, was proposed by the eminent scientist Sir Robert Boyle (1627–91), who ascribed the effect to friction between waves and the atmosphere, or between waves and solid objects such as ships or rocks. Benjamin Franklin regarded it as an electrical phenomenon, until he found that sea water lost its sparkle if kept for some time in a container.[19] It was not until the second half of the eighteenth century that phosphorescence was correctly explained for what it is: the natural radiation from a large number of minute sea organisms equipped with luminescent cells.

Nearly all planktonic animals are capable of radiating phosphorescent light, often of surprising power. For instance, it has been proved by experiment that six of the little planktonic animals known as euphausiids, placed in a glass jar, will radiate just enough light to allow a person of good eyesight to read a newspaper.[20] Phosphorescence is usually seen most clearly when the surface of the sea is disturbed, as by the movement of an oar, or by the waves set up in the wake of a ship. But sometimes the planktonic animals are so numerous as to produce a universal radiance. For example, the famous oceanographer Sir John Murray wrote concerning a concentration of plankton he encountered in the Straits of Gibraltar: 'The surface water here was so full of phosphorescent *Noctiluca* as to be almost as thick as broth, and . . . in the evening the sea resembled a star-spangled sky.'[21] Charles Darwin, too, was deeply impressed by the phenomenon, and wrote in *The Voyage of the Beagle*:

'While sailing in these latitudes [i.e. off eastern South America] near the River Plate on one very dark night, the sea presented a wonderful and most beautiful spectacle. There was a fresh breeze, and every part of the surface, which during the

85

day is seen as foam, now glowed with a pale light. The vessel drove before her bows two billows of liquid phosphorus, and in her wake she was followed by a milky train. As far as the eye reached, the crest of every wave was bright, and the sky above the horizon, from the reflected glare of these livid flames, was not so utterly obscure as over the rest of the heavens.'[22]

Now, what is the nature of this planktonic life, drifting endlessly with the currents of the world ocean, and revealing itself to the wondering spectator in vivid hues of red and green, or the soft, mysterious radiance emanating from the night sea? Plankton, as we have seen, includes both animal and vegetable forms, and even some organisms that have the characteristics of both. The vegetable plankton is known as phytoplankton, from the Greek *phyton*, meaning a plant; the animal plankton as the zooplankton, from the Greek *zōon*, meaning an animal.

The phytoplankton has been aptly called the pasturage of the sea. The tiny diatoms and other algae to which we have already referred are the ultimate food supply of the oceans. By the complicated process of photosynthesis they use the sun's rays and the chemicals of their environment to nourish and sustain their bodies without need of other food. But just as the pasturage of the earth provides sustenance for terrestial herbivores, so does the phytoplankton give nourishment to a multitude of tiny plant-eating animals in the same drifting community. These animals are in turn preyed upon by the small sea carnivores, and so on until the chain of eaters and eaten culminates in man, who derives so much of his sustenance from the animals of the sea.

It is interesting to note that some of the vitamins so necessary to human health can trace back their origin to the diatoms of the plankton. For example, we all know the value of cod-liver oil as a nutritive substance for our own bodies. The vitamin contained in cod-liver oil is in fact manufactured by diatoms. It then passes into the stomachs of small planktonic animals which use the diatoms for food, and thence into the little fish known as the capelin (*Mallotus villosus*). This fish is commonly found in northern waters, where it forms the main food of the cod. Thus the vitamin of the diatom is passed along the food chain until eventually it reaches our own stomachs by way of the familiar bottle on the chemist's shelves.

The animals of the zooplankton are not drawn from any single natural phylum. There are, of course, a large number of single-celled protozoans, but many higher forms of life are also represented. In fact, nearly every invertebrate phylum has produced a number of purely planktonic forms, and several of the lower chordates are present as well. This community of drifters can be divided into two main groups. First there are animals that remain members of the plankton for the whole of their lives. A large proportion of marine plankton, and nearly all the plankton found in fresh water, belong to this group, which is known as the holoplankton (Greek *holos*, 'whole' or 'entire'). The second group, known as the meroplankton (Greek *meros*, 'a part') consists of the larval forms of free-swimming and bottom-living animals, which are temporary members of the plankton only while they go through the earliest stages of their development. These partially planktonic animals form a large proportion of the drifting populations of the sea, but are hardly represented in fresh water. According to R. E. Coker this fact may be partly accounted for by the higher specific gravity of sea water, which favours the development of free-swimming habits at some stage in an organism's development.[23]

Before continuing with some more general issues, let us look at a few typical members of the zooplankton. By far the most important planktonic animals are the copepods, or 'oar-feet', a group of diminutive crustaceans widely distributed in both fresh and salt water. They are not only found at all depths in the sea, but in lakes, ponds, subterranean waters, and even in wet sand, debris or moss above the water level. No member of the group exceeds ten millimetres in length, the average being two to three millimetres. Yet in spite of their small size, no other class of aquatic invertebrates is so widely distributed, nor plays such an important part in the economy of the seas.

There are numerous species of copepods, and their penetration into so many habitats has led to a great variety of specialization. Yet a typical copepod can generally be recognized by its shape. The body is oval, with a tail-like extension behind; two antennae project sideways from the head, and there are four or five pairs of oar-like legs. With these and the antennae the copepods row themselves through the water in a series of jerks. The range of colour is considerable, and some of the larger forms, especially in the tropics, gleam red or bronze with the lustre of burnished metal.

The sex life of copepods is intriguing, although some of us may feel that the subtler and more pleasurable refinements of physical communion are lacking. The mature male does not in fact copulate with the female at all, but deposits his sperm in a bottle-shaped container of his own manufacture. This is made of a plastic-like substance secreted by a gland. Thus equipped, he swims off in search of a female and seeks to attach the bottle to a hole in the foremost section of her segmented abdomen. Not surprisingly, the female is inclined to resent this unromantic method of approach, and the male often has to use a certain amount of force. Some species have one of their antennae hinged so that the female can be firmly held and her attempts at resistance overcome. Two of the thoracic limbs are also modified into pincers to assist in the delicate operation. Once the bottle (or 'spermatophore' as it is correctly termed) is fastened in position, the sperms pass through its neck into a storage cavity in the body of the female. This in turn is connected with the ducts leading from the ovary. As the eggs pass down the ducts, they are fertilized from the store of sperm before being extruded into the water. In some species the fertilized eggs remain for some time attached to the underside of the body, either as a simple cluster or in a pair of egg sacs. The supply of sperms in the body cavity of the female may be sufficient to last the rest of her spawning life, and thus, after only one mating, she may be rendered entirely independent of male society. The fact that this rather frosty pattern of nuptial behaviour has been superseded in the higher animals is distinctly encouraging to those who believe in the purposeful direction of evolution.

In our northern waters the most important copepod is known as *Calanus finmarchicus*. In common with other plankton, it is caught for study in a conical net towed behind a ship, and the catches show that it exists in inconceivable numbers. Thus on one occasion when a net just over three feet in diameter, was towed for fifteen minutes in the Gulf of Maine, it was found when raised to contain no fewer than $2\frac{1}{2}$ million specimens of *Calanus*. This copepod is one of the main ingredients in the diet of that important food-fish, the herring, and surprisingly enough, it is also consumed in vast quantities by whales. The herring shoals naturally congregate where *Calanus* exists in the largest numbers, a fact which is well known and most useful to fishermen. The fish swim through the dense mass of plankton, engulfing thousands of copepods at a time. As many as 6,000 *Calanus* have been found in the body of a single herring, and the crops of sea birds such as albatrosses and petrels are likewise often found to be crammed to capacity with their remains.

Apart from the copepods the most important group of plank-tonic crustaceans are the euphausiids, already briefly referred to in connection with luminescence. There are many species and, like *Calanus*, they are an important item in the diet of the blue, fin and humpback whales. Norwegian whalers refer to the euphausiids collectively as 'krill', a word that has now passed into common use among marine biologists and oceanographers.

The general appearance of the euphausiids is shrimp-like. They are among the largest planktonic animals, some species, such as *Meganyctiphanes norvegica* from the waters round our own coasts, measuring nearly two inches in length. Most euphausiids are transparent and colourless, although there are some notable exceptions which are bright red. They inhabit the colder waters of the northern and southern hemispheres, where they some-times collect together in such prodigious numbers that the whole sea is stained the colour of blood. At such times, fish and sea birds come in from miles around to share the feast with the giant whalebone whales which always appear when there are large congregations of krill. When dusk falls, the light organs, which are one of the main features of the euphausiid body, cause the whole surface of the ocean to glow with a ghostly radiance.

The breeding habits of the euphausiids are similar to those of the copepods, the eggs being fertilized internally by sperm attached by the male to the female body in a bottle-shaped spermatophore. But in the euphausiids the pincer-like modi-fication of the limbs (in this case the first abdominal, not the last thoracic, pair as in the copepods) is even more extreme. The limbs are equipped with a number of devices which have been compared by Professor Sir Alister Hardy of Oxford to the blades of a complex jack-knife. These devices are prehensile, like fingers, and are used with the utmost precision and delicacy to insert the neck of the spermatophore into the appropriate aperture in the female's body.[24]

The eyes of the euphausiids are particularly distinctive, being proportionately as huge and black as those of gypsies. For this reason Scottish fishermen refer to the animals as *Suil dhu* or 'black eyes'. The crustacean eye is a compound structure not unlike that of an insect. It is made up of a vast number of individual tubular lenses, each pointing in a slightly different direction. This enables the animal to take in a very wide field of vision, which in the planktonic crustacea, where the eyes are frequently mounted on stalks, may exceed 180°. There is a corresponding disadvantage, however, for the presence of many eyes instead of one means that instead of a single image the visual impression consists of a mosaic of small pieces. Thus the crustacean cannot 'see' as we see, but can only obtain a generalized picture of the outside world based on patterns of light and shade on the mosaic. The mechanism is nevertheless adequate to enable the animal to judge the distance and direction of external objects, and the wide field of vision must be of particular value to planktonic creatures, whose foes may lurk above or below, to back or to front, or on either side.

The copepods and euphausiids represent the best known members of the permanent, or holoplankton, but there is also a profusion of bizarre and unusual forms. Among these, the commonest belong to the group known as the Chaetognatha, or arrow-worms, whose ancestors are known from fossils dating back at least 500 million years. A typical arrow-worm of the genus *Sagitta* resembles a little glass rod about three-quarters of an inch long with a number of protuberances. But in spite of its small size and delicate appearance it is one of the fiercest and most voracious creatures in the sea. For minutes at a time it may hang poised motionless in the water, waiting for some other planktonic animal to come within range. Then suddenly it will shoot towards its prey with the speed of an arrow, propelled by rapid movements of the tail. With jaws wide open it will seize upon the luckless animal and devour it, even though its victim may sometimes be almost the length of its own body. It is only when thus gorged with food that *Sagitta* can be easily seen, for its own body is transparent and almost invisible.

Another member of the zooplankton of somewhat violent

habits is the crustacean *Phronima*. Its favourite prey is a brilliantly phosphorescent colonial animal known as *Pyrosoma*, which inhabits tropical and subtropical seas. *Pyrosoma* is a pelagic tunicate (one of the primitive chordates referred to in the preceding chapter), consisting of a large number of small individuals formed by budding. A small colony may be only an inch or two long, but one species produces colonies measuring up to four feet long. *Phronima* eats its way round a small

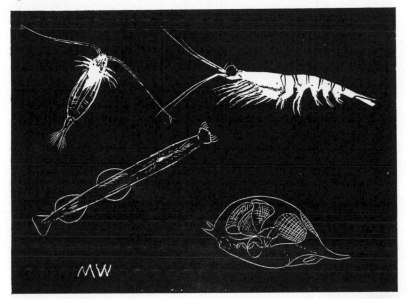

Planktonic animals: *Calanus finmarchicus* (top left); a large euphausiid; *Meganyctiphanes norvegica* (top right); the arrow-worm *Sagitta* (bottom left); and *Oikopleura* in its envelope. *After Hardy* (1956), *p.* 155.

Pyrosoma colony, consuming the individual animals one by one, until only the barrel-shaped bag of skin which formed the point of attachment is left. It then takes possession of this structure as a home for itself and a cosy dwelling in which to rear its young. *Phronima* has sometimes been seen to swim through the water pushing a barrel-load of youngsters in front of it with no more conscience than a mother wheeling her children in a pram.

So far in this chapter we have been dealing mainly with the crustacea, which belong to the phylum Arthropoda, but many of the other phyla have equally interesting planktonic representatives. One of these is *Pleurobrachia*, commonly known as the 'sea-gooseberry', which is usually classified with the coelenterates but is in fact so different from them that it could well be assigned to a distinct phylum. As its popular name suggests, the animal is shaped very like a gooseberry. It is an inch or more in length, with a mouth at the lower end and, at the upper, a remarkable device enabling it to stabilize itself in the water. This consists of a mass of tiny calcareous granules enclosed in a glass-like dome. The exact method by which the 'stabilizer' functions is unknown, but it enables the sea-gooseberry to correct any tendency to tilt in the water with considerable efficiency.

The food-catching mechanism of this animal is most remarkable. Two whip-like tentacles, about ten times longer than the *Pleurobrachia* itself, grow from little pockets on either side of its body. From these, shorter lashes project at right angles, covered with small adhesive knobs which, when touched, exude a sticky secretion. The movements of the lashes are beautifully controlled by two fibres, one elastic, which runs the length of the lash, the other coiled round the first like a spring. The tentacles and lashes are in constant motion, propelling their owner through the surrounding plankton. When one of the lashes makes contact with a potential victim, the adhesive knobs exude their secretion and attach themselves to the creature's body. In its struggles to escape it becomes entangled in other lashes, and is eventually drawn by the tentacles into the *Pleurobrachia*'s mouth. If the intended victim is particularly large, the *Pleurobrachia* will 'play' it as an angler plays a fish, by alternately expanding and contracting the tentacle. This operation may go on for half an hour or more before the struggling animal is 'landed'. Sometimes, as happens also to human fishermen who play their fish badly, the 'line breaks'; in other words, the tentacle snaps and is carried away by the intended prey.

An even more unusual feeder among the zooplankton is the minute creature known as *Oikopleura*. This is one of the commonest and smallest planktonic animals, with an oval body no more than one-sixth of an inch in length and a thin tail about four times as long. It has devised a means of catching its prey that must rank among the most marvellous adaptations produced by the evolutionary process. This is no other than an elaborate and efficient plankton-catching machine which is produced in a most wonderful way from the tissues of the animal's own body. It first secretes from its surface an extremely thin, transparent substance so that its body is encased in a membranous envelope. This envelope is elastic, and the *Oikopleura* next separates it from its body by vigorous movements of its tail. It then undulates the tail so that a stream of water flows between it and the inner wall of its 'house', as the envelope is usually called; this inflates the membrane so that the animal is enclosed in a kind of miniature, transparent barrage balloon. The water enters the envelope through two 'windows' at the rear, over which are stretched a network of fine threads like a very much more delicate version of the perforated zinc covering of a meat safe. It passes out by a hole at the front. Also towards the front of the house are two cone-shaped nets of gossamer-like thread which lead to the mouth of the *Oikopleura*. The grids over the rear windows filter out all but the tiniest microplanktonic animals and plants. These last are then carried forward by the current system to the nets, where they are trapped by the threads and conveyed to the animal's mouth. When we remember that the whole body of *Oikopleura* is no bigger than a match-head we will gain some idea of how extremely minute the captured organisms must be; some of them, in fact, measure less than a five hundredth of a *millimetre* across, and cannot be caught in any form of net so far devised by man.

Once the *Oikopleura* has constructed its marvellous apparatus it uses it throughout its life. But in case of danger, when the house and nets might prove an encumbrance, there is a back door, or 'emergency exit' situated below the rear windows. If alarmed, the animal simply shoots through this bolt hole, and darts away to safety with a few quick lashes of its tail. When calm is restored it quickly secretes a new house, with all the same elaborate refinements. The almost incredible beauty and ingenuity of nature are nowhere better manifested than in these life activities of *Oikopleura*, which emphasize so well and so strongly the essential harmony between evolutionary principles and the concept of God.

Although the great majority of planktonic animals are at most an inch or two in length, there are some exceptions to this rule. Notable among these are the group of coelenterates known as medusae, or jellyfish, which range in size from tiny polyps to creatures measuring several feet across. The jellyfish which commonly cause consternation among bathing parties along the shores of Britain usually belong to the species *Aurelia aurita* or *Cyanea capillata*. The former is the more common, and is easily recognized by the four purple ovals which adorn the top of the umbrella. This species may grow to be eighteen inches across, but has very short tentacles and is harmless to man. *Cyanea capillata*, on the other hand, can give a nasty sting. This is the largest of all jellyfish, and although specimens more than two feet across are rare off British coasts, specimens three times that size have been recorded from arctic waters. The colour ranges from brown to bright orange, deep red, or even purple, and a vast number of whip-like tentacles, which may be as much as six or eight feet long, are attached to the umbrella. As *Cyanea* drifts with the currents these tentacles spread out in a graceful fringe on every side of its body. But this attractive appearance is deceptive. The tentacles are equipped with numerous powerful stinging cells, which paralyse any small animal unfortunate enough to come in contact with them. Even man is not large enough to be immune, and the sting makes the skin red and tender for several hours. Yet in spite of this unpleasant trait certain sea animals enjoy a most interesting association with *Cyanea*. For instance, young whiting are commonly found sheltering beneath the umbrella, as are the odd bulbous-headed crustaceans known as *Hyperia galba*. It seems that these animals are there to steal the planktonic food paralysed by their host's tentacles, but how they avoid being stung themselves is still a mystery.

So far we have been discussing only members of the permanent plankton, or holoplankton, but, as mentioned earlier, many other sea animals are planktonic in the early stages of their development. In fact there is hardly a member of the benthos or nekton which does not (like some human beings in a different context) pass through a drifting phase in its youth. The importance of the planktonic phase is particularly strong among the creatures of the benthos. Bottom dwellers are handicapped in comparison with the free-swimmers of the nekton, or even with the permanent drifters, by their inability to move from place to place. Many of them are as immobile as plants and, like plants, must find some way of scattering their offspring over as wide an area as possible. The answer that many species have devised is to cast their young on the waters as plankton, so that they may be carried by the currents to new areas just as the seeds of plants are distributed by the wind. Crabs, lobsters, oysters, limpets, sea-urchins, and starfish are all among the familiar bottom-dwellers that produce planktonic young.

The difference between the planktonic larvae and their benthic or nektonic parents is often so great that even an experienced naturalist would not always think of associating the two. In fact, such differences have sometimes caused students to make some amusing mistakes in classification. For example in the drawings on the next page are shown three stages in the development of the common edible crab, *Cancer pagurus*. Early investigators, it must be admitted with every excuse, regarded these as three different animals. The first development stage was named *Zoea*; the second, *Megalopa*. It is now known, of course, that *Zoea*, *Megalopa* and the adult *Cancer* are all the same animal at different levels of development, the first being the planktonic stage, the second the intermediate stage. But the reader will recognize from the illustration that it would have been quite impossible to discover this without a complete series of observations of the creature's life history.

One interesting feature of the zooplankton, both permanent and temporary, is the way in which the different animals have become adapted to a drifting life. The transparency of some species of plankton has already been referred to, and this is found to be almost universal. The explanation lies in the advantage this characteristic gives the otherwise almost helpless drifters in avoiding predators. An even more basic adaptation is that made for suspension in the water. It may have already occurred to the reader to ask why members of the plankton, many of whom are incapable of making any but the most rudimentary swimming movements, should not sink to the bottom of the sea. One of the most obvious expedients open to them is to reduce their specific gravity to that of the surrounding sea water, and this is in fact achieved in a number of interesting ways.

The reader will observe in the illustrations accompanying this chapter that a marked characteristic of the plankton is the presence of spines and feather-like processes projecting

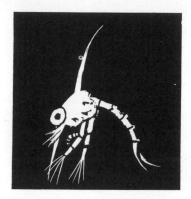

Zoea (left) and *Megalopa* (right), the two earliest stages in the development of the edible crab.

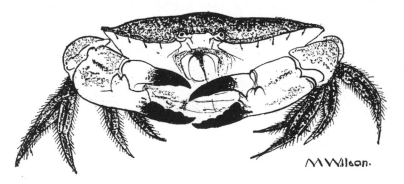

The adult edible crab, *Cancer pagurus*.

from the body. These add greatly to the beauty of the organisms, but their value is far from being purely aesthetic. The effect of these processes is greatly to increase the surface area of the body in proportion to its weight. This in turn causes an increase in the frictional resistance set up between the body and the sea water as gravity tends to drag it down towards the ocean floor. As a result it falls very much more slowly than it would if the processes were not present.

Another characteristic found in some species of plankton which fulfils the same function is a marked horizontal flattening of the body. This has the same effect as the spines or other processes, causing an increase in resistance and therefore slower sinking. The effect can be compared to a tea tray falling through the water. If the tray is kept parallel with the surface it will sink very slowly, but if it is turned at right angles to it it will swiftly slide to the bottom. Similarly we know from our own experience of bathing that we can only float if we lie stretched out at full length along the surface of the sea.

The importance of maintaining a certain angle relative to the water surface may be one reason why many planktonic organisms have developed elaborate stabilizing devices, such as that already mentioned in connection with *Pleurabrachia*, the sea gooseberry. An even more remarkable mechanism of this kind is found in the little medusa *Obelia*. Spaced round the umbrella of this animal are eight hollow cell-lined spheres known as statocysts. Each sphere contains a small calcareous nodule which rolls about like a marble in a teacup as *Obelia* dips to one side or the other. If the animal dips too far in one direction all the nodules fetch up on the corresponding side of their own spheres. Here their pressure effects a number of little hair-like sensory processes attached to the sphere walls, which in turn stimulate the muscles of the umbrella on that side, causing them to contract, and thus bringing *Obelia* back to the level position.

To return to suspension problems, it is clear that although spines, feathery processes and horizontal flattening may reduce the rate of sinking to a very great extent, they cannot entirely arrest it. They must be supplemented by some other device which actually counteracts the force of gravity and tends to bring the organism towards the surface. The most extreme example of this is the gas-filled bladder of the Portuguese man-o'-war, and the smaller but no less effective float of its ally *Velella velella*, the 'By-the-wind-sailor'. But many smaller creatures have made steps in the same direction by the use of oily substances secreted by their own bodies. Such substances are lighter than water and therefore tend to float to the surface.

They thereby counteract the action of gravity on the body of the organism and, in conjunction with the effect of spines, horizontal flattening and the other devices already referred to, a satisfactory equilibrium is achieved.

To conclude this chapter one other characteristic of the plankton must be briefly referred to: this is their habit of vertical migration. Their horizontal movements are almost entirely dictated by current movements over which the organism has no control, but with vertical movements the picture is somewhat different. Although, as stated earlier, different planktonic organisms are found at different depths according to their own peculiar specializations, the population does move up and down in a most decided way according to changes in the environment. The most important of such changes, it has been found, are almost certainly due to differences in the intensity of light reaching the different levels from the sun's rays above. These are in turn dependent on the yearly cycle of the seasons and the regular alternation of day and night.

It has been found that at high noon, and particularly in summer time, the upper levels of the sea are almost devoid of plankton. To obtain a good catch it is necessary to tow one's nets at a depth of at least ten fathoms. But as the sun declines, the limit of life begins to move gradually upwards, and during the hours of darkness the region immediately below the surface is as densely populated as the waters below. At sunrise the opposite effect can be observed, and the planktonic organisms gradually sink. Moreover the depth to which they sink is greater in summer, when the sun's rays are strongest, than it is in winter. This confirms the view that light intensity is the deciding factor in vertical migration.

A further interesting phenomenon has been observed. Whereas in the daytime organisms of different kinds are largely 'sorted out' into layers one above the other, at night this is not the case. The organisms of different layers then join together in a single conglomeration. The upward limit of this conglomeration, as stated above, is now raised to the surface of the sea, but the lower limit is not raised to a corresponding extent. The organisms wander at random between the lowest level and the highest. It thus seems that each group of planktonic organisms has its own critical light tolerance, which in the daytime determines the depth at which it is most at home, and sorts the whole planktonic population into layers. At night this sorting influence is removed, and the organisms move about at will.

One fact that is clearly underlined by these observations is the beautiful and fundamental relationship between an organism and its surroundings. Like all living things, the animals and plants of the plankton are an intrinsic part of their environment, completely responsive to its laws, yet able by their different adaptations to evolve within the special context of the sea a number of richly varied answers to the problem of living.

Chapter Ten

LIFE ON THE SEA FLOOR

OWING to the misconceptions concerning pressure described in Chapter 7, it was once believed that life could not exist in the sea below a comparatively shallow depth. The first evidence to the contrary was provided in 1860 by the raising of a broken submarine cable in the Mediterranean from a depth of over a thousand fathoms. To the surprise of marine biologists, this was found to be encrusted with a rich fauna of bivalve molluscs, worms, gastropods and other animals.[25] Later investigations made with dredges, trawls and similar devices have shown that there is no region of the ocean bed in which some form of bottom-living organism is not present.

This rich benthic life can be broadly divided into two categories. First there are those creatures, such as gastropods and crustaceans which, although bound to the bottom by the weight of their shells and bodies, are yet able to move about within a restricted range. Second there are creatures which are actually fixed to the bottom in one position throughout their lives. These include oysters, limpets, corals, sponges, sea anemones, sea lilies, certain worms and echinoderms, and a large number of other sea animals. For those who find satisfaction in using long words it has been proposed that the first category should be known as the herpetobenthos (Greek *herpo*, to creep), and the second as the edreobenthos (Greek *edraios*, sedentary). But for our purpose it will be enough to refer to them as the mobile and static benthos respectively.

The static animals of the benthos are particularly interesting, for they have adopted a way of life that would be entirely impossible except in an aquatic environment. Only the plants on land can afford to remain static, for they can extract their nourishment direct from the sun and the soil by photosynthesis. A land animal must be able to move about in search of its food, whether this be vegetable matter or other animals taken as prey, or it would die of starvation. But in the sea these laws do not apply. Sea water is almost always in motion, and thus a fixed animal can nourish itself satisfactorily on planktonic plants and animals, organic detritus, and other substances that are constantly carried past it by currents or which rain down on it through the liquid medium above. Sometimes, it is true, certain animals, such as sponges and some coelenterates, produce artificial currents which carry food into their body cavities; but this is simply reinforcing a natural characteristic of the environment. The ability to support a large population of static benthic animals is a unique property of the oceans. Even a wholly carnivorous animal can remain fixed to a rock for the whole of its life, nourishing itself on the prey and carrion brought to it by the constantly moving water.

Although it is now known that benthic animals are to be found on all parts of the sea floor, from the intertidal beaches to the depths of the abyss, their distribution and concentration varies greatly from place to place. As with all other living things, aquatic and terrestial, the distribution of the benthos is mainly determined by the interaction between the physiological make-up of the animal and the nature of the physical and chemical environment. This problem has been brilliantly worked out by the Swedish biologist Sven Ekman in his book *Zoogeography of the Sea*, but the subject is far too complex to be dealt with here.[26] It must suffice to indicate the areas in which the main types of benthic animals are found.

As might be expected, the littoral zone has the largest population, for this is the well-lighted region where there is a high concentration of marine plants to serve as vegetable food. On the continental slopes the benthic population decreases with depth, reaching a minimum on the floor of the abyss. This again is what we might expect, for plant life decreases in proportion to the intensity of the light, and when we reach the regions of everlasting darkness it ceases altogether. The animals of the deep must be either carnivores or scavengers, depending in the last analysis on the rain of organic detritus descending from above. The supply of such food is limited, and the extent of the population may also be kept in bounds by a shortage of oxygen at great depths.

The horizontal distribution of the benthos likewise follows a well-defined pattern. As with the marine fauna in general, there are a greater number of *individual* benthic animals, although fewer *species*, in temperate and polar seas. In the tropics there is a far greater number of species, but the total population is less. The reasons for this particular type of distribution are probably the widespread climatic changes which took place during the Tertiary period of geological time. The cooling of the circumpolar waters had a strong selective effect on the organisms in these zones. Many genera and species were killed off, and the survivors, who were well adapted to the harsher environment, increased in numbers to fill the vacuum. Towards the equator, on the other hand, conditions were little changed, and the marine population continued to flourish in all its tropical profusion.

Let us now look at some of the animals that live on the floor of the sea. It will be quite impossible to consider any but a purely arbitrary selection, and we must therefore restrict ourselves to a few especially important or representative forms. In general we shall try to move outward from the shore-line into deeper water, so that the reader can at least think of the animals under discussion in some kind of orderly sequence.

The region where benthic organisms can be most easily studied is on the seashore between the tides. Strictly speaking, the benthos can be said to begin only below the level of the lowest tide, but as the animals on either side of this boundary are identical, the intertidal zone is always included. As any child knows who has spent time paddling among the tidal rock pools with a shrimping net, no region is more abundantly provided with colourful and intriguing forms of life.

The problems of living in this region are at once lesser and greater than those encountered by deep water organisms. On the one hand there is an abundance of food and light, and of well-aerated water rich in chemicals; on the other, conditions are experienced which impose a considerable strain on the organism's powers of adaptation. For example, there are far greater extremes of temperature, salinity and pressure along the seashore than in the deep sea, and its inhabitants are exposed to the ceaseless pounding of the waves and to the danger of desiccation during the twice-daily retreat of the tides.

To minimize the effect of wave action many shore animals

show a marked flattening or stream-lining of the body. The water thus tends to flow round and over them more easily instead of tearing them from the shore and pounding them to pieces. Examples of this can be seen in the familiar crabs and starfishes, and the little sea slug which goes, rather pleasingly, under the scientific name of *Doris*. Other animals protect themselves by fastening themselves firmly to the rocks. A good example is the limpet, whose refusal to be dislodged from its chosen position has become proverbial. Incidentally, it is interesting to observe that limpets exposed to the full force of the sea have a high conical shell with a comparatively narrow base, whereas those in more sheltered situations are normally low and broad-based. The probable explanation is that the exposed animals must apply more force in pulling down their shells to resist wave action. This continued muscular action tends to pull in the margins of the tissues attaching the shell to the body, and the shape of the animal is thereby altered. The surface of the shell nevertheless remains smooth and stream-lined so as to offer the least possible resistance to the water.

To avoid the onslaught of the waves the sheltered positions on the seashore are obviously in most demand. The benthic animals seek out every nook and cranny in the rocks, just as human promenaders on the front above huddle gratefully in the shelters provided by the local council. Such retreats are crowded with a mixed population of sponges, sea-anemones, sea-urchins, mussels, starfish, tunicates, sea-cucumbers and other fascinating marine invertebrates, all intent on the single, basic problem of survival.

The problem of avoiding desiccation is second only to that of resisting the assault of the waves. Here again the limpet provides a good example of a specialized defence mechanism to a particular form of attack. To breathe and to preserve the moisture in its tissues when the tide is out, the limpet must be able to retain a small amount of moisture in its shell. This is stored in the narrow groove separating the outer rim of the central 'foot' from the shell's inner rim, where the thin leaflets of the animal's gills project from the body. If this water is to be retained when the tide recedes, it is obvious that the rim of the shell must make perfect contact with the rock at all points of its circumference. But rocks are not made flat just for the benefit of limpets, and to achieve the desired end the limpet must do one of two things. It must either grind away the rock until it exactly fits the contours of the base of its shell, or grind away the shell to fit the contours of the rock. In fact, it does both. It settles on a chosen spot and grinds out for itself a ring in the rock with the edge of its shell. If the rock is exceptionally hard, the grinding operation will also modify the contours of the edge of the shell before an exact fit is obtained. This ring then becomes the animal's permanent home, for naturally no other part of the rock surface will have precisely the right contours to fit the shell.

Now, limpets feed by browsing on the algal vegetation which coats the rocks like pasturage in a field. As soon as they are covered by the tide they begin to move off the site of their permanent homes and feed their way over an area of rock which may reach as far as three feet in any one direction. Shortly before the tide falls they return to their own site and settle down once more in their habitual grooves. This is as remarkable a behaviour pattern as any to be found in nature, and particularly marvellous when we consider the humble nature of the animal. Not only does it have the instinct to make itself a watertight home, but also to synchronize its movements so that they correspond exactly with the behaviour of the tides. We must also be impressed by the remarkable sense of direction which enables it to find its way back to its own ring on the rocks from any point on its feeding grounds.

An almost equally remarkable device to avoid desiccation is employed by the barnacle. Barnacles are small shrimp-like animals, contained in a tough shell which is firmly cemented to the rock by a glandular secretion. They are one of the commonest benthic animals round our coasts (it was once estimated that a single well-exposed shore on the Isle of Man contained no fewer than 1000 million barnacles in a stretch of one kilometre).[27] Their shells are open at one end, but can be closed by an arrangement of four plate-like processes. When the tide rises, these plates open, and the barnacle protrudes its twelve feathery legs, which grasp about in every direction like delicate hands in search of food. When the tide falls, the plates close, hermetically sealing the animal in its shell with enough water to prevent desiccation or suffocation

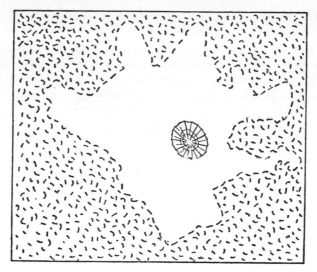

The browsing area of the limpet *Patella vulgata*. From *Yonge* (1949), *p.* 117.
Reproduced by permission of Messrs Wm. Collins, Sons & Co Ltd.

until the sea rises again. A wanderer on the sea-shore when the tide is ebbing may hear what F. D. Ommanney has called 'the whispering talk' of the barnacles,[28] a faint crepitation caused by thousands of the little creatures closing their plates like shop-keepers putting up their shutters for the night. By this device the barnacle can remain alive for days at a time without being submerged in the sea. In fact it has been calculated that in some regions near the high tide line a barnacle may spend less than a twentieth of its life under water.

Fluctuations in temperature and salinity are less obvious than the foregoing hazards, but are equally important in the lives of marine organisms. This is particularly true of the creatures of the seashore and shallow seas, where the temperature of the environment is far less stable than in the open ocean, and where the salinity is affected to a considerable extent by rivers, streams and run-off from the land. Temperature is an especially important factor in high latitudes, where wide seasonal fluctuations occur. On the whole, shore organisms in the tropics live within 9° or 10°F. of their normal favoured temperature throughout the year, but on temperate coasts this may be extended to 20°F. or even more. To avoid succumbing to such wide changes, some creatures have learnt to exist in a state of suspended animation. Thus coelenterates and sponges have been found to pass through a quiescent phase in the middle of the day and to become active again in the cool of the evening. Many protozoans also pass through a resting stage if the temperature rises above or below their normal tolerance. Where salinity is concerned, we find that coastal animals have a far greater tolerance than those found further out at sea. Many kinds of marine molluscs can exist in estuarine waters which are almost fresh. Nevertheless such creatures as oysters and mussels never grow to marketable size unless the salinity is exactly right for them. Those living elsewhere may manage to survive, but they are nearly always stunted, and often deformed.

Apart from some introductory generalizations, we have spent most of this chapter on the beaches, discussing a few representative shore animals with reference to the special problems of their lives. The time has now come to plunge beneath the waves and examine some of the benthic organisms of the upper, or eulittoral, section of the continental shelf. In the region closest to low tide level we find that, broadly speaking, the sea bed can be divided into five main natural zones, or 'biotopes', distinguished partly by the nature of the sea bed and partly by differences in the population of animals and plants. First there is the so-called Laminarian zone, named after *Laminaria*, its characteristic seaweed. This has long broad fronds, and is attached to the rocks of the sea bottom by a massive hold-fast. Although normally submerged, beds of *Laminaria* may sometimes be uncovered in dramatic fashion by the low spring tides. Second there is the Zosteral zone, named after *Zostera*, the eel-grass, mentioned in Chapter 8. This grass is typical of estuaries and lagoons where the bottom is sufficiently soft for it to put down the true roots with which it draws nourishment from the soil. The remaining three biotopes are the hard bottom zone, the sandy bottom zone, and the muddy bottom zone. The names of these are self-explanatory, so we can proceed straight away to describe a few of the characteristic organisms of each zone. For reasons of space we shall have to be extremely selective, and also limit ourselves mainly to creatures found in temperate waters.

The Laminarian zone is a dense underwater jungle in which

a wide diversity of creatures lurk and prey upon each other. Under the huge branching fronds of the weeds, which must seem to these tiny animals as great as forest trees, a microcosmic drama is continually enacted. Hydroids and sponges prey on the tiny protozoans teeming in the water, and themselves fall victim to the sea-slugs that creep between the swaying weeds. Blue-striped limpets (*Patina pellucida*) browse among the hold-fasts, while overhead the grotesque ghost-shrimp *Caprella* moves up and down the stems and over the bodies of the hydroids with an irregular motion like the looping of a caterpillar. Mussels are spread in beds across the bottom, worms and gastropods of many kinds move among the weeds, while here and there, distinctive in its familiar radial symmetry, is the colourful body of a starfish.

By comparison with this diversity of life under the fronds of the *Laminaria*, the fauna of the Zosteral zone is sparse. Nevertheless, it contains some very interesting species. The little three-spined stickleback will be well known to every small boy who has gone hunting with a jam jar, but this is an estuarine and freshwater form rather than a typical marine animal. More unusual are the three genera of pipe-fish, scientifically known as *Nerophis*, *Entelurus* and *Syngnathus*. These are relatives of the sea-horses, but with more elongated bodies, as their popular name suggests. They swim in the upright position, propelling themselves forward by undulations of a narrow fin in the middle of the back. The breeding habits of pipe-fish, like those of sea-horses, are unusual, for it is the male and not the female that carries the eggs. The female *Nerophis* or *Entelurus*, after producing her eggs, simply glues them to the under side of the male body; in *Syngnathus* the male is equipped with a marsupial pouch comparable to that of a kangaroo. When the eggs first hatch, the young fish always remain close to their father, and return to the pouch for protection whenever danger threatens.

The fauna of the hard bottom zone is a very large one, including many attached animals and a number of mobile molluscs and crustaceans. One of the most interesting and beautiful creatures of this zone found in British waters is the little mollusc known as *Lima hians*. This is a bivalve – in other words it has a shell consisting of two hinged plates. In *Lima* these are white in colour, and their shape resembles that of the scallop shell depicted in the famous petroleum advertisement. Projecting from the shell is a fringe of delicate reddish-orange tentacles which wave gracefully about in the water like the hair of a red-headed mermaid. Unlike similar attachments in other bivalves, these cannot be withdrawn into the shell, so the animal is extremely vulnerable to the attacks of predators. To overcome this disadvantage it adopts a remarkable procedure;

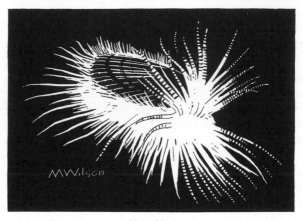

Lima hians.

it builds itself a nest of shells and stones bound together with tough thread-like tissue secreted by a special gland in its foot. The nest entirely encloses the animal except for a hole at either end through which a stream of water is drawn by the tentacles. This ensures that a regular supply of planktonic organisms is carried to the mouth. Owing to the elaborate nature of the nest, *Lima hians* does not often change position; but it is capable of locomotion to a limited extent, wafting its way gracefully through the water with the aid of its colourful fringe.

Many starfish are found in the hard bottom zone as well as other areas in the sea, and here also lives the beautiful black brittle-star *Ophiocomina nigra* with its five delicate red limbs. Worms and burrowing animals are not at home in such regions owing to the nature of the bottom, but there is the usual assortment of crustaceans, including edible crabs, lobsters and other gourmets' delights. Perhaps the most remarkable crustacean is the sponge-crab, *Dromia vulgaris*, of the Mediterranean. This creature has brought the art of camouflage to an exceptional peak of perfection. The last pair of legs are bent in acrobatic fashion over the back, and two pincers at their extremities hold a fragment of sponge over the shell like an umbrella. As this grows it gradually covers the shell so that the crab, when motionless, is quite unrecognizable. Crab-eating fish are often entirely baffled by this disguise, which must also cause great despondency, if not alarm, among sponge eaters that investigate the crustacean too closely.

Turning now to our last two biotopes, we find that the characteristic animals of sandy and muddy bottoms are the burrowers. These include numerous burrowing bivalves, the burrowing starfish *Astropecten*, anemones which dig themselves so deeply into the sea bed that only their mouths and tentacles protrude, and many varieties of worms. Mud is also the favourite environment of some of the holothurians, or sea-cucumbers, which are also, however, found in hard bottom areas. These odd animals are relatives of the starfishes but, as their name suggests, they are shaped rather like cucumbers. One species (*Holothuria nigra*) has developed a most effective, if somewhat unmannerly, method of dealing with its attackers. When approached by any hostile or suspicious character it ejects from its body a mass of glutinous threads. These swell up in the water, leaving the attacker baffled by a sticky wall of fibres, or, worse still, hopelessly entangled. If really frightened, it suddenly ejects the whole of its stomach and viscera. It seems to be quite unaffected by this loss of its vital organs, however, and when the danger is past calmly begins to grow a new set.

So much for the five typical habitats of the eulittoral zone, with some of their associated animals. We must now broaden our field of exploration and move out towards the edge of the continental shelf. At about 60 fathoms we leave behind the region of bottom-growing plants and enter the sublittoral zone. It is still fairly light here, and remains so until we reach the edge of the shelf; but the flora consists entirely of planktonic plants drifting through the waters of the neritic province above. The bottom is mostly of sand, or mud, or muddy clay, mixed with a certain amount of rock. In spite of the disappearance of benthic plants, there is still a profusion of attached animals.

109

Some of these are already familiar to us, for they also inhabit regions closer inshore.

Among the attached animals one of the most characteristic is the sea-fan, *Gorgonia verrucosa*. This is so named because of the fan-like shape of its delicate red branches, which always radiate in the same plane from a short stem. Whole beds of this beautiful creature can be found in rocky areas alongside rich growths of anemones and hydroids. Anyone but a naturalist who was suddenly transported to this submarine world would have difficulty in believing that these were indeed animals he was looking at, and not exotic tropical plants.

Hermit crabs are among the most typical and entertaining animals of the continental shelf (Plate 11*b*). They do not secrete shells of their own, but occupy old snail shells, their abdomens being spirally twisted to obtain an exact fit. Hook-like structures at the end of their bodies enable them to cling to the shell so strongly that they will nearly always permit themselves to be pulled in half rather than surrender their hold. The crab does not kill the snail in order to obtain its shell, but always waits till it comes across a shell that is already empty. It then inspects it with great care, turning it over with its claws, until it is thoroughly satisfied that this is just the kind of home it wants. If the shell passes muster, the crab's next move is to back into it and test it for size and comfort. This part of the operation can be most entertaining. The animal wriggles about from side to side, seeing how the lines of the shell fit the contours of its body rather as a fussy female customer tries on a dress in a store. If it is dissatisfied it comes out again and sets off in search of another shell; but if it finds the shell to its liking it takes up residence forthwith. Later, of course, as the crab gets bigger, its home becomes rather too tight for it, and it has to look for a new one. The whole process is repeated at intervals until the animal is fully grown.

Shells are not the only homes used by hermit crabs. One species living in the Indian Ocean habitually occupies pieces of bamboo. This is apparently by choice, not necessity, for the animal's abdomen is not spiralled as in other species, but tubular to fit the hole in the bamboo. In emergencies, when lack of suitable shells causes a housing shortage on the sea floor, hermit crabs will camp out in almost anything. One of the most amusing examples of this was noted by G. E. and Nettie MacGinitie of the Kerckhoff Marine Laboratory, California, who describe finding a piece of worm tubing occupied by two hermit crabs, one at each end. The determination of the animals to go in opposite directions, despite the obvious advantage of co-operation, was reminiscent of the behaviour of rival delegates at a Russo-American conference.[29]

Many other creatures live in the sublittoral zone, including the crawfish, *Palinurus vulgaris* (Plate 14*a*), an assortment of crabs and shrimps, and numerous species of barnacles and burrowing worms. One barnacle known as *Scalpellum* is particularly remarkable. There is a great difference in size between the males and the females, and it is customary to find the female living attached to a hydroid, with the male (a minute and puny creature) clinging to his partner's shell.

Beyond the edge of the continental shelf the sea bed falls away steeply towards the abyss. The light that still filters through the upper layers of water gets less and less, and soon disappears altogether. The creatures of the continental slopes thus live either in a ghostly twilight or, at greater depths, in total darkness. As stated earlier, their numbers grow less as one descends, but even on the floor of the abyss there are numerous species of benthic organisms.

In trawling or dredging down the continental slopes and over the abyssal plain one of the main features of the catch will often be glass-sponges, of the class Hexactinellida. These vary in height from a few inches to two or three feet, and some examples such as *Euplecta* (more poetically known as Venus's flower basket) are among the most beautiful members of the sponge family. The hexactinellids anchor themselves to the sea floor with long threads or spicules of silica. These have been compared to bunches of glass wool, and the more elaborate examples may be twisted into strands so they appear like lengths of opalescent rope.

Several members of the deep sea benthos are luminescent. These include a coelenterate called *Umbellula*, which has a bulbous hold-fast for anchoring itself to the deep sea sediments, and a beautiful species of sea-fan with branching plant-like arms called *Chrysogorgia*. The commonest fixed animals of the abyss are sea-anemones, which are found in vast numbers on the continental slopes, the abyssal plain and even in the deepest trenches. Also characteristic are the sea-lilies (Crinoidea). These, like the sea-fans and anemones, have a strong super-ficial resemblance to plants, but are in fact echinoderms. They are also found in shallow waters, but there they do not develop the long stalks which characterize the deep sea forms. About eight hundred living species are known, but owing to the diffi-culty of direct observation at great depths much of their natural history is still obscure. Each sea-lily consists of a stalk and a head with an upward-pointing mouth surrounded by a large number of branched arms. The branches are equipped with grooves down which detritus and small organisms taken from the water are carried to the mouth by cilia. The animal normally anchors itself by its stalk to the sea bed, but in some forms, after a stalked phase in youth, the top breaks away. In such cases that part of the stalk which is still attached to the animal develops short attaching organs. These enable it to fix itself directly to the rocks and it then feeds in exactly the same way as the stalked forms. It also has the advantage of certain limited powers of locomotion. It can creep slowly along the sea bed, and even detach itself and paddle laboriously to a new situation by much frenzied waving of its arms. Certain stalkless sea-lilies occur in the deep sea, but this variation is better suited to shallow waters where the sea floor is generally more rocky. The long stalk of the abyssal forms is, of course, excel-lently suited to anchoring the animal in the deep sediments and oozes which are there most commonly found.

There is a temptation when dealing with such a fascinating subject as the animals of the ocean floor to enthuse indefinitely about their charms. Many more benthic creatures demand the attention of the inquisitive naturalist; for example, the giant sea-spiders of the genus *Colossendeis*, whose legs measure up to two feet long, the polychaete worms which dwell in exquisite tubes fashioned from shells bound with threads of silica, and the many extraordinary species of sea-cucumbers and bivalve molluscs. Unfortunately, to deal even briefly with such animals would take us far beyond the scope of this book. Instead we must now leave the benthos and turn our attention to the open waters overhead, the home of the free-swimming animals of the nekton.

9*a* The common octopus, *Octopus vulgaris*

9*b* The brilliantly patterned cuttlefish *Sepia officinalis*

10a Underwater photograph of an oceanic squid
at a depth of about 650 metres

10b Two squids of contrasted shape: *Ommastrephes sloanii*
(*left*) and the abyssal squid *Loligopsis veranyi*

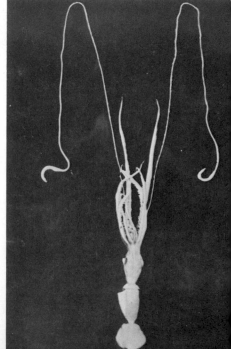

11*a* A sea urchin. These echinoderms are a popular
table delicacy

11*b* (*Left*) A hermit crab shares a whelk shell with an annelid
worm while an anemone clings to the shell's exterior.
(*Right*) Sea-horses

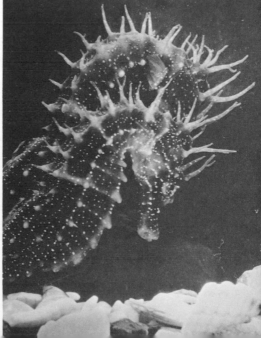

12 and 13 Life of the Devonian seas

The large fish in the centre is *Dinichthys*; above are three specimens of the shark-like sponge, a eurypterid, a group of crinoids, and a trilobite climbing up the rocks. animals in the top left-hand

three hundred million years ago

Cladoselache and an early cephalopod. Below (left to right) are cup-corals, a glass
Two brachiopods are attached to the rocks in the left foreground. The seaweed-like
corner are colonial graptolites

14*a* A rock lobster or crawfish (*Palinurus vulgaris*)

14*b* The spiny spider crab (*Maia squinado*) may measure a yard across the legs and weigh half a stone

15*a* The leopard shark (*Calliscyllium venustum*), an inhabitant of eastern waters

15*b* A group of cow-nosed rays (*Rhinoptera*)

16*a* A fanciful reconstruction of ichthyosaurs and plesiosaurs
from *The Book of the Great Sea Dragons* (1840)
by Thomas Hawkins

16*b* The extinct *Anthropornis*. These giant penguins, which
lived twenty million years ago, were as tall as a man

Chapter Eleven

THE FREE-SWIMMERS

THE animals of the nekton, free-swimming and generally more intelligent than their benthic cousins, are the most highly evolved members of the ocean community. But in the sea, as in human society on land, it is not given to many individuals to rise above their fellows, so the nekton includes only a comparatively limited number of animal groups. Among those nektonic creatures that live and breathe entirely under water the most important are the fishes, all of whom, of course, are vertebrates, or animals with backbones. Invertebrates are very poorly represented, the only genuinely nektonic forms being the larger octopuses, the squids, and, if we are prepared to stretch a point, a few of the larger crustaceans. In addition there are several air-breathing animals that have taken to an oceanic habitat. These may be mammals, such as whales and seals, or reptiles such as sea-snakes and marine turtles. Strangely enough, not a single species of amphibian is found in the ocean proper, although representatives of the class do occur in brackish waters at the mouths of rivers.[30]

The meaning of the word nektonic has been given as 'free-swimming', but it now needs somewhat closer definition. In one sense, many planktonic organisms are as capable of progression through the water as the creatures of the nekton, and this is certainly true swimming of a kind. But the point is that planktonic animals are so small that their movements can only be local. For example, a copepod may well be capable of travelling many hundreds of times the length of its own body in one day, but its small size still makes this movement negligible in comparison with the vast size of the ocean. We must therefore define nektonic animals more precisely as free-swimmers who can make their way purposefully through the sea *in opposition to any current they may encounter*. At the same time we should remember that most of the animals coming within this definition are not nektonic for the whole of their lives; as stated earlier, the larvae of nearly all the fishes and invertebrates are

113

members of the plankton, and only graduate to the nekton at a later stage.

Nektonic mammals and reptiles will fit more logically into the story when we come to consider marine life from an evolutionary point of view. Here we shall be concerned only with a general survey of the fish and larger invertebrates living in the sea today. To begin with the fish, it is worth spending a few moments sorting out the main types clearly in our minds. For our present purpose, all the fish in the sea can be loosely divided into two main groups. These are, first, the elasmobranchs or cartilaginous fishes and, second, the teleosts or bony fishes. The elasmobranchs are more primitive than the teleosts, and are survivors from an earlier phase in the evolution of life. This group includes the sharks, skates and rays, all of which have skeletons made of the hard transparent material known as cartilage. The teleosts are more advanced in the evolutionary scale, and have skeletons made of true bone. This group includes the great majority of the fish in the sea, ranging from the tiny sardine to the gigantic tuna, and the homely herring or plaice to the grotesque fishes of the abyss. In addition to these two groups there is a small class of nektonic animals known as the Cyclostomata. This includes the lampreys, or round-mouthed eels, and the hagfishes, or slime eels. The cyclostomes are not true fishes like the elasmobranchs and teleosts, but may legitimately be grouped with them here to simplify the presentation.

Before discussing the natural history of some of the more representative and bizarre kinds of fish we must first dispose of a few general issues. As has been said, the distinctive characteristic of nektonic animals is their ability to move from place to place. This not only includes local movements in restricted areas, but vast migrations covering many hundreds of miles. Owing to the comparatively helpless condition of the planktonic larvae the choice of a suitable spawning ground is extremely important. Thus it is common to find fish travelling long distances to deposit their young in exactly the right place. In choosing this, the direction of the prevailing currents is allowed for in a most marvellous way. To take only one example, plaice living in the southern North Sea always move southwards to spawn, so that their young may drift with the currents into their nurseries along the sandy coasts of Holland. Salmon and eels perform even more remarkable spawning migrations which will be referred to later on.

The essentially mobile nature of the nekton has caused nearly all its members to evolve bodies that will pass easily through the water. Compare, for instance, the flapping planktonic jelly-fish with the smooth, torpedo-like shape of the typical teleost. Nearly all fish have developed this stream-lined form to a greater or lesser extent, and in some species the speeds that can be achieved are remarkable. A salmon has little difficulty in travelling at over ten miles an hour, while some members of the mackerel family can almost double this speed. We should remember, moreover, that the resistance of water is vastly greater than the resistance of air. A javelin thrown into the sea will travel at most ten feet before losing its momentum, whereas on land three hundred feet is by no means an uncommon throw.

In spite of the motility of the typical fish, it does not enjoy an unlimited freedom of range. It was emphasized in an earlier chapter that, although the oceans all belong to one great system, their populations are nevertheless divided by a number of natural but invisible barriers. Salinity, temperature, viscosity, light, and other physical factors, as well as the availability of a suitable food supply, restrict many organisms to one particular region. Likewise, the nature of the bottom may cause certain species to make extreme specializations which, once acquired, unfit them for life in any other habitat. This is as true of certain kinds of fish (the flatfishes for example) as it is of the benthos itself. Such facts should be borne in mind when we employ the term 'free-swimming'. The movements of the widely ranging animals of the nekton are still governed by the nature of the physical environment, and some highly specialized types are as closely confined to one spot as if they were cattle in a field.

A question of general interest arising from the horizontal zoning of fish populations is how they maintain their chosen level in the water. We have already described in Chapter 9 how planktonic organisms are aided in this respect by spiny processes, a horizontal flattening of the body, and the secretion of oily substances which counteract the action of gravity. In the fishes quite different mechanisms are used. The typical elasmobranch has no special hydrostatic organ, and must maintain its level by constant movements of its muscular fins and tail. In most teleosts, however, there is a remarkable structure known as the swim-bladder which enables the fish to enjoy hydrostatic equilibrium at a selected depth. At this level it has no tendency either to rise or fall, and can thus devote all its muscular energy to the act of moving horizontally through the water.

Physically, the swim-bladder consists of a pouch budded off from the gullet. This is filled with gas originating in the breakdown of cells in the bladder lining. In spite of its value in allowing the fish to keep its vertical position without undue effort, it has certain corresponding disadvantages. It was stated earlier that fish which move higher than their accustomed habitat are in danger of being carried to the surface due to the disequilibrium between the internal pressure in the swim-bladder and the external pressure of the water. Conversely fish that stray too low are in danger of sinking to the bed of the sea. The external pressure of the water so compresses the air in their bladders that they lose their buoyancy, and may sink helplessly to the bottom. Certain adjustments can be made in the volume of gas by the individual fish, and these normally allow a satisfactory equilibrium to be maintained. But such adjustments only operate within fairly narrow limits and, once a certain critical level has been passed, a fish may find it impossible to return to its proper habitat. In a natural state fish suffering this fate must inevitably die, but under artificial conditions a simple remedy can be applied – at least to those fish that 'fall upwards'. The distended belly of the helpless fish, floating upside down on the surface of the sea, may be pierced with a sharp instrument, whereupon the air swiftly escapes and the animal resumes its normal activities at the new level.[31]

Apart from its role as a hydrostatic organ the swim-bladder fulfils several other interesting functions. The reader who has always thought of the sea as a silent world may be surprised to learn that one of these is to assist in the production of sound. Fish are in fact quite noisy creatures, and can make a wide range of grunts, gurgles and barks, as well as grating and croaking sounds caused by friction between the hard parts of their bodies. Consider for example, the trigger-fish, *Balistes aculeatus*, of Mauritius. This animal rubs together the bones of the arch supporting the pectoral fin, and the noise is then amplified by the swim-bladder into a loud drumming sound. The expulsion of air from the bladder is also very probably the cause of the 'bark' of the conger eel when it is taken out of the water.

In addition, there are a number of fish noises which are not connected with the swim-bladder at all. For example, the grating sound produced by sticklebacks is caused by friction of the first dorsal spine against the backbone. This technique, in modified form, is also adopted by certain species of catfish. The bullhead (*Cottus*) produces a rasping noise with a portion of its gill-covers, and the flying gurnard (*Dactylopterus*) uses the hardened cartilage of its jaws for the same purpose. The horse mackerel (*Trachurus*) and the sun-fish (*Mola*) adopt the simple expedient of grinding their teeth together, while the loaches make a somewhat indelicate popping noise by expelling air bubbles rapidly through the anus. Such revelations show that the study of fish sounds is a fascinating one, but we unfortunately have no space to pursue it here. Instead we must embark on a discussion of some of the more representative nektonic animals.

The most primitive fish-like vertebrates found in the sea are the cyclostomes. Their best-known representatives, the lampreys, are the creatures to whom the Romans used to throw Christians and political prisoners when lions were for some reason unavailable; taken internally, and to excess, they are also alleged to have accounted for at least one English monarch. The lamprey has indeed many unendearing qualities. It is an eel-like creature ranging in length from eighteen inches to three feet. The mouth is a round disc which acts as a sucker enabling it to attach itself firmly to the body of its prey. It then gets to work with its muscular, tooth-studded tongue, which rasp and penetrate the skin so that the blood and flesh may be extracted.

For the first three or four years of its life the lamprey is a freshwater animal. It then migrates into the open ocean, where it becomes typically marine except for the periods when it returns to the rivers and streams to breed. On these journeys the peculiarly constructed mouth fulfils a quite different function from that described above. If the animal meets obstructions such as rapids or falls which it cannot negotiate by swimming, it makes a lunge upstream and then fastens itself by its mouth to

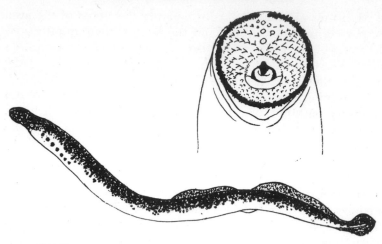

M.Wilson

The lamprey, a primitive eel-like vertebrate, fixes itself to its prey by a
sucker surrounding its mouth (top right).

a rock. After some minutes' rest it makes another lunge forward
and finds a new anchorage. The process continues until the
obstacle has been overcome. In the breeding season, when large
numbers of lampreys are migrating upstream, their glistening
grey bodies may be concentrated in such numbers on the rocks
bordering rapids or falls that hardly a space is left between them.
The eggs themselves are laid in holes in the beds of rivers, the
stones being removed with the mouth one by one so as to form a
suitable depression.

Another form of cyclostome is the hagfish. This animal is not
unlike the lamprey in general appearance, but the mouth is
much smaller, and is surrounded by a number of short finger-
like processes, or tentacles. Hagfishes do not make incursions
into fresh water like lampreys, but are strictly marine in habit.
They live near the sea bed on most coasts at depths of between
five and twenty fathoms. Their normal prey is carrion, and
they have been aptly termed the vultures of the sea; they never
attack anything capable of defending itself but, like the hyena
on land, will speedily polish off a fish that is weak or diseased.
They enter the body of their victim through the anus and make
a meal of its internal organs while it is still alive. In spite of

these unattractive traits, hagfishes are of great interest to naturalists as being the only vertebrate hermaphrodites. That is to say, in one breeding season an individual may produce eggs, and in the next, sperm, and so on. The alternative name of the animal, which is slime eel, derives from its habit of secreting large quantities of slime when it is touched or otherwise alarmed. According to G. E. and Nettie MacGinitie, who have studied these creatures widely under laboratory conditions, the amount of slime secreted is quite extraordinary; after placing two hagfishes of average size in a half-bucket of water and then agitating it the MacGinities were able to lift the hagfishes and the water out together in one congealed blob of slime.[32]

Of the true fishes we will deal first with the elasmobranchs. The best known of these are the sharks, of which many lurid and blood-curdling tales have been told. At the risk of incurring the wrath of sensational journalists and the more unscrupulous naturalists it must be said at once that most of these are without foundation. Although carnivorous in habit, sharks are in general harmless to man. Their reputation as man-eaters is based on very few well-authenticated cases, and they are only really dangerous when there is a scent of blood in the water. This arouses in them the same lust to kill as a retreating fox inspires in the more moronic members of the human species, and it is then advisable to give them a wide berth. In normal circumstances, however, the shark is a peaceable member of the ocean community whose only wish is to be left to mind his own business while others mind theirs.

The limited numbers of substantiated attacks on human beings have mainly been the work of one species, the great white shark, *Carcharodon rondeleti*. This is found in all the warm seas of the world, and is an occasional visitor to temperate waters. The average length of the animal is between twenty and forty feet, but much larger specimens are known to exist. Thus some white shark teeth dredged from the floor of the Pacific during the famous *Challenger* expedition of the last century measured no less than five inches long. By comparison with the teeth of specimens whose length is known, it can be deduced that the owner of these teeth must have measured at least seventy feet from nose to tail.

The animal is exceptionally voracious, and many kinds of

fish and even young sea lions form part of its diet. It not only takes living prey, but is also a scavenger, feeding on the refuse and offal discharged from ships in harbour. The stomach of one great white shark was found to contain a tin can, a number of mutton bones, the hind quarters of a pig, the head and forequarters of a bulldog, and a quantity of horseflesh; another had consumed a large Newfoundland dog ('with his collar on', the report adds). Such animals, even though their attacks on human beings may be rare, are to be discouraged near bathing places. The late Sir Frederick McCoy described one method of dealing with the problem as it presented itself at Port Philip, Australia, where a large specimen (the same, in fact, that was later found to have eaten the Newfoundland) had been pestering holiday makers. He wrote: 'It had been observed for several days swimming round the ladies' baths, looking in through the picket fence in such a disagreeable manner that the station master had a strong hook and iron chain made . . . and this, being baited with a large piece of pork, made to look as much like a piece of a lady as possible, was swallowed greedily; and then, with the aid of a crowd of helpers, the monster was got on shore.'[33]

Large as the white shark is, it is probably exceeded in size by the whale shark, *Rhineodon typus*. Fifty feet is by no means an uncommon length for this shark, and it may grow to sixty feet or even more. It is a beautiful animal, brownish-grey in colour, and peppered with round white or yellow spots, which on the body are separated by narrow vertical lines of the same colour. In spite of its large size it is quite harmless, and habitually feeds on small planktonic animals which it sieves out from the water by structures in its mouth known as gill-rakers. In this respect it closely resembles the whalebone whales which we shall be discussing later on. To obtain its food the shark swims slowly through the plankton, its mouth wide open in a somewhat fatuous way for such a dignified animal. The mouth has, in fact, so wide a gape that all sorts of foreign bodies are inclined to be ingested by the animal accidentally. Thus one whale shark captured off the Philippine Islands was found to have swallowed a number of shoes, leggings, belts, and other oddments, while another from Japan had a piece of wood a foot long reposing in its stomach.[34]

A close relation of the whale shark is the basking shark,

M Wilson.

Three contrasted elasmobranchs: Top to bottom: Basking shark (*Cetorhinus*);
hammer-head (*Sphyrna*); and saw-fish (*Pristis*).

Cetorhinus, found off our own shores. This grows to a length of
thirty or forty feet and its name derives from its habit of swimming about slowly over the surface of the water as if enjoying
the rays of the sun. Whether it actually finds these agreeable
only a basking shark would know, but this is certainly not the
main cause of its behaviour. The animal's motive is simply to
obtain a supply of the surface plankton which form its main
food.

The oddest shark in appearance is the hammer-head, of which the five known species are grouped together in the genus *Sphyrna*. These are comparatively small animals, ranging from four to fifteen feet in length. They feed mainly on other fishes, but if these are in short supply, or the shark is feeling too indolent for an energetic chase, it will browse quite happily on benthic animals such as crabs, small lobsters and even barnacles. Its name comes from the extraordinary structure of the head, which is unique among marine vertebrates. Instead of the pointed shape characteristic of the fishes it has two outgrowths, one on either side, with the eyes mounted at their extremities. Marine biologists are full of theories concerning the evolutionary purpose of this odd arrangement, the most popular explanation being that the outgrowths permit of a wider field of vision, with increased ability to manoeuvre swiftly in the water; but this has not yet been definitely established.

Many other genera of sharks are found throughout the length and breadth of the world ocean. These include the tiger shark, which is restricted to the warmer parts of the sea, but for some reason best known to taxonomists is called *Galeocerdo arcticus*; the elfin or goblin shark, an extraordinary creature with a cut-away chin and a tail fluke like that of a futuristic aeroplane; the carpet shark, or 'wobbegong', to give it its more pleasing name; the cow shark, the zebra shark, and the fox shark; and the nurse shark, or 'gata', found in tropical waters in the Atlantic, Pacific and Indian Oceans. This last creature, incidentally, derives its name from the word 'nusse', which was once in common usage to denote any large fish; but as the late Mr J. R. Norman used to emphasize, it should not necessarily be regarded as good with children.

For reasons of space we must restrict this brief survey of the sharks to only one other species. This is the odd-looking monk-fish, *Squatina squatina*, whose popular name is derived from the monk-like cowl of skin on its head. Superficially this animal looks less like a true shark than a typical member of the second great group of elasmobranch fishes, the rays. Its body, which sometimes attains a length of eight feet, is broad and horizontally flattened, and it has a blunt, rounded snout. It is nevertheless distinguished from the rays by its internal anatomy and several other technical criteria, such as the position of the gill-slits. The superficial resemblance is due to the fact that the way of life of the two types of animals is largely the same. Both are mainly bottom-dwellers which feed on crustaceans, flatfish and other animals living on or near the floor of the sea. Specialization for this habitat and diet makes a flattened shape of greater evolutionary importance than the high speed which can be attained by the more stream-lined varieties of fish. The tendency of animals of different natural groups to acquire similar adaptations to a common environment is by no means rare in the history of life. An extreme example in the sea is the likeness between the larger fishes and the whales. The latter in spite of their fish-like shape are, of course, warm-blooded mammals, and are much more closely related to other mammals, including the human race, than to the cold-blooded fish they so much resemble.

Turning now to the rays, we find that the same principles of evolutionary convergence sometimes apply. Most people, if asked to describe a typical ray, would say it had a much flattened body shaped like an irregular disc or quadrilateral, with a long, whip-like tail. This is indeed a good rough and ready description of many well-known species, but it does not represent the whole truth. Just as the monk-fish is a ray-like type of shark, so are there several shark-like types of rays. For example, the saw-fishes have only partially flattened bodies and swim with the oar-like motions of the tail which are so typical of sharks; yet in all other essential characters they show themselves to have much more right to be grouped with the rays.

As stated above, the characteristic habitat of the rays is the sea bottom. They are clumsy, rather sluggish creatures, and are commonest close inshore where the sea is fairly shallow and there is a good supply of the benthic organisms which form their main food. Apart from their flattened shape they have made several other interesting adaptations to their habitat. For instance, whereas the colour of the underside of the body is normally very pale, the upper surface always harmonizes closely with the ground on which the animal lives. Another adaptation concerns the organs known as spiracles, which are generally situated close behind the eyes on top of the head. At an early stage of evolution these were functional gill-clefts, but through the long ages of geological time they have in most species of fish either become vestigial or been eliminated altogether. Only very few species of teleosts, or bony fishes, retain their spiracles, and in the sharks they serve no practical function. But in the rays they perform an entirely new and very important duty which is directly related to the animals' environment. In sharks and bony fishes the normal method of breathing is to take in water through the gill slits, extracting the oxygen from it on the way. Rays also breathe in this fashion when swimming in open water, but when lying on the bottom there is a danger of their taking in particles of sand or other foreign bodies which might damage the delicate gills. This is particularly the case because the mouth of the typical ray is on the underside of the body to assist it in feeding. This is where the spiracles come in. In rays they are always exceptionally large, and are used instead of the mouth for taking in water when the fish is at rest on the ocean floor. Moreover they are equipped with special shutter-like valves so that the flow of water into the gills may be strictly regulated.

The size of the different rays varies from one or two feet across the disc in the smaller species, such as some of the skates, to over twenty feet in the enormous devil-fishes, *Mobula mobular* and *Manta birostris*. This last animal, incidentally, has largely given up life on the sea bottom, and ranges widely in surface waters. In spite of its large size it swims most gracefully, seeming to glide along with the effortless motion of a soaring bird. Occasionally it will leap high in the air, descending on the surface of the sea with a sound like the report of a cannon.

The protective coloration on the back is the main means used by rays to avoid their enemies, but they can also discourage the attention of predators by more active means. In some species the back is armed with spines, and the animal can roll itself into a ball like a hedgehog. Another effective weapon is the tail, which is often equipped with a sharp spike, or even with electric organs that can impart an unpleasant shock. Electrical defence among the rays is brought to its highest peak of perfection in the genus *Torpedo* where, however, the electrical organs are not situated in the tail but between the pectoral fins and the head. They are reminiscent of a highly specialized car battery, and consist of a large number of hexagonal tubes containing a clear, jelly-like substance corresponding to electrolyte. Each tube is divided into compartments, and each compartment contains a flat electric plate. There may be between nine hundred and a thousand such tubes in any one fish, grouped in two flat structures, each connected by nerves to a special lobe of the brain. The rate of shocks that can be given is very high – 150 per second according to one estimate. This naturally exhausts the animal in a fairly short space of time but, after a brief period for recharging, the battery is restored to its former effectiveness.

As briefly mentioned above, one of the least characteristic of the rays in shape is the saw-fish, *Pristis pectinatus*, and its related species. In addition to its semi-cylindrical shape this is distinguished from other rays by the extraordinary saw-like rostrum which gives it its name. This is a long, flat structure projecting forward from the head and equipped on either side with a row of sharp pointed processes, or 'teeth'. A large saw-fish may measure between twenty and thirty feet in length, of which six feet or more will be taken up by the 'saw'. In spite of its size and the possession of this formidable weapon the saw-fish is sufficiently sensible not to pick on creatures of its own size as prey if a supply of smaller animals is available. It feeds either by grubbing about in the mud of the sea floor, or by charging rapidly into a shoal of small fish and laying about energetically with its saw. By this means it knocks out a large number of fish, which seldom manage to recover their wits before the sawfish has returned from its charge to swallow them.

We must now leave the elasmobranchs and turn our attention to the bony fishes, or teleosts. As stated above, these represent the largest group of marine vertebrates, outnumbering the elasmobranchs by many hundreds of species to one. They are found at all depths and in all regions, and include many bizarre forms, as well as all the familiar food fish to be found on the fishmonger's slab. We shall only have space here to mention a few characteristic or unusual species of the upper waters, reserving a description of the grotesque fishes of the abyss for the next chapter.

One of the most typical teleosts is the Atlantic salmon, which is also a good example of the migrating habits of many teleost fishes. Adult salmon live habitually in the sea, but return to fresh waters in autumn and winter to spawn. Spawning takes place in a trough, known as a redd, formed by lashing movements of the tail, which pile up the gravelly bed of the river into an encircling mound. The young fish do not normally migrate during their first year (although up to 5% may occasionally do so), and during this phase of their development they are known as parr. But at two years old about 70% reach the migrating stage, and descend the rivers to the sea. These young migrating salmon are no longer known as parr, but as smolt. In the third year the remaining 25% to 30% of parr are likewise transformed into smolt and follow their more precocious comrades seaward.

The parr, smolt and adult salmon differ so much in appearance that they were once thought to belong to different species. The parr is characterized by ten or eleven dark bands on an orange ground, with round black spots on the gill covers. As it is transformed into a smolt the bands gradually disappear and the orange is replaced by silver, until the characteristic silvery appearance of the adult salmon is attained. The salmon spends the whole of its first year at sea, and at this time is known as a grilse; thereafter it makes an annual ascent of the river to spawn, and the life cycle is complete.

The above description applies mainly to the Atlantic salmon, *Salar salar*, but other species show some interesting variations. For instance, typical Pacific forms appear to lack the vitality for an annual breeding operation. They remain in the sea for one or two seasons, and then make their way upstream in the usual way to spawn. But this creative act is also their own suicide, for after the eggs are laid their strength is spent and the adult salmon die.

Another even more remarkable migration, which is in the reverse direction to the salmon's, is performed by the eel, *Anguilla*. The life cycle of this eel has puzzled naturalists for hundreds of years, and only in comparatively recent times has the problem been clarified. Adult eels are freshwater animals, commonly found in the rivers and streams of the North American and European coasts of the Atlantic. The American species is known as *Anguilla rostrata*, the European as *Anguilla anguilla*. In the ordinary way the life cycle of such a familiar animal would have been quickly described by scientists, who would then have passed on to more challenging problems. But the eel proved to be a more formidable object of research than one might have expected, for one very simple reason: no one could discover its young.

The lack of larval forms of the eel in fresh water led the old naturalists to put forward some intriguing, if scientifically dubious, theories. Thus Aristotle stated that they did not obey the normal laws of sexual reproduction, but were spontaneously generated in mud and putrid earth, while later writers believed that young eels could be produced by dropping horsehairs into water, or placing two sods of wet grass together in the sun. In the eighteenth century leading scientific opinion had abandoned the idea of spontaneous generation and a search began to be made for the eel's generative organs by dissection. Even so there were difficulties and anatomical misunderstandings, and it was not until 1874 that the generative organs of both sexes of eels had been located and fully described.

Meanwhile naturalists had observed that a two-way traffic of eels was occurring between fresh and salt waters. Mature eels were seen to migrate downstream every autumn and enter the sea. Similarly in the spring young eels, or elvers, could be seen making their way upstream into fresh water. These migrations were often on a gigantic scale. Thus Professor Romer quotes one estimate of the total number of eels leaving the fresh waters of southern Europe in a single season as in the region of 25 thousand million.[35] It became obvious that the eel was practising a salmon-like migration, but on an even larger scale, and in reverse. The animals spent their adult lives in the rivers and streams, and then went in vast numbers into salt water to breed.

The next step was to find out where their breeding grounds were. It was at first thought that they probably lay close to the mouths of the rivers formerly occupied by the adults, but this was made unlikely by the fact that breeding eels and small larvae were never fished up from these waters. Then a discovery was made that greatly helped the investigators. Two Italian scientists named Grassi and Calandruccio were making some experiments with a small, flat, transparent, leaf-shaped fish named *Leptocephalus*. This fish had been known for many years, but had never been kept for any length of time in an aquarium. After some weeks, to the amazement of the investigators, the specimens of *Leptocephalus* under observation gradually began to transform themselves into elvers. It became obvious that *Leptocephalus* was not after all a fish in its own right, but a larval form of the eel.

Now, *Leptocephalus* was known to exist in many parts of the Atlantic, and as the animal had at last been recognized as a clue to the great eel mystery, research on its distribution was redoubled. Much charting of catches took place, and eventually the breeding grounds of the eel were narrowed down to a comparatively small area south-east of Bermuda. The astonishing truth about the life cycle of the eel therefore is probably that the adult fish, after some five or six years of life in fresh waters, leave their home rivers and set out on a journey of some three thousand miles to their Bermuda spawning grounds. There in spring they spawn and then die, exhausted by the effort of their long journey and their breeding activities. The eggs then begin to drift slowly eastwards with the current at a depth of about 600 feet, hatching eventually into tiny *Leptocephalus*. By the end of that summer the larvae have travelled some four hundred miles and have an average length of about an inch. They then gradually move into shallower water and carry on eastwards at an average depth of 120 feet. After a year they are in mid-Atlantic, and a further year brings them to the coasts of Europe. Here, as three-inch *Leptocephalus*, they change into elvers and swim up the rivers and streams, where they remain for some five or six years as mature animals. Finally, in response to the same mysterious urge that afflicted their parents, they forsake their homes and undertake anew the long journey to their spawning grounds – and death. The sense of direction shown in these journeys is even more remarkable than that possessed by migrating birds, for there are no fixed landmarks in the open sea, and physical factors such as salinity and temperature gradients are too slight and variable to give effective aid.*

As is shown by a comparison between the two types of teleosts we have already mentioned, the group shows a wide diversity of shape. Many more extreme forms also exist, such as the odd trunk-fish (*Ostracion*), with a head like a cow and an entirely

* The classical theory of eel migration has recently been severely criticized in the scientific Press, but the author feels that the present description should stand while the matter is *sub judice*.

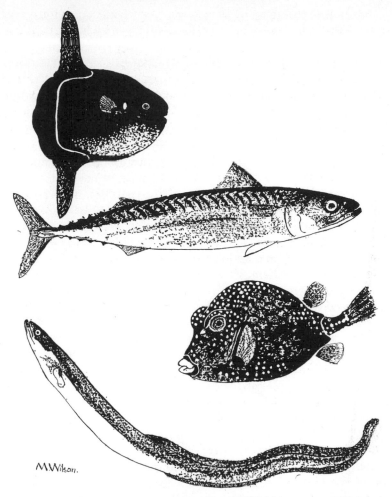

Four contrasted teleosts. Top to bottom: Sun-fish (*Mola*); mackerel (*Scomber*); trunk-fish (*Ostracion*); and eel (*Anguilla*).

rigid body with only the fins movable; the sun-fish (*Mola*), vertically flattened and disc-shaped, with two long, pointed fins, one above and one below the semi-circular fringe-like tail; the nearly spherical globe-fish (*Chilomycterus*), with its surprised expression and coating of short spines; and the sea-horse (*Hippocampus*), resembling a knight on the chess board brought to life.

More familiar than these, but no less highly specialized, are the flatfish. The commonest of these, such as the plaice and sole, are too well known at the dinner table, even when disguised by breadcrumbs or *sauce bonne femme*, to need description here, but one or two aspects of their natural history are most intriguing. All flatfish are, of course, specialized for a bottom-dwelling life, and often harmonize so closely with the sea bed as to be invisible except for their raised eyes. To achieve this, many species are capable of chameleon-like changes of colour on their upper surface. For example, the well-known orange-red spots of the plaice become white if the animal moves to a part of the sea bed where there are white pebbles. Experiments made with the Mediterranean turbot (*Bothus podas*) show even greater versatility. An obliging specimen was induced to lie at rest on a succession of different chequered patterns placed in the bottom of its tank, and made a very brave attempt at adapting itself to all of them. Flounders of the genus *Paralichthys* were tried on backgrounds of white, black, grey, brown, blue, green, pink, and yellow. They made an excellent approximation to each one, the yellows and browns being copied with nonchalant ease and the greens and blues with only little more difficulty. The red was not achieved quite so accurately, but the fish showed a fine sporting spirit and its performance was by no means discreditable.[36]

These colour changes are made possible by the presence in the dermal layer of the skin of a number of pigmented cells called 'chromatophores'. The pigments may be red, orange, yellow or black, and their appearance is controlled by a complex system of fine muscular fibres and nerves. The colours may either be displayed singly, or in combinations to give other shades. The main stimulus to colour change in flatfish is, of course, the nature of the sea bed, but, in common with many other kinds of fish, they also change colour as a result of emotional factors. The behaviour of fish in this respect corresponds with that of human beings, although the colours associated with the various emotions are often different. Thus a frightened fish does not go 'as white as a sheet', but usually turns several shades darker. Conversely, many fish are known to go red on occasion, but they cannot therefore be regarded as blushing with embarrassment; the chances are that they are simply excited by food or some glamorous member of the opposite sex. It should be mentioned in passing that the chromatophores are not the only factors influencing the colour of fish. An important part is played by the presence in the skin of a number of peculiar reflecting structures known as iridocytes. These originate in a waste product given off from the blood, and are responsible for the characteristic silvery appearance of so many of the bony fishes.

One other aspect of flatfish is worthy of mention before we leave the teleosts for the nektonic invertebrates. This is connected with the eyes of the young fish. We all know that the adult flatfish has its two eyes situated on the upper side of its body; if this were not the case the lower eye would be no use. But flatfish have not become horizontally flattened from top to bottom like the skates and rays. They have evolved from fish of more conventional shape, and have adapted themselves to a bottom-dwelling life by the simple expedient of lying on their sides. The process is well shown in the larvae which, like the ancestral flatfish, are quite conventional in appearance and swim upright in the water with one eye on either side of their heads. But at an early stage the larva grows thinner and flatter, finally lying down on its side on the bottom. At this point a wonderful metamorphosis takes place. The head likewise becomes gradually flattened, and at the same time the centre part of the skull rotates so that the two eyes point upwards. This is what some writers mean when they say that the lower eye 'migrates' to the upper side of the head, which is not a strictly accurate or clear way of putting it. The unusual physical behaviour of flatfish is one of the most remarkable phenomena in nature, and is the reason why soles, plaice, and other members of the group, gaze at one from the fishmonger's slab with such a twisted grimace.

As we said at the beginning of this chapter, the number of nektonic invertebrates is extremely limited, and here it must suffice to mention only one outstandingly spectacular species. This is the giant squid, *Architeuthis princeps*. Squids are molluscs belonging to the natural class of the cephalopods, or 'head-feet', and *Architeuthis* is their largest representative. It is a grotesque creature, with a tubular body between ten and fifteen feet long. Two tentacles, which may reach a length of fifty feet, and eight

M.W.

The giant squid (*Architeuthis princeps*).

somewhat shorter tentacles, or 'arms', all studded with suckers, project from its head. Its mouth is equipped with a cruel, curving beak, like that of a parrot.

The giant squid can propel itself through the water at considerable speed. It normally travels backwards with a jerking movement controlled by an interesting mechanism closely connected with the breathing arrangements. The animal has no external shell, but nearly the whole of its body is covered by a muscular 'mantle', which also encloses on the underside a cavity containing two feathery gills. This cavity is alternately expanded and contracted, so that water is first drawn in and then ejected through a funnel-like opening. When the squid is at rest these movements are slow and rhythmic, their main function being to bring a constant supply of water to bathe the gills; but when it is alarmed the movements are speeded up drastically so that water is repeatedly ejected from the funnel in a series of violent squirts. By this simple form of jet-propulsion the animal can make a quick escape. It is sometimes stated that squids are incapable of forward movement, but this is incorrect, for the funnel can be turned back on itself. In this case, however, progression is less rapid as there is no stream-lining on the head to help the animal pass through the water.

Architeuthis has a wide range both horizontally and vertically, but is commonest in fairly deep water. On rare occasions it can be seen floating right at the surface, an event which causes great consternation among mariners. It is probable that several good sea serpent yarns are based on a quick sight of the tentacles or pointed mantle of a giant squid, and it may also be one of the animals responsible for the Norwegian legend of the kraken. The reader interested in such matters is referred to my book *Mermaids and Mastodons*, where marine legends are considered at some length. But in the present context it is time to leave the nektonic animals of the middle and upper waters and consider their cousins who live in the depths of the abyss.

Chapter Twelve

INTO THE ABYSS

THE deep sea remains the most mysterious and challenging region of the earth's surface. Man has now stood on the summits of the highest mountains, crossed the whole breadth of the Antarctic continent, and penetrated to the heart of the remotest deserts and jungles; but to the depths of the abyss he has not yet been able to venture. The main obstacle to exploring these regions is of course the immense pressure that must be withstood by any machine designed to transport living things to the floor of the deep sea. Even though the invention of the bathyscaph, to be referred to in Part 3 of this book, has demonstrated that the problem is by no means insoluble, it will still be some time before humans can hope to make a detailed examination of the deepest submarine levels by direct observation. The journey we shall make to the abyss in this chapter must therefore be an imaginative one, based mainly on the catches made in deep sea trawls and the evidence provided by underwater photography.

We have already dealt with some aspects of deep sea biology in previous chapters. For instance, reference was made to the pressure gradient in Chapter 7, and to a few characteristic benthic organisms in Chapter 10. Here we shall restrict ourselves mainly to two kinds of life: first, the nektonic animals that swim in the region of partial or total darkness prevailing over all the deeper regions of the sea; second, the micro-organisms which live on the bed of the abyss, and have recently been recovered in samples taken from the deepest oceanic trenches.

To begin with the deep sea nekton, we find that, as with the nekton of the middle and upper waters, two main groups are represented. These are the active and fast-swimming vertebrates, and the more mobile species of invertebrates such as cephalopods and large crustaceans. The fish are particularly interesting, many of them being extremely unfamiliar in shape, and exhibiting several fascinating specializations to their environment.

As we have seen earlier, fish are not exposed to any special hazards as a result of living under conditions of great pressure. This is because the pressure is uniform inside and outside their bodies. Only if they possessed large swim-bladders incapable of rapid adjustment to pressure would they be in danger of collapsing during rapid descents or exploding if they rose too rapidly towards the surface. As a matter of fact, many deep sea fishes have reduced swim-bladders invested with fats, while others have lost these organs altogether. The fats provide some of the buoyancy which would otherwise be provided by the gas in the swim-bladder, and the bladderless species normally have such fragile tissues and poorly ossified skeletons that they are not much heavier than their environment. This means that slight movements of their fins and tails alone are sufficient for them to maintain their level in the water.

The reduction, transformation, or elimination of the swim-bladder can thus be regarded as an adaptation made by deep sea fish to one important aspect of their environment, namely pressure; but it is not on the whole so basic as that made to the other main physical characteristic of the abyss, the absence of light. We have told earlier how minute particles suspended in the sea cause the sun's rays to be reflected, scattered, or absorbed so that light intensity decreases rapidly with depth. The animals at different levels tend to adapt themselves to this effect in three ways. The first is in their tone and coloration, the second is in the structure of their eyes, and the third is in the evolution of light-producing organs, some of which may enable them to see as efficiently in the dark as a motorist whose car is equipped with a powerful pair of headlamps.

Gradations of colour are not strictly defined, but nevertheless occur fairly consistently with depth. In the surface waters the animals tend to have bluish bodies, or to be wholly or partially transparent. At a depth of between 150 and 500 metres silvery and greyish creatures predominate, especially among the fish. Below the 500 metre level the animals are usually black or otherwise dark-coloured, and there are also a number of red forms. As stated earlier, many fish of the upper and middle levels are darkish above and light below; this is an obvious protective adaptation to the environment, their bodies toning in with the light background as seen from below and the dark background as seen from above. The blueness or transparency of surface forms is likewise easily explicable as a device for making them less conspicuous, and this also applies to the dark forms of the abyss. The red coloration of some abyssal fish is more difficult to account for. The most favoured explanation at present is that this colour is less conspicuous than any other in the light emitted by fish with luminescent organs. But this is a matter on which only a luminescent fish could afford to dogmatize.

The eyes of deep sea fishes are astonishing organs beautifully adapted for maximum efficiency in the dark waters of the abyss. As we might expect, nearly all of them are of exceptionally large size, their orbits sometimes occupying nearly half the length of the skull. But size alone does not allow them to make the most of the near-dark conditions. A large eye has no more advantages over a small one than a large camera over a miniature; the important point is that the pupil, or 'aperture', must be widened to a proportionately greater extent than the diameter of the eyeball. In such a case the lens, which collects the light rays and focuses them on the retina, must also be considerably enlarged. Amateur photographers will recognize the principle of this arrangement at once. The eyes of fishes living in the light surface waters correspond with the small lenses of ordinary Box Brownies with an aperture of $f11$ or even smaller. Those of the abyssal fish, on the other hand, correspond with the wide $f1·5$ and $f2$ lenses of, say, the Leica and the Contax, which enable these cameras to take pictures in exceptionally dark conditions. In some species the pupil is so enlarged as to occupy nearly three-quarters of the vertical diameter of the eyeball.

In spite of what has just been said, it does not always follow that the eyes of fish become consistently larger with depth. In fact it seems that a maximum size is reached at a certain level, after which the size of the eye decreases again. This level probably corresponds with the greatest depth at which vision as we understand it is physically possible; below this point the eye must resign itself to being simply a light-sensitive organ, capable of determining the direction of illuminated objects, but not their actual shape. If this theory is true it would account for the fact, otherwise difficult to explain, that some deep water fish have smaller eyes than those that live in the twilight zone above.

The internal structure of the eyes of deep sea fish is distinctive and remarkable. The retina possesses few, if any, 'cones' – the visual cells controlling colour and sharpness of vision – but is well equipped with a number of rod-shaped structures containing pigments, such as rhodopsin and chrysopsin, which respond exceptionally well to very faint light. N. B. Marshall has compared the arrangement of these rods to the close-packed pile of a thick carpet.[37] They are almost inconceivably small, and in some species of deep sea fish one square millimetre of the retinal surface may contain as many as twenty million of them. The rods are connected in groups to a complex of optic nerve fibres, many dozens or even hundreds of rods feeding light impulses into a single fibre. By thus concentrating the stimulae received by many rods into one channel there is a greater chance that a nervous reaction will be produced than if each rod were designed to act in isolation. The arrangement can be compared to using a number of cells in series in an accumulator to produce a higher voltage than could be produced by one cell alone.

In the very deepest waters the eyes are often small or degenerate. In this region the only light comes from naturally luminescent creatures, and the function of the eye is to receive signals rather than to register shapes. Thus *Cetomimus*, the 'whale mimic', which grows to a length of four inches, has eyes only $\frac{1}{25}$ inch across, while those of the snipe-eel, *Cyema atrum*, are proportionately even smaller. Some fish living at these depths lack eyes altogether, but in such cases the optic nerve often branches out on the surface of the head in the region normally occupied by the eye, and may be capable of receiving stimulae direct.

In contrast to such small or degenerate structures many fish of the twilight zone and abyss are distinguished by large eyes of peculiar shape. Some bulge out like tennis balls, and at least nine families have developed eyes in the form of tubes. These point either forward, as in such genera as *Winteria* and *Gigantura*, or upward, as in *Opisthoproctus* and *Argyropelecus*. The biological function of such odd-shaped eyes is a subject of controversy. Some authorities believe that they act like a telephoto lens in a camera, because the distance between lens and retina (the 'focal length' in photographic terminology) is greater than in normal-shaped eyes. Others simply regard them as a special adaptation for receiving signals from the luminescent organs of predators or prey. In any case they are extremely complicated in structure, having an accessory retina of short rods which acts in conjunction with a principal retina of the type described above.

The time has now come to say something more about luminescence itself. We have already seen in Chapter 9 how planktonic animals are often equipped with light organs that impart to the surface of the sea a ghostly phosphorescent radiance. We have also stated that in the abyss these organs are commonly found among the nekton, being probably possessed by well over 60% of all the species living there. The light is produced by structures known as photophores, of which more than a dozen different kinds may be found in any one species, ranging from simple to highly elaborate structures. They are arranged in definite patterns which are usually similar in closely related species, but vary widely between fish of different groups, and particularly between fish and the larger nektonic invertebrates.

The biochemical cause of luminescence is too technical to be gone into here. It must suffice to say that it is produced by the interaction of two substances in the body of the animal exhibiting it. These are known respectively as 'luciferin' and 'luciferase', words derived from the Latin *lux* 'light' and *ferre* 'to bring', but not in this context to be associated with Satan and hell fire. Little is known about either substance, but luciferase seems to have some of the properties of protein, one of the essential substances composing the bodies of living things, while luciferin is non-protein in character. The substances seem to react on each other in different ways in different types of animals, and luciferin taken from one species will not necessarily produce light if mixed with luciferase from another. On the other hand, if the substances are taken from the same species, luminescence can easily be caused artificially. It is essential that they should be mixed in the presence of oxygen, but if this condition is fulfilled the result is a sudden bright glow which after a few seconds gradually fades. This characteristic has led to the two substances being used in some rather unexpected contexts. For example, Japanese officers in the last war were often equipped with powdered luciferin and luciferase extracted from the bodies of the ostracod crustacean *Cypridina*. When moistened and rubbed in the palm of the hand this provided sufficient light for messages to be read in conditions where the use of an electric torch would have been dangerous.

In deep sea fishes luminescence is not distributed evenly over the whole body of the animal. The light organs are localized in different regions in different species. They may occur on the trunk, on the head, on the fins, or even, in some genera such as *Chauliodus* and *Dactylostomias*, inside the mouth. The colour ranges from purplish-orange to blue-green, and the organs can be switched on and off at will.

Perhaps the most remarkable of all deep sea fish are the angler-fishes, not only for their luminescent organs but for the extraordinary 'angling' device that gives them their name. This is possessed only by the females, and consists of a structure reminiscent of a fishing rod which projects from the end of the snout. The rod can be raised or lowered by two sets of muscles fastened to a supporting basal bone, and at its extremity is a luminescent organ which acts as a lure, or bait. In some species the rod is comparatively short, but in others, such as *Gigantactis macronema*, it may be several times the length of the fish. To catch its prey the animal probably swims slowly through the water with the rod extended forward and the luminous bait winking provocatively as it is twitched by the controlling muscles. When the prey approaches to investigate the source of light, disturbing the water around it and perhaps even touching it, the angler-fish opens its mouth and darts rapidly forward. The chances are that the prey will be swiftly engulfed.

One exceptionally remarkable species of angler-fish, which has the light-lure inside the mouth, is known as *Galatheathauma axeli*, a name which commemorates the *Galathea* deep sea expedition of 1950–52 (on which the fish was first discovered) and also H.R.H. Prince Axel of Denmark, chairman of the expedition committee. The specimen captured on the expedition was 47 centimetres long, and the forked light organ was suspended from the roof of the mouth behind a row of pointed comb-like teeth. It was suggested that the fish captured its prey by lying on the bottom with its large mouth wide open; other creatures were then attracted by the light, and swam or crawled into the

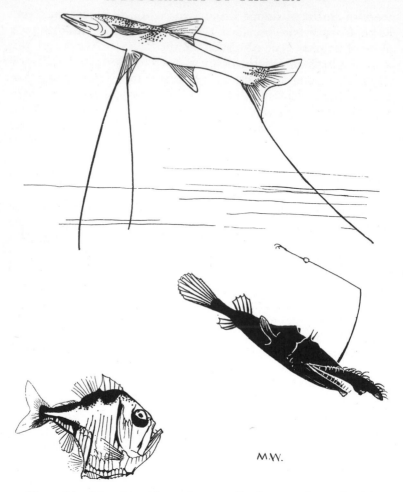

Three fish of the abyss. Top to bottom: *Benthosaurus*; the angler-fish
Lasiognathus; and the hatchet-fish *Argyropelecus*.

mouth to investigate, whereupon the fish simply closed its jaws.
If these assumptions are correct *Galatheathauma* can be con-
gratulated on devising one of the least energetic methods of
capturing prey known in any animal.

The efficiency of light as a lure is well known. I have described
elsewhere [38] how Mediterranean fishermen go out after dark
and use a lamp to attract the fish to their nets, while off the

coast of Portugal living tissue is used for the same purpose. E. N. Harvey has described how Portuguese fishermen take a piece of dogfish flesh which they intend to use as bait and rub it on the belly of the rat-tailed fish, *Malacocephalus laevis*; this coats it with luminous bacteria which live in a gland near the anus of the animal. In the East Indies also, flesh taken from near the eye of the fish *Photoblepharon* is widely used as bait, because there is a gland in this region containing luminous bacteria.[39]

The use of light organs as a lure for prey is only one of their functions, and we have mentioned that they also act as head-lamps or for general illumination. It is quite common to find a pair of luminous organs close behind the eyes capable of throwing a beam of light forward for two feet or more. In addition to their use as a lure these also illuminate the prey, and enable their owner to chase it with a greater chance of success. The direction of the beams can be varied to a con-siderable extent by the action of the cheek muscles. Some fish, such as *Bathophilus* and *Chirostomias* are equipped with a double row of lights on either side of the under part of the body. These throw a stream of light obliquely outward and down-ward, and illuminate a wide segment of the water below. The bodies of these fish as they glide through the dark waters resemble the fuselages of airliners with the light streaming from the windows along their sides.

Other arrangements of light organs are found in the hatchet-fishes and lantern-fishes. The former have a grotesque hatchet-like shape, and between a hundred and five hundred light organs may be scattered in regular patterns over the surface of their bodies. The latter are more conventional in appearance, and their lights are smaller and fewer in number. The main purpose of the lights does not seem to be to illuminate the visual field, but to act as a signal to fish of the same kind.

Many other aspects of luminescence could be discussed, but we must now pass on to some further aspects of deep sea biology. To return to the angler-fishes, the reader may be wondering why only the female is equipped with a rod, and what the male does while his partner is engaged in her fishing operations. The answer is rather shaming to masculine vanity, for the male angler-fish lives a most degenerate life compared with the female. To begin with, he is minute in size and it is his habit simply to grip at random with his jaws some part of the body of the first female who comes along. Sometimes two or more diminutive males may attach themselves to the body of a single female. It might be thought that this behaviour alone would be enough to kill any hope of a fruitful romance, but worse is to follow. In some species, the mouth of the male becomes gradually fused to the skin of the female, and the male organs, except for the sex organs, completely degenerate. Thereafter he ceases to have any physiological identity, and is nourished entirely by the blood of the female. His role in life is simply to fertilize the eggs after the female has laid them. Several explanations for this extraordinary behaviour pattern have been put forward, but none is really satisfactory. Perhaps we can best regard it as an awful warning provided by nature of what can happen when feminism is allowed to run away with itself.

A noticeable characteristic of many deep sea fishes is the size of their mouths. Compared with the inhabitants of shallow waters these are exceptionally large, and are also capable of an extremely wide gape. This is probably because the waters of the abyss are so sparsely populated that meals are few and far between, and it is therefore advisable for each one to be as large as possible. It is certainly true that many deep sea fish are capable of swallowing fish of at least their own size. The record is probably held by the angler-fish *Melanocetus johnsoni*. One specimen of this fish caught on the *Dana* expedition of 1920–22 was found to contain a large lantern fish (*Lampanyctus crocodilus*) approximately twice its own length. Fish of the genera *Idiacanthus*, *Chiasmodus*, *Gigantura* and *Evermannella*, among others, are also capable of feats of this kind.

It is astonishing what a grotesque distension of stomach and abdomen can be endured by some deep sea fishes in thus dealing with large prey. The avoidance of damage to gill arches, heart and aorta in some species is still more remarkable, and has formed the subject of a paper by the Russian-English scientist Dr V. V. Tchernavin. Tchernavin puts forward the suggestion that special muscles must pull the heart and gill arches out of harm's way at the moment of swallowing. The reconstruction he gives of the fish *Chauliodus sloani* performing this feat shows the enormous degree of distortion that must occur before the prey is successfully ingested.

Apart from 'fishing rods', light organs, and specially adapted jaws, several abyssal fish possess structures whose function is more difficult to explain. One example is the strange creature known as *Benthosaurus*, which has long feeler-like extensions of the fins. It was at first suggested that the fish glided low over the sea floor, using these feelers to discover any substance it encountered that might be worth investigating as food. But more recently photographs have been taken from a bathyscaph which suggest that the fish not only uses the structures as feelers, but can also support its body with them on the bottom. It is alleged to rest there, rather like a camera on a tripod, and even on occasions to move about on the feelers by hopping. There is nothing intrinsically impossible about this suggestion, but it must be regarded as a little unlikely until someone brings back a film as incontrovertible evidence.

We must now turn to the deep sea micro-organisms. These are dealt with here rather than in the earlier discussion of the benthos because the most exciting recent developments in the field have occurred mainly in connection with deep sea bacteria. The work was begun on the *Galathea* expedition mentioned above, when mud samples were obtained from depths never previously probed. It has since been continued in the microbiological laboratories of the Scripps Institution of Oceanography in the University of California, and elsewhere.

Bacteria are single-celled micro-organisms reproducing by the simple process of dividing in two. They are commonly regarded as being more plant-like than animal-like in character, but the existence of bacteria in the deep sea has shown that this concept presents certain difficulties. An essential characteristic of plants is that they need light to synthesize the chemical elements in their environment into food. But deep sea bacteria live in a world of total darkness, and can therefore only be plant-like in a very special sense. It has in fact been discovered that there are two main kinds of bacteria in the abyss, one kind needing organic compounds for their nourishment and growth, the other able to synthesize inorganic substances like ordinary green plants. The latter, which are known by the somewhat formidable name of 'chemosynthetic autotrophs', have been found to use such inorganic substances as molecular hydrogen, methane, ammonium, and nitrite as a source of energy instead of light. Whether, on this basis, they can still be regarded as plants is not easy to decide.

Before the *Galathea* expedition the presence of organisms in the deepest ocean trenches had been regarded as unlikely. Low temperature, high pressure, absence of light, and other adverse environmental factors had persuaded many authorities that life in these regions could not be supported. It was therefore with great excitement that, on July 15th, 1951, the group of *Galathea* scientists watched the first sample of mud hauled from the bottom of the Philippine Trench, no less than 10,060 metres below the ship's keel. Would it or would it not contain organic material?

Small portions of the mud sample were removed with sterilized instruments and examined under the microscope. It was quickly seen that the bodies of many kinds of bacteria were buried in the mud – rod-shaped 'bacilli', comma-shaped 'vibrio', and spherical 'cocci'. But what the microscope failed to reveal was whether any of the organisms were actually alive. It was always possible that these were simply the bodies of dead bacteria that had drifted down from shallower levels. To settle this point, small amounts of mud were placed in a nutrient medium consisting of sea water, peptone, and yeast extract. The mud-seeded medium was placed in a small glass test tube which was in turn placed inside a stout steel cylinder. The tube was sealed with a sterilized neoprene stopper, which also acted as a piston, allowing the contents of the tube to be compressed to the extent of a thousand atmospheres; this was equivalent to the hydrostatic pressure in the Philippine Trench, where the sample was taken. The cylinders were then incubated in a refrigerator at 3°C. – the approximate temperature in the Trench – for several days. When the samples were examined, bacterial growth was found to have occurred on a large scale. This was the first certain proof that living organisms exist in the profoundest depths of the sea.

Several interesting facts are known about these deep sea bacteria. For instance, attempts made to grow them artificially at much reduced pressures were a failure, showing that the extreme pressures of the abyss are essential to their welfare.

For this reason they are known as barophilic, or 'pressure-loving', organisms. Moreover, the existence of bacteria in the abyss has several important implications. One of these has already been mentioned, namely the doubt it throws on their status as plants. Another point of interest concerns the possible role of these organisms in the deep sea food chain. It was said earlier that the larger abyssal animals are usually assumed to live entirely on each other, or on the rain of organic detritus descending from the waters overhead. But the presence of bacteria shows that they have another living source of food close at hand. It is not known to what extent bacteria are eaten by other creatures of the deep sea; but the fact that they are known to have a very high reproduction rate certainly suggests that some agency is keeping their numbers in check.

Another interesting question is the possibility that bacteria are the cause of infectious diseases in the creatures of the abyss. Their role in this respect is well known among land animals and in the creatures of shallow waters, but it has not yet been fully investigated at great depths. It is certainly a fact that they sometimes embed themselves in the surface slime of fish and marine invertebrates, and also infect wounded organisms. In such cases, as we have seen, some species of bacteria have a luminescent effect; but whether they also exercise a harmful influence on their hosts is not yet certainly known.

Chapter Thirteen

A JOURNEY THROUGH TIME

I N the last six chapters we have looked at some of the aspects of marine biology that can be directly studied today, and considered a few characteristic plants and animals that pass the whole of their lives beneath the surface of the oceans. In this chapter we are going back many hundreds of millions of years to see how these different organisms evolved and how the life of the land gradually emerged from beneath the waves. Finally, in the last three chapters of this Part, we shall describe how several interesting groups of reptiles, birds and mammals have partially abandoned land life, and returned to dependence on the ancestral ocean.

The reader will recall that in Chapter 3 I explained how the history of our earth is divided into four great eras, which are themselves subdivided into a number of geological periods. A glance at the chart on p. 25 will refresh his memory on these points. The rocks of each period are, of course, of different geological age, and it is from the fossil remains of animals buried in the various strata that we can build up a picture of the life of the past and the way it evolved. In the present context I shall only have space to describe the actual sequence of events, leaving the evidence for my account to be taken on trust.*

The earliest marine fossils occur in the pre-Cambrian rocks of well over 500 million years ago. Apart from carbonaceous material suggesting the presence of marine algae, there are sponge spicules, tracks and burrows of polychaete worms, and a number of dubious fossils which some authorities believe to be those of coelenterates and arthropods.[40] But the evidence is shadowy and incomplete, and it is not until the Cambrian period itself that we begin to gain a clearer picture of the development of marine life.

This period lasted from 500 to 426 million years ago and, as was stated in Chapter 3, the geography of the earth at that time

---

* For a simple description of palaeontological techniques the reader is referred to Simpson (1953) and Carrington (1956).

was very different from what it is today (see map page 26). The climate also was much more equable, and the period was characterized by warm, shallow seas which encroached on present-day land areas as far apart as Greenland, Morocco and Antarctica. There was no land life, and marine life was represented entirely by plants and invertebrates, for the backboned animals had not yet appeared on the scene. The main plant fossils of the period were of marine algae, such as *Epiphyton* from Antarctica, but invertebrates flourished in profusion. By the end of the period we can find examples of most of the main invertebrate phyla of today, including several species at a very advanced level of organization.

The dominant creatures of the time were known as trilobites, a group of marine arthropods superficially resembling large woodlice. These animals flourished to such an extent that they made up more than 50% of the known fauna of Cambrian seas. Their success continued into the succeeding Ordovician and Silurian periods, but they then rapidly declined as a result of competition with more advanced creatures. They finally became extinct towards the end of the Carboniferous period, after a dramatic career lasting nearly 300 million years.

The length of the average Cambrian trilobite was between one and four inches, but occasional giants reached a length of eighteen inches. In later times even larger forms appeared, such as the Devonian genus *Dalmanites*, which was nearly two and a half feet long. The name trilobite is derived from the three divisions, or lobes, of the chitinous shell which covered the animal's back. The body itself was segmented, each segment being equipped with a pair of legs; the total number of pairs exceeded two dozen in some species. The feeding habits of the trilobites are not certainly known, but it seems likely that the group included both predators and scavengers. Most species were probably benthic in habit, and a few were eyeless burrowers which derived their sustenance from the organic content of the mud of the sea floor.

Apart from the trilobites, the Cambrian saw the rise of many other groups of curious creatures which are now entirely extinct. One of the best known was the group of colonial coelenterates known as graptolites. These were mostly planktonic, and drifted freely across the oceans to nearly every part

147

of the world. They had beautiful branching skeletons, often fantastically shaped, which are preserved in the succeeding Silurian period in black shales from places as far apart as Canada, the United States, Wales, France, Bolivia, Australia and New Zealand. Another extinct group contained the Archaeocyathinae, or 'coralline sponges', mentioned earlier. These were reef-building animals with cylindrical calcite skeletons, consisting of two walls, one inside the other. The walls were sieve-like in appearance, and were separated by limy plates or bars. The immense range of these animals is shown by the black dots on the palaeographical map on page 26.

The mild conditions of the Cambrian period persisted throughout the succeeding Ordovician and Silurian. During these two periods, which together lasted over a hundred million years (426 to 312 million years ago), seaweeds and the great hosts of marine invertebrates continued to differentiate and increase. Sponges and corals were abundant, but were still exceeded in numbers by the brachiopods that lived in the shallow seas. Many of these brachiopods are now extinct, but one Ordovician genus known as *Lingula* has persisted unaltered in to modern times, and is still commonly found on the shores of Japan, Queensland and the East Indies.

Among other marine invertebrates of the time the most important were the eurypterids, or sea-scorpions. These flourished in large numbers in the late Silurian, but became extinct before the end of the Palaeozoic era. They were voracious predators, probably inhabiting estuaries and salt water lagoons, and the largest species attained a length of nine feet. Although their general structure suggests that they crawled on the bottom, they could probably also swim fairly well. Their name literally means 'broad-finned', and derives from their possession of two large paddle-like appendages which must have enabled them to propel themselves quite efficiently through the water.

Impressive as were the trilobites and eurypterids in the world of their day, another development was occurring in the Silurian seas which was to doom them to extinction. This was the evolution of the first vertebrates, the line that was to lead to all the higher sea animals, as well as to all land vertebrates, including man himself. The most primitive known forerunner of the vertebrates was a little fish-like chordate known as *Jamoytius*, whose remains have been discovered in the Silurian shales of Lanarkshire. It was probably an estuarine animal not unlike the living *Amphioxus*, or lancelet. Other primitive vertebrates of the time were the ostracoderms. These looked superficially like fish, but were in fact only jawless cousins of the fish, and later became extinct.

The Devonian period, which lasted from 312 to 270 million years ago, saw a great expansion of vertebrate life in the seas. Henceforward the vertebrates became the dominant marine animals, and the invertebrates which had formerly ruled the waters of the earth were compelled to surrender their privileged position. The reason for this change was the much greater efficiency of the vertebrates in the struggle for existence. Backboned animals are in general more mobile, more powerful, and more intelligent than the static or slow-moving invertebrates and even when one of these advantages is lacking their superiority in the other two is usually sufficient to give them an exceptionally high chance of evolutionary success.

The marine vertebrates must have originated from an earlier invertebrate group, and there has been much scientific argument as to which group this could have been. If we press the matter back far enough in time the likelihood is that we shall arrive at the coelenterates. These lowly animals, represented today by the jellyfish, corals and sea-anemones, are now in fact generally presumed to have given rise to every other higher form of life except the sponges. But between the coelenterates and the vertebrates it seems that there must have been an intermediate stage represented by some other invertebrate phylum. For a time the annelid worms were regarded as being most fitted for the role of vertebrate ancestors, but it was eventually realized that there were insuperable anatomical objections to this theory. The subdivision of the Arthropoda which gave rise to spiders and water scorpions was likewise considered and rejected. Today the favoured phylum is the one that at first sight seems the most unlikely – the Echinodermata. If this theory is proved to be correct, we shall be faced with the odd fact that not only all the higher fishes, but every land vertebrate, including man, shares a common ancestor with the starfish of the seashore.

The boundaries of oceans and continents in Devonian times had shifted considerably from their earlier positions. Earth movements caused a gradual elevation of mountain ranges, and land appeared in many regions that had formerly been covered by sea. Wind, rain, and other erosive forces wore down these newly-formed mountains, and large quantities of pebbles, sand and mud were deposited in inland basins and formed vast coastal deltas. These deposits belong to the formations called collectively the 'Old Red Sandstone' – a term which will be familiar to readers of Hugh Miller and other nineteenth century geologists. Elsewhere shales and slates were formed from compressed mud, and the abundant coral reefs of the warm shallow seas were gradually worn away to form deposits of submarine lime. These majestic geological processes formed the background to the evolution of the first true fish in the earth's history.

The earliest Devonian fish fossils are found in strata (such as the Old Red Sandstone) which were laid down in fresh water, but many species invaded the open sea during the period. The scientific names of all the groups represented at this time need not concern us here, but we must make brief reference to some of the characteristic genera. The most spectacular, and one of the best known, was called *Dinichthys*, meaning 'terrible' or 'huge' fish (Plates 12 and 13). This animal grew to an average length of between twenty and thirty feet, and was the first of the great vertebrate predators of the seas. It was equipped with an armour of thick bony plates covering the whole of the head and forepart of the body. The mouth contained no true teeth, but the plates covering the jaws were developed into razor-edged cutting instruments that could sever the body of a smaller fish in two with the efficiency of a pair of well-sharpened shears. But in spite of this formidable armament *Dinichthys* seems to have been too highly specialized for survival, and its domination of the seas lasted only for the geologically brief period of about 25 million years.

Apart from *Dinichthys*, which belonged to a specialized side branch of the main line of fish evolution, several true elasmobranchs existed in the Devonian seas. The best known is the primitive shark-like fish *Cladoselache*, whose fossil remains have been found in large numbers in the Cleveland shale. The remains include not only teeth and the calcified outlines of the hard parts of the animal, but even impressions of the skin, the body silhouette, and such soft parts as muscle and kidney. This allows us to build up a very clear picture of the animal, which had a torpedo-shaped body between 1½ and 4 feet in length, with an exceptionally large pair of pectoral fins. The pelvic fins were also well developed, but smaller, and a third pair of fins was probably placed just forward of the anus. These last are absent in all later species of shark.

No true teleosts evolved in Devonian times, for this now-dominant group was unknown before the Jurassic period some 150 million years ago. There were, however, a number of primitive bony fishes belonging to orders now extinct, or only represented by one or two comparatively rare species. Most of these were inhabitants of fresh water, but others later migrated into the sea. In the present context we shall only have space to consider one group, the Crossopterygii, or 'fringe fins', which were of immense significance in the future development of life.

The crossopterygians were closely related to the three genera of lungfish that still exist in the fresh waters of Australia, Africa and South America respectively. The distinguishing feature of the lungfish is that not only can it extract oxygen from the water by means of its gills, but can also breathe air, the swim-bladder having become adapted to function as a rudimentary lung. The need for such an adaptation must be sought in the animal's environment. In the wet season a typical lungfish, such as the African *Protopterus*, swims happily about in the rivers and fresh-water lagoons in the ordinary way. But in the dry season, when the streams and swamps dry up, it makes itself a chamber in the mud where it lies in a state of suspended animation comparable to hibernation. At this time it can only breathe by means of its swim-bladder, which has developed a complex of blood vessels capable of absorbing oxygen and discharging carbon dioxide like the lung of an ordinary land vertebrate.

Devonian crossopterygians showed a parallel adaptation, doubtless resulting from the seasonal alternation of heavy rainfall and drought which characterized the period. Moreover the structure of their fins showed that these were adapted to a certain extent for four-limbed progression. The fins were

A Devonian crossopterygian (*Eusthenopteron*).

mounted in two pairs on the underside of the body, and sprang from fleshy lobes which were themselves supported by projections of the internal skeleton. With the aid of these rudimentary limbs it is probable that the Devonian crossopterygians could make short overland excursions from a desiccated region to one that possessed a higher degree of moisture. From such simple beginnings the emancipation of vertebrate life from the water was able to proceed by logical steps.

A full account of the invasion of the land by sea organisms would not be relevant to the story of ocean life, and it will be sufficient to state here that the descendants of such crossopterygian fish as we have just described followed in the train of certain species of algae and a number of aquatic invertebrates in conquering the new environment. Freshwater forms were probably the spearhead of the advance, for the comparatively calm conditions along the banks of rivers and on the shores of lakes were more suited to the transitional stages of the process than the wave-battered coastlines of the open ocean. Nevertheless several cousins of the invaders were also present in the sea, and some of their descendants and relations have survived to this day. The most famous is the coelacanth *Latimeria*, discovered in comparatively recent times off south-east Africa. This is a crossopterygian fish of a type closely resembling the first vertebrate animals to make an invasion of the land.

Little is known of the development of marine algae and other oceanic plants because of the rarity of fossil specimens, but the history of marine animals is fairly well documented. Already in the Upper and Lower Carboniferous periods, which succeeded the Devonian, many vertebrate and invertebrate fossils are found. To begin with the invertebrates, there was an abundant fauna of molluscs, brachiopods, corals, and the beautiful crinoids, or sea-lilies. Numerous reefs were formed in the clear shallow seas, but less now by the corals, which had been the great reef-builders of earlier times, than by brachiopods, molluscs, and bryozoa. Holothurians, or sea-cucumbers, appeared for the first time, and the sea-lilies flourished to such an extent that their bodies accumulated on the ocean bed to form thick beds of crinoid limestone.

Vertebrate life was represented by many species of fish, especially sharks, which were the dominant sea animals of the period. Other fishes beginning to play an important role were the heavily scaled palaeniscoids, which had first appeared in the Devonian but were then greatly outnumbered by the crossopterygians and lungfish. They were primarily inhabitants of rivers, lakes and streams, but may also have ventured into the brackish waters of estuaries. Of truly marine forms the best known were four families of bottom-dwellers collectively known as bradyodonts. The modern chimaera, or 'rabbit fish', can probably trace its origin to this group. The bradyodonts had a flattened shape resembling that of the skates and rays of later times. They skimmed along the beds of the ancient seas searching for the molluscs that formed their main food, and probably fell victim in their turn to the voracious sharks that hunted in the waters overhead.

The Permian period, which succeeded the Upper Carboniferous, represents a great crisis in earth history. Deep-seated geological processes caused radical changes in the patterns of sea and land. In the northern hemisphere great oceanic inlets were sealed off by upheavals in the earth's crust, leading to the creation of huge inland seas. High mountain ranges were formed by the forces set up by the shrinking earth on its own rocky skin, and there was violent volcanic activity. These geological events altered the circulation of the atmosphere, with a marked effect on climate, while the redrawing of the boundaries between sea and land affected the behaviour of ocean currents. Such major changes in the environment presented a great challenge to living things – a challenge which sea organisms did not escape. In the Permian more than in any other period until the end of the Mesozoic a physical revolution invoked the inescapable natural law of adaptation or extinction.

The effect of the geological crisis on marine life can best be studied in the invertebrates. Fossil fish are scarce in the strata of this period, and the other vertebrates belonged exclusively to the land. As might be expected, many characteristic groups of earlier times became extinct. The Permian saw the last of several primitive kinds of corals, of the globular or spindle-shaped foraminifera known as fusulinids, and of the whole dynasty of the trilobites. Other groups (the cephalopods, for example) went through rapid evolutionary changes, and in some seas, such as that which then covered the north-east of England, the fauna showed a progressive decrease in size.

As a result of such events the cast that was assembled in the seas at the opening of the Mesozoic drama had many new members. These not only included several new kinds of fish and invertebrates, but also a number of sea reptiles which had returned to a marine environment after many millions of years of evolution on land. These were distant relations of the great dinosaurs which at this time ruled the land surface of the earth. They will be more fully dealt with in the next chapter, but it should be noted here that their arrival had an extremely important effect on the ecology of the oceans. The marine reptiles were new and powerful predators, as dominant in the Mesozoic seas as were such creatures as *Dinichthys* and the sharks in the seas of earlier ages.

The Mesozoic era lasted from about 200 million to 63 million years ago, and is divided into three periods, the Triassic, the Jurassic, and the Cretaceous. Throughout the era marine plants were still exclusively represented by the algae, red algae being particularly characteristic of the Jurassic. Among the invertebrates, bivalve molluscs and marine snails became increasingly common, while modern types of sea-urchins were gradually making their appearance. By the beginning of the Triassic all the main groups of echinoderms known in the sea today were already in existence. The modern group of corals known as the hexacorals had come into being, and these as well as several kinds of calcareous sponges built reefs in the warm, shallow seas. Brachiopods were in decline, but continued to be represented by two important types known respectively by the tongue-twisting names of terabratulids and rhynchonellids. Crabs appeared for the first time during the Jurassic, and have increased in numbers and diversity ever since.

Two of the most typical invertebrate groups of the Mesozoic were the ammonites and belemnites. These animals existed in fantastic numbers and great variety throughout the era. Their fossils can still be picked up by the dozen in such places as Lyme Regis in Dorset and Whitby in Yorkshire, where there are outcrops of the shale beds known as the blue lias. The typical ammonite had a coiled form like an unignited catherine wheel; belemnites were shaped like miniature projectiles, and their fossils are still sometimes mistaken by simple people for thunder-bolts.

Among vertebrates few creatures could rival the great marine reptiles. Their effect on the life of the sea was augmented in the Jurassic by the appearance of the flying reptiles known as pterosaurs or 'pterodactyls', and in the Cretaceous by the first sea birds, such as *Ichthyornis*. All these creatures commonly fed on fish and other marine organisms, and thus exercised an important influence on the evolution of ocean life. The dominant indigenous vertebrates were still the sharks, although these had declined greatly in importance since Carboniferous times, and now took second place to the reptiles. Several kinds of Mesozoic sharks were identical with shark genera alive today. The coelacanths were on the wane and, until the first description of *Latimeria* by Professor J. L. B. Smith off south-east Africa in 1938, were thought to have died out during the era. The last rare descendants of the palaeniscoid dynasty of the Carboniferous period struggled on until the Cretaceous and then became extinct.

By contrast with this decline of primitive types the great group of teleost fishes was coming into its own. Its earliest representatives evolved in the sea at the beginning of the Jurassic, and the group then embarked on a spectacular radiation which led without a setback to its present position of dominance. By the end of the Jurassic the numbers of teleost fishes were already approaching those of other types; by the end of the Cretaceous they had almost entirely supplanted them. Superficially there is no marked difference between the teleosts and their more primitive ancestors, but they are in fact distinguishable by a number of technical criteria. The vertebrae have become completely ossified, there are differences in the bones of the head, the fins of the tail appear to be generally more symmetrical, and the scales are either reduced in size or entirely absent.

The modern teleosts vary enormously in shape and size, and the group includes such widely different creatures as the eel, the cod, the plaice, and the sea-horse. A similar, if rather less extreme divergence, was already apparent in Mesozoic times. Some teleosts, such as *Leptotrachelus* of the Cretaceous period, had a thin tubular body reminiscent of an arrow; others, such as the Cretaceous *Aipichthys*, had a deep body with an exaggerated dorsal fin. Some of these early teleosts were only a few inches long, while others, such as the giant *Portheus molossus*, attained a length of twelve feet. Many Mesozoic teleosts are closely related to genera existing today.

The Mesozoic era was in the main warm and equable, and the physical and climatic environment offered few challenges to the inhabitants of land or sea. But at the end of the era there was a further period of crisis and catastrophe comparable with that which had occurred in the Permian. The harsher conditions swept away the ruling reptiles of the sea and the great dinosaurs on land with ruthless finality, and the smaller, more intelligent, and more adaptable mammals rose to the dominant position. When our own era, the Cenozoic, dawned about 63 million years ago a great sifting out of life forms had occurred. New genera on land and in the sea pointed the way to many of the familiar creatures of today, and we can begin to see with increasing clearness the pattern of events that was to lead to our own times.

The Cenozoic is the shortest of the geological eras, being as yet a mere 63 million years old. But being nearest to us in time it is extremely well documented, and the fossil record can be interpreted with a greater degree of certainty. As a result it lends itself to more precise chronological treatment, and its two main periods, the Tertiary and the Quaternary, are customarily divided into a number of well defined shorter periods, or 'epochs'. The four epochs of the Tertiary period are known as the Eocene, or 'dawn of the recent', the Oligocene or 'few of the recent', the Miocene or 'less recent', and the

Pliocene or 'more recent'. The two epochs of the Quaternary period are known as the Pleistocene, or 'most recent', and the Holocene, or 'wholly recent'. The Holocene began only ten thousand years ago and is the epoch in which we now live.

Apart from a few groups of mammals which had returned to the sea, and some insignificant survivors of the marine reptiles, ocean life in the Cenozoic pursued the general pattern of evolution that had been initiated in the Jurassic period with the rise of the teleost fishes. As early as the Eocene the marine flora and fauna was almost modern in general character. The fauna did, however, include several groups that later became extinct, such as the last survivors of the belemnites and vast numbers of the foraminifer *Nummulites*. The shells of *Nummulites* accumulated on the sea floor to form thick beds of limestone, some of which were later upraised above sea level. The pyramids of Giza were partly built of nummulitic limestone, and other formations of this rock occur high up in the Swiss Alps.

Among Eocene invertebrates that still flourish in modern seas were numbered cockles, mussels, oysters, crinoids, starfish, brittle-stars, sea-urchins, and crabs. The fish were mainly teleosts, but sharks and shark-like fishes were now holding their own. In the succeeding Oligocene epoch nummulites and large foraminifers such as *Lepidocyclina* (which was nearly three inches across) remained abundant, and there were many modern species of hexacorals and sponges. In the Miocene a huge species of shark known as *Carcharodon megalodon* appeared. If we are to judge from the length of its teeth, which measured six inches from root to point, it must have been at least sixty feet long.

Carcharodon megalodon continued to live into the Pliocene epoch and then became extinct. By this time many marine plants and animals were already identical with those of today, although several species did not manage to survive into modern times. The distribution of many groups was also very different due to climatic factors. This was true also of the succeeding Pleistocene epoch when, as a result of the harsh conditions of the Great Ice Age, tropical forms retreated into a comparatively narrow belt on either side of the equator. During this epoch a great ice sheet made four separate advances from the poles, retreating in between and allowing somewhat milder conditions to supervene. As a result many of the less hardy species of marine animals were compelled to move backwards and forwards with the changes in temperature.

Since the last retreat of the ice at the end of the Pleistocene epoch conditions have grown progressively more mild. Sea life has undergone a period of expansion, and tropical forms are once more moving slowly outwards towards the poles. If this trend continues the pattern of former ages may well repeat itself. Sponges and corals will again spread through warm, clear waters off the coasts of Greenland and Siberia, and Antarctica itself will be girdled by a glittering tropic sea.

It will be seen from the foregoing that the marine plants and animals of today are the successful survivors of a process of evolution that has probably lasted over a thousand million years. Each has developed along a different path, some at a fast pace, undergoing many changes of structure and spreading into many different environments, others, to whom life offered fewer challenges, more slowly, or hardly at all. Yet whatever the shape or size or habits which an organism has acquired as a result of its evolutionary history it is exciting to recall that it is in a very real sense a cousin of every other living thing; seaweeds and shrimps, whitebait and whales, mackerel and men, can all trace back their ancestry to the protoplasmic froth that floated on the surface of the Pre-Cambrian seas.

Chapter Fourteen

SEA REPTILES

W E have seen in the last chapter how some time during the Devonian period of geological time an air-breathing crossopterygian fish was the first vertebrate to leave its ancestral environment and pioneer life on land. The fascinating history of the growth of land vertebrates from these simple beginnings does not belong to our present story, but we must briefly summarize the general pattern of events in order to understand the effect that land vertebrates had later on the history of the sea.

The four great classes of land vertebrates evolved in the following order: amphibians, reptiles, birds and mammals – the last two appearing at approximately the same time, although on quite distinct evolutionary paths. The amphibians appeared in the Devonian period and represent the transitional phase between the ancestral crossopterygian fish and the reptiles. Although modern amphibians, such as the frogs, toads, newts, caecilians, and salamanders represent a rather lowly form of vertebrate life, we should not forget that they belong to the natural class which made the whole of vertebrate land life possible. They are able to breathe air, and are adapted in several important ways to land life. Their great disadvantage is that in general they still have to return to the water to breed.

The reptiles, which represent the next stage of advance, first appeared in the Upper Carboniferous period. During the Permian, and throughout the whole of the Mesozoic era, they enjoyed a tremendous period of flowering, and dominated the whole surface of the earth. The best-known and most spectacular reptiles of the time were the larger species of dinosaurs, which ruled the land, but other reptiles achieved the conquest of the air, and others again re-entered the sea and established domination there. The reptiles had an immense advantage over the amphibians in that they had developed a new kind of egg with a hard shell and a plentiful supply of food, or yoke, for the embryo. This made it possible for them to breed without returning to the water; they also had a much modified skeleton, better adapted to land life than that of their crossopterygian and amphibian predecessors. But one disadvantage they retained: like the reptiles of today, they had no internal mechanism for regulating their body temperature and were thus ill-adapted to withstand protracted periods of cold. Because of this they were restricted, like most modern forms, to the warmer parts of the earth, and if the temperature fell for long below a certain level they were in danger of extinction.

The birds and mammals both learnt to overcome this disadvantage. They were already evolving during the period of the reptiles' domination, but did not come into their own until the beginning of the Cenozoic era some 63 million years ago. Although specialized for different functions and evolving in different directions, both groups developed a heat-regulating mechanism that made them to some extent independent of their thermal environment. The mammals acquired the additional advantage of much increased brain capacity relative to their body size. Apart from their value in land life such factors as these were of great importance in determining the evolutionary success of the mammals who took up a marine existence at the beginning of the Cenozoic.

We must now come back to the reptiles of the past and present who have returned to the sea. This return began nearly 200 million years ago, and although superficially it might seem like a retreat, it was in fact nothing of the kind. It was an adventurous reinvasion of a once familiar environment by animals that now had the advantage of over 60 million years of evolutionary experience, and the profusion of fossil forms found in marine strata throughout the Mesozoic are a measure of its success.

The earliest aquatic reptiles probably lived in fresh water and therefore do not strictly concern the story of the sea. But some of them, such as the crocodiles, later developed marine forms. The earliest crocodile-like reptiles were a group known as phytosaurs which flourished during the Triassic period. These were not ancestral to the crocodiles of later times, but belonged to a different branch of the reptiles, which died out about 170 million years ago. The true crocodiles developed alongside the phytosaurs towards the end of the Triassic. These early members of the group were mainly freshwater or estuarine forms, but in the following period several marine crocodiles appeared. One example, known as *Geosaurus*, was superficially not unlike a modern gharial with a slender body and long, pointed snout. Some of the contemporaries of *Geosaurus* were extremely small, one species measuring no more than a foot in length.

Later, in the Cretaceous period, at least one giant crocodile evolved, which probably lived in the brackish waters of estuaries. This was known as *Phobosuchus*, and a cast of its skull in the British Museum (Natural History) measures some six feet long and four feet broad. This suggests that the total length of the animal could hardly have been less than fifty feet. Other aberrant forms were known in the Cenozoic era, as well as forms transitional between the ancestral members of the group and the species alive today. These last were nearly all inhabitants of fresh water, which suggests that the main line of crocodile evolution took place in the rivers and estuaries rather than in the sea.

The dominant marine reptiles of the Mesozoic belong to three groups, the ichthyosaurs, the plesiosaurs, and the mosasaurs. The flying reptiles known as pterosaurs may also be regarded in a certain sense as marine, for it is probable that several of them, such as the huge *Pteranodon*, lived by making gliding flights over the sea and swooping down on shoals of fish (Plates 20 and 21). The fossil remains of ichthyosaurs and plesiosaurs were first discovered in the early nineteenth century near the English seaside town of Lyme Regis, and have since come to light elsewhere. The word ichthyosaur means 'fish-reptile' or 'fish-lizard', and ichthyosaurs were indeed very fish-like in shape. The skull was sharply pointed, and the head and body followed a single stream-lined curve to the twin-fluked caudal fin, or 'tail'. Impressions of the soft parts left in some fossil localities show that there was a fleshy dorsal fin of large size, which was not, however, supported by bone. The limbs were transformed into flippers and had entirely lost their former power of progression on land. In the sea, however, the ichthyosaur was able to propel itself through the water with great speed and grace by propulsive movements of the tail, using the flippers as rudders to determine its course.

A particularly distinctive feature of the animal was its bony, saw-like jaws. Another was the enormous eye sockets, which were reinforced at the circumference by hard bony plates and sometimes attained the size of a human head. These and other characteristics of the ichthyosaurs moved the palaeontologist Blackie to an entertaining composition in verse, which reads as follows:

> Behold a strange monster our wonder engages!
>   If dolphin or lizard your wit may defy.
> Some thirty feet long on the shore of Lyme Regis,
>   With a saw for a jaw, and a big staring eye.
> A fish or a lizard? An ichthyosaurus,
>   With a big goggle eye, and a very small brain,
> And paddles like mill-wheels in chattering chorus,
>   Smiting tremendous the dread-sounding main.

The comparison with a dolphin has more significance than that derived from the superficial physical resemblance between the two animals, for it seems that the ichthyosaurs fulfilled the same ecological function in the Mesozoic seas as do the whales, dolphins and porpoises in the seas today. They were particularly common in the Jurassic period, but their life-span continued until the end of the era. Their domination was probably only brought to an end by the onset of harsh conditions which brought the Cretaceous to its close, and gave a greater evolutionary advantage to the warm-blooded mammals. Nevertheless they had a long and successful evolutionary run lasting nearly a hundred million years.

The plesiosaurs were the main rivals of the ichthyosaurs in the Mesozoic seas, but made a different set of adaptations to the problems of marine life. Many of them were large creatures, with a length of between thirty and fifty feet. Their bodies were usually barrel-shaped, with a long tail and often an exceptionally long, snake-like neck. (The geologist William Buckland used to say that they resembled 'a snake threaded through the body of a tortoise'.) The rather ungainly structure of the long-necked forms was less suited to speedy progression than that of the ichthyosaurs, and instead of gliding about with fish-like movements of the body the plesiosaurs were compelled to rely entirely on their four large paddle-like limbs to pull them through the water. Nevertheless they could probably achieve a good turn of speed over short distances, and their highly flexible necks gave them a great advantage in making rapid movements of the head. This was most necessary in catching the swift-moving fish that formed their main prey.

Many genera and species of plesiosaurs already existed at the opening of the Jurassic. Their early development must therefore have occurred in the late Triassic, but only very few fossil specimens have been found from this period. They seem to have held their own very well throughout the rest of the Mesozoic and, like the ichthyosaurs, did not die out until the time of general reptilian extinction at the end of the era.

Our third group of marine reptiles must now be briefly considered. These are the mosasaurs, or 'Meuse reptiles', whose name derives from the locality on the French river Meuse where their fossils were first found. The mosasaurs were only very distantly related to the other groups of marine reptiles we have been discussing. They were, in fact, lizards which had made adaptations to life in an aquatic environment, and are cousins of the modern *Varanus*. Their immediate ancestors were probably a group of lizards known as the aigialosaurs which lived part of their lives on land; but by the time the mosasaurs evolved at the end of the Cretaceous period they were entirely marine in habit.

One of the best known mosasaurs is *Tylosaurus dispar*, from the Niobrara Chalk of Kansas. This creature grew to a length of between twenty and thirty feet, with a long head, short neck, a long, slim body, and an exceptionally long tail. There were four flipper-like limbs, but these were used for steering, not propulsion, the motive power being supplied by the tail. The teeth of the animal suggest that it fed mainly on other water reptiles and fish. Were it not for the extinction of the mosasaurs at the end of the Cretaceous, it is possible that they and the plesiosaurs between them might have had an important effect on the population of primitive teleosts with whom they shared the sea.

Apart from these strange sea reptiles which vanished for ever from the earth some 63 million years ago, fossil remains exist of several creatures more closely resembling the marine reptiles of today. Mention has already been made of the phytosaurs and primitive crocodiles, but a more typically

163

marine group is that containing the turtles. Turtles have come down from Triassic times almost unchanged, and are as successful today as they were in the seas of a hundred and eighty million years ago. Their present familiarity causes us to take them for granted, but, if they were extinct, their fossil shells, or carapaces, would probably be regarded as some of the most remarkable fossils known to science. The turtle shell is, in its way, quite as bizarre and wonderful a piece of armament as was ever assumed by any prehistoric animal, not excepting the great armoured dinosaurs of the late Cretaceous.

Remains of turtles are known from nearly the whole range of marine strata from the early Mesozoic until recent times. In the earliest Triassic forms it is probable that the animal was not yet able to withdraw its head and legs into its shell, but this faculty was later acquired by two suborders of turtles known respectively as the cryptodires and the pleurodires. The first group includes the typical turtles of today, which draw the head straight back into the shell by an S-shaped bending of the neck. The members of the second group, whose name means 'sidenecks', were more primitive, and their neck vertebrae show that they were unable to draw the neck straight back like the cryptodires. Instead, as their name indicates, they tucked it in to one side.

Mesozoic cryptodires included several large marine forms, the best known being *Protostega* and *Archelon* of the Cretaceous period. Some of these ancient sea turtles reached a length of twelve feet, and must have been well able to defend themselves against all comers except perhaps the larger and more formidable mosasaurs. These giant turtles all died out before the end of the Cretaceous, but others of the period, including several members of the genus *Chelonia*, have survived almost unchanged to the present day. The pleurodires have been in general less successful, and the modern representatives of the suborder are restricted to the three southern continents. All are aquatic, or semi-aquatic, but there are no genuinely marine forms.

The sea turtles of today comprise only six species, but these differ so much among themselves that four genera have had to be created to contain them. The names of the species are the green turtle (*Chelonia mydas*), the hawksbill turtle (*Eretmochelys imbricata*), the loggerhead turtle (*Caretta caretta*), the leathery turtle (*Dermochelys coriacea*), the Atlantic ridley (*Lepidochelys kempi*) and the Pacific ridley (*Lepidochelys olivacea*). It is probable that all these turtles belong to different lines of descent which diverged and began to follow separate evolutionary paths as much as 100 million years ago.

Although an occasional stray has been reported from temperate waters, the marine turtles typically live and breed in tropical and subtropical seas. They are mainly pelagic, and have been observed several hundred miles from the nearest coast, but they must return each year to the shore to breed. Here the female laboriously climbs the sandy beach by convulsive movements of her flippers, which are quite unsuited for locomotion on land. When she has reached a point well above high tide level she digs, with even greater effort, a deep hole in which she deposits her eggs. She then fills this with sand and, completely exhausted, makes her way once more down the beach to the sea. The whole operation is an extremely dangerous one, for a turtle on shore is quite defenceless. For this reason egg laying is carried out at night.

The eggs, which are spherical or nearly so, may number over a hundred. When they hatch, the baby turtles scratch their way to the surface and then scurry down the beach to the sea. On their journey they have to run the gauntlet of many enemies, especially sea birds, which congregate in the region in large numbers. How the young turtles know which way to go to find the comparative safety of the waves was for some time a mystery, but it is now believed that the slope of the shore is the deciding factor. Elaborate experiments have shown that the sentimental idea that they could 'smell the sea' has no scientific basis.

The largest marine turtles are the leathery turtle (Plate 17*b*), the green turtle and the loggerhead. A large green turtle may measure nearly four feet from nose to tail and weigh over 800 pounds. Leathery turtles and loggerheads are even longer and heavier, the former being the largest species in the world. Turtles feed on both animal and vegetable food, and the species vary greatly in temperament. Surprisingly, the green turtle (which is the kind that has been so much persecuted by Lord Mayors and others for its gastronomic qualities) is a gentle creature and can be easily handled. On the other hand the Atlantic ridley, which is the smallest of all the marine turtles,

The sea-iguana (*Amblyrhynchus cristatus*).

is extremely bad tempered, and according to one authority becomes quite hysterical with rage when captured.[41]

No living crocodile or lizard can be regarded as truly marine in habit, although the salt-water crocodile, *Crocodylus porosus*, which ranges from India to northern Australia, is widely distributed in the estuaries of great rivers, and the sea-iguana, *Amblyrhynchus cristatus*, of the Galapagos islands regularly enters the ocean in search of the seaweed which forms its only food. But when we turn to the last great group of living reptiles, the snakes, we find there are many genuinely marine forms. These are grouped together in a single family, the Hydrophiidae, including many species that never leave the sea, even bringing forth their young there alive, and others that come ashore each year to lay eggs. Anatomically the two kinds of sea-snakes can be roughly distinguished by the scales on the underside of the body, properly called the ventral plates. Typical land snakes have exceptionally large ventral plates as an aid to easy locomotion, and these persist, although generally in reduced form, in those sea-snakes that habitually venture ashore to breed. On the other hand, in the snakes that never leave the sea, the plates are unnecessary and have therefore disappeared.

The structure of all sea-snakes shows certain adaptations to the marine environment. The tail is greatly flattened from side to side to allow the snake to scull its way more efficiently through the water. The body is likewise flattened to some extent in the same direction. The nostrils are usually placed on the upper side of the snout, allowing the snake to breathe without exposing the whole of its head. Valves are also found in the nasal passages, excluding water when the animal is submerged.

Of the fifty-odd species of sea-snakes the majority are restricted to warm waters close inshore on tropic coasts. But there is one species, *Pelamis platurus*, which seems to be more widely distributed, and has probably learnt to prey on pelagic fish. This animal is the only species to have ventured both eastwards and westwards from the main centre of distribution of sea-snakes, which lies in the waters of south-east Asia and Indonesia. It is found along the east African coast as far as the Cape and has even crossed the Pacific to the west coast of America. So far the cold southern waters have prevented any species of sea-snake rounding the Cape of Good Hope or Cape Horn into the Atlantic, but it is quite possible that the adventurous *Pelamis* may one day arrive there by way of the Panama Canal.

Sea-snakes are quite as venomous as cobras, which are their nearest land relatives, and a bite from one of them can easily prove fatal. Yet their disposition is generally so mild that they have hardly ever been known to molest bathers, while fishermen handle them without fear when they become entangled in their nets. Their biting apparatus is said to be inefficient compared with that of ordinary vipers, and this too reduces the danger of a fatal attack. In spite of such assurances, however, the curious naturalist will usually be content to manipulate them only in thick gloves or with the aid of a pair of forceps. Incidentally the venom acts on the sea-snake's victim exactly as does that of cobras: the central nervous system is paralysed, the respiratory system ceases to work, and death occurs through asphyxiation.

In pursuing their prey, sea-snakes must spend long periods under water, and there was formerly much speculation on the length of time they could remain submerged without rising to draw breath. Estimates based on the animals' metabolism, the capacity of their lungs, and other factors, gave many different results according to how the evidence was interpreted, and eventually on the *Galathea* Deep Sea Expedition it was decided to put the matter to the decisive if rather crude test of drowning some of the animals. The victims were placed in a sealed container, and although the vigorous movements they made in their initial efforts to escape caused them to use up more oxygen than would normally have been the case, they did not die for over two hours. This is indeed a remarkable fact, but even with the most impeccable scientific motive it must have been difficult to explain the need for the operation to the snakes themselves.[42]

Those sea-snakes that are best adapted for marine life are quite helpless when removed from the water. They writhe about in a frenzied and unco-ordinated way, but do not move more than a few inches from their starting point. Moreover the lateral flattening of the body and tail mentioned above causes them, when on land, to fall on their sides. It is only the comparatively few species that habitually breed on shore whose enlarged ventral scales allow of land movements of a reasonably effective kind.

Sea-snakes show great variation in size, appearance, and coloration. The largest species may grow to a length of nine or ten feet, but the majority seldom exceed a length of four feet. The shape and placing of the eyes, mouth, and nostrils also varies between the different species, suggesting adaptations to special environments and feeding habits, and the animal is not always of the uniform tubular shape we normally associate with snakes on land. Thus in one genus, known as *Microcephalophis*, the head and forepart of the body are no thicker than a pencil, while the hinder part is as thick as a man's arm. It has been suggested that this snake very probably uses its thin forepart for exploring narrow crevices in the rocks and coral reefs of the sea floor in search of food which it could not otherwise obtain.[43]

The coloration and markings of many sea-snakes are splendid and beautiful. The whole length of the body is often striped with alternate dark and light bands, and the scales gleam and glisten like polished metal. The banding has a practical function apart from the pleasure it gives to the eye, for it helps to break the contours of the body so that the animal merges into the background of the sea bed. This kind of camouflage is particularly effective among the branching shapes of corals where sea-snakes often hunt their prey. The animals also differ in colour above and below, the upper parts being dark and the lower parts light. This repeats the plan found in crocodiles and many fishes, and helps to compensate for the incidence of light in the sea which is, of course, always from above.

No discussion of sea-snakes would be complete without a brief reference to the Great Sea Serpent which has played such a large part in the folklore of the sea. It is quite certain that a

Sea-snake or Great Sea Serpent? A poetical view of the subject. *From Forbes* (1841), *p.* 243.

real and almost certainly a known animal is behind some sea serpent reports, and I have suggested elsewhere [44] what this animal may have been. But whether sea serpents are to be identified with seals, whales, oar-fish, porpoises, or giant eels, or simply regarded as animals of an unknown species, one thing is clear: none of the hydrophiid sea-snakes so far described can have played any part in the growth of the legend. There are three main reasons for this. First, the most characteristic attribute of the sea serpent, even as described by the soberest and most responsible mariners, is its enormous size, and we must remember that no sea-snake yet known exceeds a length of ten feet. Second, sea-snakes are typically inshore animals, whereas the traditional sea serpent is a creature of the open ocean. Third, the majority of sea serpent reports have come from the Atlantic, an ocean to which hydrophiids do not yet seem to have penetrated.

It is, of course, always possible that a giant member of the family Hydrophiidæ may one day be discovered. But in the meantime responsible naturalists will subscribe to the opinion that the sea serpent can be explained in terms of animals (and not necessarily snakes, or even reptiles) already known to science.

Sentimentalists may at first find something a little prosaic and unromantic in this view, but they would be as wrong as sentimentalists always are. We have only to think of some of the bizarre and extraordinary animals already described in this book to realize that the wonder of superstition can never stir the imagination like the wonder of truth.

Chapter Fifteen

SEA BIRDS

SEA birds play an extremely important part in the ecology of the oceans. They exist in countless millions, and for many of them the sea is their main or only source of food. Some are primarily coastal birds and only fly out to sea to feed, but others are truly pelagic, spending the whole of their lives in or over the oceans except when they return to land to lay their eggs. The depredations of both types of sea birds among the populations of the sea are enormous, and they certainly account for more marine organisms than all the commercial fisheries of the world put together.

Approximately 8,600 species of birds of all kinds are now recognized, and of these only about 200 are truly oceanic. The most important belong to five main natural orders. These are the penguins (order Sphenisciformes); the albatrosses and petrels (order Procellariiformes); the tropic-birds, pelicans, gannets, boobies, cormorants, and man-o'-war or frigate-birds (order Pelecaniformes); the geese and ducks (order Anseriformes); and the oyster-catchers, phalaropes, sheath-bills, skuas, jaegers, gulls, terns, skimmers, auks, guillemots and puffins (order Charadriiformes). These orders also contain many non-oceanic forms, but I shall limit myself here to those which are most commonly found in or over the open sea.

The penguins, probably the most primitive of all living birds, are particularly remarkable in that they have entirely lost the power of flight. But their torpedo-shaped bodies, although ungainly on land, are excellently adapted for making swift progress through the water. Underwater speeds of fifteen miles an hour are by no means uncommon, and maximum speeds of 18 and 22·2 miles per hour have been recorded for the blue and gentoo penguins respectively. The birds' movements resemble a kind of underwater flying rather than true swimming, for the propulsion is provided entirely by the blade-like wings. The legs and feet are generally inactive or are used only for steering.

There are fifteen species of living penguins, all except the tropical Galapagos penguin (*Spheniscus mendiculus*) being confined to cold southern waters. The largest is the emperor penguin (*Aptenodytes forsteri*) which may stand four feet high and weigh seventy-five pounds. Among the smaller species are the little rock-hopper penguin (*Eudyptes crestatus*) which inhabits islands in all the southern oceans, and the Adelie penguin (*Pygoscelis adeliae*) which looks more like a child's toy than a living bird (Plate 18*a*). Others include the macaroni penguin (so named from its peculiar head feathers), the jackass penguin with its donkey-like bray, and the crested penguin from the Snares Islands south of New Zealand.

Penguins are truly pelagic birds, and may spend many months out of sight of land. In an exuberant mood they will plunge in and out of the waves like porpoises, and seem as little worried by the most violent tempests in the open ocean as by the storm-lashed surf pounding on some wild Atlantic shore. Their food consists mainly of fish and molluscs, and they in turn are eaten by killer whales, leopard seals and other marine predators. Although the cold southern oceans may be a harsh and forbidding environment, these very conditions are essential to the bird's survival. They form a barrier to the incursions of many kinds of predators against which the penguins would not be able to hold their own. The birds have been forced back into these inhospitable regions as a result of the evolutionary struggle, and are quite incapable of surviving for any length of time in areas inhabited by man and other voracious carnivores.

The albatrosses are another largely pelagic group. They can live for months on end in the remotest wastes of the ocean, returning to land only to breed. There are thirteen species in the albatross family of which nine are restricted to the southern hemisphere south of the tropic of Capricorn. The tenth, known as the Galapagos or waved albatross (*Diomedea irrorata*), is entirely confined to the tropical waters of western South America, while the remaining three inhabit the north Pacific. The best-known member of the group is the wandering albatross (*Diomedea exulans*) of the southern oceans (Plate 19*b*). This is a huge bird with a wing span of ten feet or more; it is mainly white with black primaries and a distinctively hooked yellowish bill. All the albatrosses feed mainly at night, when the cuttlefish and other marine animals composing their diet tend to come close to the surface. Like penguins they can sleep on the surface of the sea and drink sea water.

The name albatross does not relate to the whiteness of the bird as is commonly supposed, but is a corruption of the Spanish word *alacatraz*, meaning 'pelican'. Seamen often refer to the birds as mollymawks or goonies, and, as readers of *The Ancient Mariner* will recall, they were once commonly held in superstitious veneration. The more simple-minded sailors still look at them askance to this day. A solitary albatross, or several in a group, will sometimes follow a ship for many miles, scanning the sea below for edible refuse. When there is a good breeze the birds may soar for hours without flapping their wings, rising in a slanting direction against the wind, then turning in a broad circle to make a swift down-wind descent.

A favourite pastime among sailors is to 'fish' for albatrosses with a hook and line baited with salt pork. The hook does not harm the bird, for it cannot penetrate the bill, and once the albatross is hauled on deck it cannot take off again, as it needs a very long run; on shore the birds normally launch themselves into the air from the edges of cliffs. Owing to the superstitious awe in which albatrosses were once held, the captured specimens are seldom killed; they are carried for the remainder of the voyage as pets and then released. But sometimes the sailors are prepared to tempt providence by using their skins to make feather rugs, a practice which may explain why they are sometimes referred to as 'Cape sheep'. The long hollow bones were at one time made into pipe stems, and the webs of the feet were used for making purses or tobacco pouches.

Earlier this century albatrosses were ruthlessly hunted in their breeding grounds for the purposes of the feather trade. This was a profitable business, and could be carried out without difficulty or danger to the hunters, the birds being simply approached on their nests and hit on the head. Gradually laws were introduced to protect the albatross from such depredations but not before almost complete disaster had overtaken one species. This was the beautiful Steller's albatross (*Diomedea albatrus*) which nothing but a miracle can now save from extinction. Of the main colony on the Japanese island of Torishima, out of a breeding population which a century ago numbered many thousands, only a handful of pairs still remain.

Petrels are small relations of the albatrosses, and are likewise truly pelagic. Including the shearwaters and the fulmars, there are fifty-three species, all of fairly uniform habits but distinguished by wide variations in size and appearance. Apart from internal skeletal features the hooked bill of the petrels clearly suggests their affinity with the albatrosses.

Petrels of various kinds are found in all the oceans of the world. They either settle on the water to feed on small cephalopods, plankton or decomposing matter, or perform short dives beneath the surface; some of the larger species prey on other sea birds.

Each year petrels migrate vast distances to their ancestral breeding grounds, which are often remote oceanic islands lost in the wastes of the sea. After a period of mass courtship a single egg is laid in a shallow burrow hollowed out by the breeding pair in the turf. When the young birds leave the nest they are normally abandoned by their parents, who fly back to the wintering area many thousands of miles away. The young birds then shuffle to the edge of the cliff and drop unconcernedly into the sea, where they are at once completely at home. After a short time they too fly off to join the adult birds in the wintering area.

The method by which these birds, both adults and young, can find their way over the featureless ocean has been for long a subject of speculation. Among the more remarkable suggestions put forward to explain this phenomenon is that petrels can navigate, like humans, by reference to celestial bodies. In one experiment to test this theory the British ornithologist Dr G. V. T. Matthews captured a Manx shearwater off the Welsh coast and, after ringing it, released it 3,200 miles away at Boston. It was recaptured in its original home 12½ days later. Apart from the intrinsic interest of this feat it is noteworthy that the journey was made in completely clear conditions, and that birds released under overcast skies took far longer to reach their destination.

The possibility that petrels are capable of astra-navigation is also born out by some experiments made by Dr Franz Sauer of Hamburg. The birds in this case were warblers, but the same principles could fairly be said to apply. Dr Sauer released his subjects in the Hamburg Planetarium and found that their direction of flight could be quite clearly correlated with the setting of the stars on the dome. Experiments made in such extremely artificial conditions may not be accepted as conclusive, but they at least suggest a possible explanation of the extraordinary navigational powers of pelagic birds.[45]

The smallest of all petrels, and in fact the smallest of all sea birds, are the storm-petrels of the family Hydrobatidae. These are the birds known to mariners as 'Mother Carey's chickens' (a name derived from the term Mater Cara, used to describe the Virgin Mary), and as readers of Marryat's *Poor Jack* will know, they are the subject of several superstitious beliefs. In particular their presence in large numbers near a ship is supposed to herald the onset of a storm. Like many superstitions this is based on a substratum of fact. In high seas storm-petrels do frequently congregate near ships, as the wake tends to flatten the surface of the water and this helps them to obtain their food.

A typical storm-petrel is no larger than a swallow, most species being sooty in colour, usually with white rumps. The legs are long and thin and the wings narrow and pointed. All storm-petrels are night fliers, and can often be seen by the light of the moon flitting in ghostly fashion among the waves. Sometimes as they do so they utter twittering, chirping, or squealing notes which produce on the suggestible listener a profound sense of melancholy, and even fear. In calm weather and when feeding, the birds often assist their progress along the surface of the water by patting it with their webbed feet. Generally the two feet are used together, and the bird progresses by a series of hops; less frequently they are used alternately, so that it literally runs along the surface of the sea. This may be the origin of the name petrel, which is believed by some to be derived from St Peter. The prowess of this apostle in walking on the water is of course well known from Biblical reports.

Although less far-ranging than the albatrosses and the petrels, the tropic-birds also make long flights over the open ocean. They are about the size of large pigeons, but far more streamlined and graceful, and are distinguished from all other sea birds by a pair of very much elongated tail feathers. As their name suggests, they are birds of the warm waters and are commonly met with over shallow fishing grounds fringing

Tropic-bird.

oceanic islands. The white plumage of the tropic-birds reflects the glittering blues and greens of the tropic sea, imparting to them in certain lights a radiance of extraordinary beauty. Despite their charm and grace in their oceanic home they are clumsy on land. They have webbed feet and short legs, and often have to steady themselves with their wings to prevent themselves from toppling over. They can only take off from a level surface with great difficulty, and usually launch themselves into the air by stepping off the edge of a cliff. In this respect the tropic-birds resemble the petrels, many of which cannot stand without the support of their wings, and progress in the most ungainly manner by pushing themselves along on their breasts.

Pelicans, gannets, boobies and cormorants are not pelagic, but are found mostly in coastal waters. These birds are too well known to need description, but the last three are especially interesting for their methods of fishing. Gannets and boobies habitually plunge into the sea with half-closed wings from heights of a hundred feet or more, and can stun fish six feet below the surface. The screaming descent, reminiscent of the attack of a dive bomber, is extremely impressive to watch, and at the moment of impact a cloud of spray sometimes rises ten or twelve feet into the air. Cormorants can swim long distances under water, twisting and turning in pursuit of their prey with the agility of otters. In the Far East they are trained to hunt on behalf of man, the birds being attached to a long

17a Shaw's sea snake (*Lapemis curtus*)

17b The leathery turtle (*Dermochelys coriacea*) may weigh over 8 cwt.

18a Adelie penguins passing between their rookery and the sea

18b Ring or 'chinstrap' penguins in the Antarctic

19a Gannet in flight

19b The courtship of the wandering albatross

20 and 21 Life of the Upper Cretaceous

Pteranodon (top left) and *Ichthyornis* fly above an inlet containing (left centre) the
right, just in front of the rocky promontory, are a mosasaur and the great crocodile
and sand while the giant turtle

seas eighty million years ago

snaky-necked plesiosaur *Elasmosaurus* and the ichthyosaur *Ophthalmosaurus*. On the *Phobosuchus*. Two specimens of the wingless bird *Hesperornis* perch on a spit of rock *Archelon* swims in the foreground

22a Steller's sea cow (*Hydromalis stelleri*)

22b Manatees

23*a* Bull sea-elephants fighting, South Shetlands

23*b* An angry polar bear with her two cubs in Greenland waters

24a–d Four great ocean explorers: Vasco da Gama (*top left*);
Ferdinand Magellan (*top right*); Christopher Columbus
(*bottom left*); and James Cook (*bottom right*)

leash, and having a ring placed round their necks so that they cannot swallow the captured fish.

The last member of the order Pelecaniformes we must con sider here is the man-o'-war or frigate-bird. Paradoxically although this bird is entirely dependent on the ocean for its livelihood the ocean is also its biggest enemy. Its small light-boned body and huge sail-like wings give it exceptional powers of flight, but it is also so constructed that once it alights on the surface of the water it can never gain the air again. If this happens it starves to death. It is the fastest flying of all oceanic birds, and its names are derived from its piratical habits. The frigate-bird habitually flies over shallow waters within sight of land, its seven-foot wing spread allowing it to soar effortlessly above the waves. It may occasionally hover over the surface, dipping into the water from time to time to snatch up organic matter, but it mainly feeds by harassing other birds and stealing prey which it forces them to surrender. For example, a gull may be seen carrying a fish in its beak. Immediately a party of frigate-birds will give chase, their immense mobility in the air giving them an overwhelming advantage over the compara-tively slow-moving gull. Frightened by the onslaught of these large creatures the gull will usually drop its prey and make off, whereupon some of the frigate-birds will swoop on the fish and catch it while it is still in the air. Only the booby, a particularly tenacious creature, sometimes refuses at first to part with its lawful prize, and the frigate-birds are then compelled to make a direct attack by slashing at it with their sharp, hooked bills. They seldom fail to attain their ends by these bullying tactics.

A particularly notable feature of frigate-birds is the so-called gular pouch. This is a balloon-like ornamental structure developed in the courtship season on the underside of the throat; it is inflated with air and coloured a terra-cotta red. The legs are also feathered almost to the toes, and vestigial webbing clearly shows that the frigate-bird was once more truly oceanic than it is today. Another unique feature is the tail, normally long and pointed like a sword, but capable of expansion into a char-acteristic structure shaped like a pair of scissors.

Of the remaining orders of oceanic birds, the Anseriformes and the Charadriiformes, nearly all are birds of the seashore rather than the open ocean. Even the gulls, which the layman regards as sea birds *par excellence*, are by no means strictly oceanic, and many of them spend a large part of their lives inland. A few species of steamer ducks have taken largely to a salt water existence, but the only other bird apart from those already mentioned which is to any genuine extent pelagic is the kittiwake (*Rissa tridactyla*). This attractive grey and white gull breeds on the shores of all the northern oceans and winters as far south as Mexico. It can often be seen several hundreds of miles from land, where it feeds on molluscs, plankton and small fish which it takes from the surface of the sea. In the breeding season it returns to the land to nest, laying its eggs on rock ledges as far to the north as cliffs extend.

These brief notes on some of the more remarkable living pelagic and semi-pelagic genera of birds must suffice in the present context, but to understand the full interest of this aspect of the biography of the sea we must now briefly refer to some of the oceanic birds of the past. Such a perspective is essential if we are to see the matter in depth.

The birds evolved from the reptiles some 150 million years ago, the earliest bird known being a gliding, fluttering creature called *Archaeopteryx*. This was an inland bird of the cycad forests, but some 50 to 55 million years later, during the last period of the Age of Reptiles, a number of typical oceanic birds had begun to make their appearance.

The two best-known genera were *Ichthyornis* ('the fish bird') and *Hesperornis* ('the bird of the west'). *Ichthyornis* was a small tern-like creature about eight inches long, with strong powers of flight. *Hesperornis*, on the other hand, was an exceptionally large bird, measuring six feet or more from beak to tail (Plates 20 and 21). It was equipped with sharp pointed teeth, and the absence of a 'keel', or breast bone, and the reduction of the wings to tiny vestigial structures show that it was flightless. The bird was probably pelagic, and the hind limbs were so highly adapted for swimming that it probably could only progress with great difficulty on land. The modern sea bird which *Hesperornis* most closely resembles is the diver, although this is of course much smaller in size.

During the Tertiary period of geological time, which began some 63 million years ago, several types of sea birds ancestral to species living today had already evolved. These included

178

pelicans, gulls and divers, but the fossil remains are often too fragmentary for us to obtain a very clear picture of what they were like. One species known as *Colymboides anglicus*, reconstructed from a single breast bone in the British Museum (Natural History), was probably intermediate between the loons and the grebes. Another Tertiary bird, with the rather pleasing scientific name of *Prophaethon shrubsolei*, lived in the London region some 50 million years ago; this was a giant species of tropic-bird, considerably larger than the three foot *Phaethon rubricauda* of the present day. Penguins existed in abundance, and there were many giant forms. One of these, known as *Anthropornis* ('the man bird'), was comparable in height with a living human being (Plate 16b). In structure the penguins of 30 to 15 million years ago were very similar to their modern descendants, although the fossil record does not, of course, reveal the colour of their feathers. Their feet were certainly webbed and they were probably mainly pelagic, only returning to the land to breed.

Auks, terns, sandpipers and other coastal birds are known from every epoch of the Tertiary period, and one of these ancient species, the great auk (*Alca impennis*), was exterminated by man little over a century ago. This bird looked superficially like a large penguin (it is indeed the 'penguin' of Anatole France's *Penguin Island*) and at one time fulfilled the same role in the ecology of the North Atlantic as the modern penguins do in the southern oceans.

I do not propose to weary the non-specialist by extending the list of extinct sea birds to the dimensions of a catalogue. Not enough is known about their habits to bring the subject fully to life, and the reader primarily interested in their anatomy can be confidentally referred to the books by Lambrecht, Heilmann, and Swinton listed in the bibliography. For the rest of us it will be sufficient to remember that the sea birds of today, with all their beauty and diversity, have a long and fascinating family tree, and that they and their ancestors have gladdened the aspect of the world ocean for well over a hundred million years.

Chapter Sixteen

SEA MAMMALS

W E have already seen in an earlier chapter how during the Mesozoic era a number of reptiles reinvaded their ancestral environment, the sea. At a somewhat later period several groups of mammals followed their example, and at the beginning of the Cenozoic, about 63 million years ago, the balance between the different classes of animals inhabiting the world ocean was very similar to what it is today. In this chapter we shall follow roughly the plan adopted in the preceding one, dealing first with the various oceanic mammals alive at the present time and then referring briefly to a few of their more remarkable forerunners.

Three natural orders of mammals have been mainly responsible for the reinvasion of the sea: the Carnivora, the Sirenia, and the Cetacea. Marine members of the Carnivora at the present time are the sea-lions, walruses and seals (suborder Pinnipedia), the sea-otter (genus *Enhydra* or *Latax*) and, if one is prepared to stretch a point, the polar bear (genus *Thalarctos*). The Sirenia, or sea-cows, are represented by two genera, the dugong (*Halicore* or *Dugong*) and the manatee (*Trichechus*), while a third (*Hydrodamalis*) became extinct only a little over a hundred years ago. The order Cetacea, which contains the whales and their allies, is divided into two suborders of living animals, the Mysticeti, or whalebone whales,* including the right whales and rorquals, and the Odontoceti, or toothed whales, including the sperm whales, porpoises and dolphins. A third suborder, the Archaeoceti, or ancient whales, contains no living representatives.

These mammals of the sea all show a different degree of specialization for marine life, ranging from the polar bear, which is still mainly a terrestial animal, to certain species of whales which are so superficially fish-like in shape that the lay observer is often reluctant to believe that they are mammals

* The whalebone whales should properly be termed 'baleen whales' for reasons that will emerge later in this chapter.

180

at all. Our description of the various groups can fittingly begin with those most charming, intelligent and attractive creatures, the sea-lions, walruses and seals.

The great naturalist Linnaeus wrote, rather unkindly, of the Pinnipedia some two hundred years ago:

'This is a dirty, curious, quarrelsome tribe, easily tamed, and polygamous; flesh succulent, tender; fat, and skin useful; they inhabit and swim under water, and crawl on land with

'A quarrelsome tribe.' A turtle watches a seal being disciplined by an eel in rather an unusual way (all species unknown to science). *From Aldrovandi* (1638*b*), *p.* 483.

difficulty, because of their retracted fore-feet and united hind-feet; feed on fish and marine productions, and swallow stones to prevent hunger, by distending the stomach.'[46]

The term 'seal' is often used loosely to denote all the pinnipeds, but taxonomists now divide the order into three distinct families – the Otariidae, or sea-lions, the Odobenidae, or walruses, and the Phocidae, or true seals. Taken together, these families contain forty-seven species and subspecies and perhaps as many as 25 million individuals, probably representing the greatest population of large carnivorous mammals in the world today. The animals are distributed widely in both hemispheres, especially in temperate and circumpolar waters, some species such as the northern fur-seal being semi-pelagic, while others such as the harbour seal spend much of their time on land.

The characteristic appearance of most species of seals is too well known to need description, but a word must be said about their place in the ecology of the seas. The world ocean, as we have seen, is a vast storehouse of life, and marine biologists can describe scores of so-called 'food-chains' representing the order in which the different creatures prey upon one another. Thus small fish and crustaceans prey on the minute creatures of the plankton, and themselves form the food of larger fish and molluscs; these in turn are eaten by still bigger fish, and so on. The seals are at the top of these food-chains. They can prey on almost any animal living on or near the surface, and their diet includes fish, cephalopods, the larger forms of plankton, sea birds, other seals, and even occasionally small whales and carrion. Their own enemies, on the other hand, are remarkably few, being represented mainly by the polar bear (*Thalarctos maritimus*), the killer whale (*Orcinus orca*), which is partial to certain species of seals, and man.

For man the seals are especially useful, for they are efficient gleaners of the smaller forms of life which he himself would not find it worth while to exploit. Thus man has hunted seals for many centuries, not only for food, but for their blubber, which is used as fuel and in several industrial processes, and for their skins, bones and teeth, which are useful for making clothes and artifacts. Some societies, such as the Eskimos, are still very largely dependent on the seal for their existence.

The hunting of pinnipeds by man has greatly reduced the numbers of several species. Thus the fur-seal known to zoologists as *Arctocephalus philippii* is now represented by only a few hundred individuals on the island of Guadalupe off Baja California, while the Japanese race of the Californian sea-lion (*Zalophus californianus japonicus*) and the Caribbean monk-seal (*Monachus tropicalis*) are in an even more precarious position. The walruses also have been much persecuted for the valuable ivory of their tusks, and during the last three hundred years have shown a progressive decline in numbers. The story of the exploitation of these remarkable animals is a shameful one, and reflects little credit on the compassion and intelligence of our own species. Walruses are devoted parents, and if their calves are threatened will immediately do all in their power to shield them from injury, even interposing their own bodies between their young and the lances of the hunter. It is the custom of professional walrus hunters to take advantage of this trait by catching a young calf and then striking it until it begins to cry. The sounds of distress bring all the adult walruses in the vicinity to attempt a rescue, and these animals then fall an easy prey to the hunters.[47]

The largest and most impressive of the pinnipeds is the elephant-seal or sea-elephant (*Mirounga*). There are two species, one inhabiting the warm waters off the western coast of North America, the other living in the cold waters bathing Antarctica and the tips of the southern continents. A large bull elephant-seal may measure well over twenty feet in length, while even the female, which is characteristically much smaller, may attain a length of eleven feet. Like other species of pinnipeds, elephant-seals have been much persecuted by man. In the eighteenth and nineteenth centuries the slaughter of the animals was on such a large scale that the species was on the verge of extinction, but nowadays hunting is only allowed under special licence and many thousands of elephant-seals can still be seen in summer on the beaches of South Georgia and other southern lands.

The elephant-seal is an indolent, unwieldy animal (Plate 23*a*), the male being characterized by a fleshy inflatable proboscis hanging down over the mouth. The females lack this structure, but can inflate the nostrils, producing a swelling and puckering of the tissues of the nose. Beneath the skin there is a thick fibrous layer loaded with oil, known as blubber, which protects the animal from the cold, and causes it to wobble as it moves like a fat man parading along a bathing beach. The blubber is the source of the oil which led man to hunt the animal with such relentless persistence.

The pinnipeds are the most gregarious of flesh-eating mammals and in the breeding season, which lasts from August to October, sea-elephants congregate in hundreds and thousands in 'rookeries' on the beaches. Each bull has a harem of from two to thirty cows, and much of his time is spent in driving off enterprising young bachelor bulls who attempt to annex the more glamorous of his mistresses from the periphery of the group. The pups take to the sea a few months after birth, but at this time they remain close inshore and are constantly hauling out to sleep. In April or May of the following year they begin to voyage further afield, and thereafter both pups and adults become mainly pelagic until the next breeding season comes round.

The sea-elephant is the largest mammal inhabiting the world ocean except for the whales. The smallest is the little creature which is the sole representative of our second group of marine carnivores, the sea-otter (*Enhydra lutris*). This animal inhabits the western coasts of North America, the Commander and Kurile Islands, and may even range as far as North-eastern Asia. Its total length seldom exceeds four feet, and it is one of the most amusing and delightful creatures living in the sea.

Sea-otters are usually observed (when they are observed at all, for they are by no means common) in small groups off rocky, broken coasts where there is an abundance of seaweed. They resemble large river otters in appearance, but habitually swim on their backs, their fore-paws resting on their chests. When dozing they sometimes put one or both paws over their large, black, intelligent eyes to shut out the light. Propulsion is provided by both hind limbs and tail, and when the sea-otter wishes to move fast it turns on its front and kicks out vigorously. In the abdominal position it can achieve a speed of ten miles an hour.

The favourite food of sea-otters is sea-urchins, but they will eat many other kinds of marine invertebrates and some small fish. The chest or abdomen is used as a table, and the animal manipulates its food with such dexterity that it seldom loses any of it, even in the choppiest sea. Large sea-urchins are bitten or cracked open and the contents extracted with the tongue or by sucking; smaller ones are eaten whole, spines and all. The sea-otter has also been observed to crack bivalves on a flat stone carried on its chest.[48]

Sea-otters are semi-pelagic in habit and may spend weeks at some considerable distance from the shore. According to Victor Cahalane they often return to the same dormitory of floating seaweed night after night, preferring ribbon-like weeds which they wrap round themselves like a bed covering.[49] They may mate at any time of year, and the single pup is born nine months later in an isolated spot on a remote island or on a bed of sea-weed in some sheltered coastal inlet. The protective instincts of the mother are extraordinarily well developed, and she will never desert her young whatever danger may threaten. As with walruses, this has led unscrupulous hunters to use the young as decoys, the fur of the animal being extremely beautiful and costly. Human exploitation of the sea-otter, which at one time threatened the animal with extinction, will be discussed more fully in Chapter 19.

Some people will dissent from the inclusion of the polar bear in a book on the sea, and indeed it is only a marine animal in a rather special sense. In appearance it is a typical terrestial mammal, and although there are certain adaptations to swim-ming, such as a streamlined head, and body and legs so jointed that they can move through an exceptionally wide arc, it is certainly not pelagic in the same sense as the pinnipeds. Yet polar bears think nothing of travelling fifteen or twenty miles across the open ocean, and can twist and turn and dive with far greater agility than some of the animals more generally regarded as nektonic. It is probable also that most of them spend considerably more of their lives in the ocean than they do on land. For these reasons it seemed essential to include them in my account.

The polar bear is so well known to most people from photo-graphs and visits to the Zoo that there would be no point in giving a description of it. Not everyone, however, is familiar with its way of life in the wild. The typical habitat of these great white bears is the fringe of the northern ice sheet, and they are circumpolar in range. The latitude of the boundary between sea and ice varies with the march of the seasons, and in winter polar bears are encountered further to the south than during the summer months.

The bears mate in June or early July and after the brief period of courtship and communion the male resumes his solitary hunting life. With the advent of the long arctic night the female digs herself a hole in a snowdrift and hibernates there until January, when usually two cubs are born. At birth the cubs are hairless and blind, and may weigh only two pounds compared with the 600 to 800 pounds of the mother. Male bears and non-pregnant females do not hibernate, but live by hunting right through the dark months of winter.

The polar bear, like the seal, is at the top of one of the great oceanic food-chains. At the bottom are the little planktonic organisms known as krill which were mentioned in an earlier chapter. These shrimp-like organisms occur in large numbers on the fringes of the ice, where the melting bergs and floes produce water of exceptionally low salinity. The fishes are attracted by the krill, the seals live on the fish, and the polar bears in their turn hunt the seals.

The polar bear cannot move sufficiently fast in water to catch a seal in straight pursuit, but on land it can travel at between 20 and 25 miles per hour. Its yellowish white coat harmonizes so well with the ice that it has a great advantage in stalking. In regions where the ice is contorted or broken the bear will approach its prey by taking advantage of every available piece of cover and then making a final dramatic rush on its intended victim. The seal, as we have seen, is a comparatively clumsy and slow-moving animal on land, and if the water is not sufficiently near it has little chance of escape. If the ice is flat, and thus unsuitable for providing cover, the bear will lie flat on its belly, the long neck and pointed head stretched out towards the unsuspecting seal. It will then gradually edge forward, pulling itself along by its front paws while the hind legs trail behind, until it is within striking distance of its prey. It then adopts the same technique as before, making a sudden rush forward, and either breaking the seal's back or crushing its skull in its powerful jaws.

So much for the marine members of the order Carnivora. We must turn next to a group whose members are strongly contrasted with the animals we have just described both in habit and habitat: the Sirenia, or sea-cows. The two living genera of sea-cows, the manatee and the dugong, are creatures of the warm tropic coasts, and are exclusively vegetarian in diet. A third genus, the famous *Hydrodamalis* or *Rhytina*, commonly known as Steller's sea-cow, was a northern animal, but this very fact led to its undoing. As we have already seen with the sea-elephant, mammals living in cold waters often have a thick layer of subcutaneous blubber to help them maintain their body temperature. This fat has great value to man as fuel, and for many other purposes, and thus any animal possessing it is in danger of persecution. Unfortunately *Hydrodamalis* was not able to sustain the onslaught of the hunters to the same degree as the sea-elephant, and before effective measures could be made for its protection it was already extinct (Plate 22*a*).

Hydrodamalis was an exceptionally large animal, sometimes attaining a length of 30 feet or more and weighing up to $3\frac{1}{2}$ tons. By comparison the manatee and the dugong are of only moderate size, seldom exceeding more than 8 or 9 feet, but their close relationship with *Hydrodamalis* is suggested by their appearance. Both are torpedo-shaped creatures, their bodies tapering in front to a round head and at the rear to a horizontally flattened tail; their colour is slate grey and the adults are almost devoid of hair. The hind limbs are absent, and the fore-limbs have evolved into flipper-like structures with which the sea cows propel themselves through the water. The main external difference between the two genera is that the manatee has a rounded tail while that of the dugong is expanded horizontally into flukes.

Manatees (Plate 22*b*) belong more to the coasts and estuaries than the open ocean and they are quite at home in the fresh waters of large rivers; dugongs are sometimes sighted several miles out at sea. The range of the manatee extends along the Atlantic shores of tropical America and western Africa, while that of the dugong is restricted to the coasts of the west Pacific and Indian oceans for some 15° north and south of the equator. Both genera are mild and inoffensive by nature and spend their lives browsing on seaweeds and other aquatic plants. Both animals, incidentally, are alleged to have played a part in the history of the mermaid legend, having been mistaken on several occasions by love-starved sailors for glamorous members of the female sex. This may in part be accounted for by the fact that the sea-cow's mammae are prominently situated on the chest in the normal human position, not just in front of the hind legs as in most quadrupeds. Nevertheless the twilight glimpse that may have caused members of a more credulous generation of mariners to dream of nights of love with some mysterious siren of the sea would surely have been rudely shattered after a close-up view of the bristly muzzle and cleft upper lip of a manatee

187

or dugong. Another fact about the Sirenia, less obviously romantic than the foregoing, except to naturalists, is that these odd aquatic mammals are one of the two natural orders most closely related to the living African and Asiatic elephants.

The last but by no means the least of the orders of marine mammals is the Cetacea, which includes the porpoises, dolphins and whales. Many of the members of this order are extremely spectacular, and it includes in the blue whale, which sometimes measures 100 feet long and weighs between 120 and 150 tons, the largest animal that has ever lived on the face of the earth. Although many species of whales have a fish-like shape, they are, of course, built on a totally different plan. Fish have spent the whole of their evolutionary history in the water, whereas cetaceans have returned to their ancestral environment after a long episode as terrestial mammals. As a result there are many differences between the two groups. The cetaceans lack the scales that are characteristic of fish, but are equipped with a layer of blubber beneath the skin, which fish never have. As warm-blooded mammals they need this blubber to help them maintain a constant body temperature, whereas the body temperature of fishes can fluctuate within fairly wide limits without having a detrimental effect. Another obvious difference is in the shape of the tail. The typical fish tail lies in a vertical plane and enables its owner to propel itself forward by vigorous lateral movements. The cetacean likewise mainly propels itself forwards by its tail but here the organ is in a horizontal plane, and the movement is up and down. This is almost certainly due to the need for the animal to rise at regular intervals to the surface to breathe.[50]

The breathing arrangements themselves exemplify another fundamental difference between fish and cetaceans. The fish, as we know, extract the oxygen they need from the water by passing it through the organs known as gills; the nostrils are mainly organs of smell, and only very few fish ever use them for breathing purposes. In the mammals, on the other hand, oxygen is extracted directly from the air by the lungs, and inhalation characteristically takes place through the nostrils. Cetaceans are no exception to this rule, but the nostrils themselves have become greatly modified as a result of the marine environment. Instead of being placed at the tip of the nose or snout they are situated almost without exception on the highest point of the head, where they form a single or double opening known as the 'blowhole'. The so-called 'spouting' of the whale is simply the exhalation from the blowhole of its breath, which in cold conditions condenses to form a white cloud of vapour just as our own breath is visible on a winter's day. The idea fostered by the old naturalists and some more recent writers that whales can eject a stream of water from their blowholes like that given off by the nozzle of a fire hose is entirely without foundation, for there is no communication in these animals between the respiratory and digestive tracts.

Whales sometimes dive to tremendous depths, several examples of dives up to 200 fathoms having been well authenticated. This habit formerly posed an interesting physiological problem, for it was by no means clear how the animals avoided the condition known as 'gaseous embolism', which causes caisson disease, or 'diver's palsy'. As is well known, when a mammal is subjected to great pressure, such as is encountered in a deep dive, nitrogen dissolves in the blood. If the subsequent decompression is too rapid, the nitrogen returns to a gaseous state and bubbles are formed in the bloodstream, the process being comparable to the sudden appearance of bubbles in a bottle of champagne or soda water when the stopper is removed. These bubbles tend to block the bloodstream and thus interfere with the workings of the circulatory system to a dangerous and sometimes fatal extent. This explains why divers and frogmen must come up from deep descents by easy stages to avoid the results of too rapid decompression.

There is no evidence to show that whales are similarly cautious in ascending from their deepest dives. In fact numerous cases have been recorded where harpooned whales have come up from depths of well over 100 fathoms in a period that can be measured in seconds. How, then, do they avoid caisson disease? For many years this was a subject of animated controversy among scientists, but the answer is in fact quite simple. It must be remembered that human divers who suffer from the condition are receiving a continuing artificial supply of air, either from a cannister strapped to their bodies or through a pipe leading to an air pump at the surface. Their ability to absorb air is therefore not limited by the supply, but only by the capacity of their blood and tissue for dissolving the gas at the incident pressure. But when a whale dives, the supply of air is restricted to the capacity of the lungs; after this is exhausted it cannot be renewed unless the animal returns to the surface. Thus the diving whale is not actually breathing air from an outside source while its body is under pressure, and in consequence the risk of caisson disease is eliminated.[51]

Any attempt to discuss the various species of whales would be, in the present context, both foolhardy and pretentious, so we must content ourselves with a few generalizations. As we have seen, the order Cetacea is divided into two great suborders; the Mysticeti, or whalebone whales, which includes the right whales and rorquals; and the Odontoceti, or toothed whales, which includes the sperm whales, porpoises and dolphins. A third suborder, the Archaeoceti, or ancient whales, is represented by a number of fossil genera, but all the members of this group are now extinct.

There are several important differences between the whalebone whales and the toothed whales, the most obvious of which relate to the structure of the mouth. The whalebone of the whalebone whales is not bone in the generally accepted sense, but a substance scientifically known as baleen. In fact the term 'baleen whales' would be a much better way of identifying this suborder, as the description 'whalebone whales' has often in the past led to confusion. Readers of Kipling should not be misled into believing that baleen consists of the remains of a raft tied together with the sock suspenders of the Mariner of infinite-resource-and-sagacity under the direction of a small 'Stute fish; its composition is in reality even more complicated. The most that we can say here is that it is glossy in appearance, hard and horny to the touch, and of varying flexibility in the different species of mysticetes. The typical whalebone whale is equipped with a number of plates of baleen which hang down into the mouth cavity from either side of the palate, the normal complement being upward of five hundred (Plate 29a). The purpose of these plates is to strain from the water the tiny planktonic animals known as euphausiids, or 'krill', which were described in Chapter 9. Oddly enough the gigantic whales of the suborder Mysticeti rely almost entirely on these tiny creatures as a source of food.

The toothed whales are in general smaller than the whale-bone whales, but pursue a far greater range of prey. Many species are equipped with powerful teeth, and a large form such as the sperm whale (*Physeter catodon*) can deal effectively with giant squids and other large cephalopods. The most voracious of all the odontocetes is the killer whale or grampus (*Orcinus orca*) which is an implacable enemy of seals, walruses, penguins and other sea creatures, as well as of members of its own order. Killers hunt in packs varying in numbers from three or four to thirty or forty and, according to Dr F. C. Fraser, their behaviour when attacking large whalebone whales can be compared with that of a pack of wolves attacking a deer. [52] They swoop onto their victim from every side, some holding its tail to prevent it from threshing, others attacking the head, and especially the lips and tongue. Although killers are fairly small as whales go, measuring between fifteen and thirty feet long, they are well able to deal with baleen whales two or three times their own length.

Several remarkable stories have been told of the intelligence of whales, and they undoubtedly have a better mental equipment than any other marine animal, not excluding the sea-lions and seals. W. J. Dakin tells in *Whalemen Adventurers* how killer whales will collaborate with the whalers in obtaining their prey. He has known of cases where, if a humpback whale or other suitable quarry comes close inshore, the killers will prevent it from getting back to the open sea by hemming it in and harrying it, and will even apprise the whalers of its presence by throwing themselves out of the water to attract their attention. When the whale is eventually harpooned the killers will help themselves to the tongue and lips and leave the rest of the carcase to the whalers.[53] Such tales may cause us to raise an eyebrow at first, but observations of captive dolphins and other cetaceans confirm the exceptional intelligence of the order. Some scientists regard this as so high that they rank the whale's cerebral powers somewhere between those of the domestic dog and the chimpanzee.

To conclude this chapter we must briefly refer to the geological history of the modern marine mammals. As with the reptiles, the return of certain mammals to their ancestral environment was not a retreat but an enterprising invasion of an ecological niche which had not formerly been exploited by the highest group of vertebrates. The fact that the marine mammals of today evolved from terrestial ancestors is clearly shown by several modified or vestigial structures in their skeletons. For example, the hind flippers of pinnipeds were obviously derived from the hind limbs of a terrestial quadruped, while the former presence of hind limbs in the sirenians is indicated by the presence of vestigial bones in several fossil species. Even whales, which are the most completely adapted of all sea mammals to the marine environment, show evidence of their terrestial ancestry. Thus all species retain vestiges of the pelvic skeleton, which not only serve as points of attachment for important abdominal muscles, but are also evidence of the former existence of hind limbs. A study of the embryos of certain whales proves the point still more clearly. The embryos of humpback whales, for example, have particularly well-defined projections of the body which at one stage of their evolution must have developed into limbs, but have now become reabsorbed.

The land ancestors of the different groups of modern sea mammals are unknown in a fossil state, but the science of comparative anatomy enables us to make some reasonable deductions concerning them. Thus it seems probable that the modern sea-lions, walruses and seals originated in a group of primitive land carnivores known as miacids, which somewhat resembled weasels, and took to the sea in early Eocene times some 55 million years ago. The ancestors of the whales were probably a group of small land mammals living at the end of the Age of Reptiles. Some members of this group seem to have evolved with extraordinary rapidity and in isolation so that by middle Eocene times they had greatly increased in size and were completely adapted to ocean life.[54]

Several remains of these ancestral whales are known from the fossil rècord. The earliest genera are *Protocetus* and *Eocetus* from the middle Eocene, but the largest and most spectacular was the upper Eocene *Basilosaurus*, commonly known as *Zeuglodon*. This animal attained a length of sixty feet and had an elongated cylindrical body and an exceptionally long tail. If *Zeuglodon* were alive today it would be excellently cast, in shape if not zoological class, as the Great Sea Serpent of popular imagination.

With this brief account of marine mammals and their possible ancestry our survey of the life of the sea must come to an end. Its many omissions and shortcomings will be apparent to all who have followed me so far, and my main hope is that these very limitations will cause readers to fill in the gaps in their knowledge by further reading. But one serious omission must be repaired at once if this book is to have any claim to be a Biography of the Sea: I refer to the relationship between the oceans and our own species, *Homo sapiens*. In the space still left to me I shall attempt to describe the role of the sea in the human adventure – its discovery and exploration, its utilization for material gain and, perhaps most important of all, the effect it has had on the spirit and imaginations of men.

PART III
MAN AND THE SEA

Chapter Seventeen

THE DISCOVERY OF THE OCEANS

U NLIKE the mammals discussed in the last chapter, which have become physically adapted to a greater or lesser extent to ocean life, man's physical specializations have always been those of a land animal. In fact the other members of the natural order Primates to which he belongs are generally so allergic to water that they will never voluntarily enter it, and for this reason even the most precocious of the anthropoid apes, such as chimpanzees and gorillas, can be safely separated from the public in zoological gardens by a comparatively narrow and shallow moat. Man himself, although able to support himself in the water after a fashion, and even to move through it at some speed, is one of the poorest and feeblest mammalian swimmers. We have only to compare his performance with that of an otter or a seal, or even such an unlikely creature as an elephant (which, if pressed, can swim across many miles of open ocean), to realize how greatly inferior are his powers in this respect.

Yet in spite of these shortcomings the human species has achieved a mastery of the oceans unrivalled by any other animal. Man has succeeded here, as he has in so many other fields of endeavour, not by physical adaptations made to a particular environment, but in the prodigious evolutionary development of his brain. With his advanced capacity for thought he has been able to acquire an impressive degree of control not only over one special environment, but over almost the whole of the earth's surface. This control has been achieved by the use of material equipment to extend the range of his own physical powers.

The various types of equipment used by man in the conquest of his environment would make a catalogue of almost infinite extent. To take a few examples at random, there are the tools, ranging from the most primitive hand-axe to the most intricate precision machinery, which have enabled him to perform tasks that would have been impossible by the use of his hands

197

alone; there are the books in which he can store his thoughts and experience for the use of future generations; there are the diverse types of wheeled vehicles which have helped him to move more quickly and easily over the surface of the earth; and there are the scientific instruments such as thermometers, theodolites and telescopes which he uses to measure the physical properties of the earth and which are now enabling him to probe the deepest recesses of the universe. It is almost entirely through the use of material equipment of this kind, especially ships and submarines and bathyscaphs, and the many elaborate instruments associated with the science of oceanography, that man has achieved his present knowledge and mastery of the oceans. It would not be appropriate to discuss the evolution of all these inventions here, although a few will be mentioned in the next chapter, but their supreme importance will be apparent to all who study the relationship between man and the sea.

To our primitive ancestors the ocean was a barrier, and we may assume that it was only by pressure of circumstances that they were first compelled to venture upon its surface. A limited food supply may have encouraged early man in his first attempts to reap the harvest of the sea. Perhaps more important still were the climatic fluctuations of the Great Ice Age, which compelled him to cross the waters in pursuit of new and more congenial environments. Conscious of his own limitations as a swimmer, man would first have pressed into service such objects as floating tree trunks to transport him over short distances from one piece of land to another. From this it would have been only a short step to the construction of primitive rafts, and then of dugouts and outrigger canoes. The building of such simple craft initiated the long development in marine architecture which has culminated in the great ocean liners and battleships of modern times.

As civilization advanced and the interchange of goods became of increasing importance in human economy the oceans came to be regarded no longer as barriers but as highways that could be used to increase the wealth of nations. With the growing mastery of the art of shipbuilding the early navigators were able to transport the riches of distant lands to the civilized centres of the ancient world. At the same time, alongside these practical developments in marine commerce, the oceans were stirring the hearts of men to a new sense of wonder. No great seaman has ever thought purely in terms of wealth and fame, and it is certain that many of the early navigators had a strong sense of the glamour of their calling. It was the lure of high adventure and a profound curiosity concerning what lay beyond the far horizon quite as much as the prospect of material gain that led them to undertake their long and dangerous voyages. This challenge of the sea has persisted into our own times, even though few coasts remain unexplored by men, and is certainly a source of inspiration to the best kind of oceanographer, whose researches are taking him further and further into the uncharted regions of the abyss.

The first voyages across the open sea were made at a much earlier period than is generally realized. Long before Homer recorded the exploits of Ulysses in the Mediterranean, sailor-traders were voyaging between the Red Sea and the Persian Gulf, and Arab ships were transporting fabrics, rare woods and precious stones from the Far East to the trading centres of the western world. Although much of this trade was carried on by small coastal vessels, the Erythraean Sea, or Indian Ocean, was certainly traversed at an early stage by ancient mariners. The first penetration of the Atlantic may also have been made at this time and it is probable, although unrecorded, that adventurous sailors pressed far down the western coasts of Africa, and perhaps even sailed across the Bay of Biscay to western France and Britain.

We can only speculate on the extent of these first attempts to explore the oceans, but in the first millenium B.C., with the beginning of written records, the picture becomes clearer. The ocean explorations of this time were mainly the work of two peoples, the Phoenicians and the Greeks. The land of Phoenicia lay in the coastal region of Syria, being roughly bounded by the island of Ruad, off Tartous, in the north, and by Carmel in the south. Its main cities were all seaports with names that figure prominently in the earliest Greek and Hebrew records: Byblos, Berytus (the modern Beirut), Tyre, Sidon, Tripoli and Aradus. From these ports, and particularly Tyre, the Phoenicians ventured forth on to the seas in a mounting wave of commercial expansion in the early centuries of the first millenium B.C. They traversed the whole of the Mediterranean, establishing trading stations on the coasts of northern Africa and southern Europe. They sailed boldly forth onto the great Atlantic itself, discovering the Canaries and, according to Humboldt, very probably reaching the Sargasso Sea.[55] In the north they discovered the Cassiterides (probably the Scilly Isles) where they went in search of tin, and it is most likely that they also landed on the coasts of Cornwall.

Whether the Phoenicians ever circumnavigated Africa, as is often asserted, has not yet been conclusively proved. This event was supposed to have taken place in the sixth century B.C., but there are no contemporary records, and the evidence is based on the testimony of the Greek historian Herodotus, which dates from well over a hundred years later. In Book IV of the *Histories* Herodotus writes:

'As for Libya, we know it to be washed on all sides by the sea, except where it is attached to Asia. This discovery was first made by Necôs, the Egyptian king, who on desisting from the canal which he had begun between the Nile and the Arabian Gulf, sent to sea a number of ships manned by Phoenicians, with orders to make for the Pillars of Hercules,* and return to Egypt through them, and by the Mediterranean. The Phoenicians took their departure from Egypt by way of the Erythraean Sea, and so sailed into the southern ocean. When autumn came, they went ashore, wherever they might happen to be, and having sown a tract of land with corn, waited until the grain was fit to cut. Having reaped it, they again set sail: and thus it came to pass that two whole years went by, and it was not till the third year that they doubled the Pillars of Hercules, and made good their voyage home. On their return, they declared – I for my part do not believe them, but perhaps others may – that in sailing round Libya† they had the sun upon their right hand. In this way was the extent of Libya first discovered.'[56]

Many critics have regarded this account as too thin to be credible, and as it was inevitably based on hearsay there are good reasons for caution. On the other hand the statement that

---

* i.e. The Straits of Gibraltar. – R.C.
† The name 'Libya' was synonomous with 'Africa' in early classical times. – R.C.

'in sailing round Libya* they had the sun upon their right hand' seems to me entirely convincing. At a time when only the northern hemisphere was known, and the midday sun was seen to the southward for most of the year, the northerly position of the sun as seen from the Cape of Good Hope would have been especially striking and unexpected. It would be odd indeed if such an unlikely observation had been the subject of pure invention, and for this reason alone we need not necessarily reject the possibility that Africa was circumnavigated at this time.

Other important voyages undertaken by the Phoenicians included an expedition by the Carthaginian admiral Hanno down the west coast of Africa and an exploration of the eastern North Atlantic by his compatriot Himilco. An account of the latter is given in a fragment by the Roman poet Rufius Festus Avienus, who was probably proconsul of Africa and of Achaia during the second half of the fourth century A.D.[57] The ocean is represented as stretching westwards without limit beyond the Pillars of Hercules; a favourable wind never blows, the air is enveloped in a mantle of mist, and sombre vapours obscure the light of day. This, as the reader will recognize, still gives an accurate enough picture of the North Atlantic in one of its most characteristic moods.

The Phoenicians were the most daring navigators of the ancient world, and would voyage far out on the open sea without a compass or coast to guide them. The Greeks, in spite of Homer's vehement propaganda, were considerably less advanced in the techniques of navigation, and in general lacked the confidence to venture far onto the deep waters. As practical mariners their range was almost entirely restricted to the Mediterranean, and it is mainly by their intellectual speculations concerning the form and extent of the oceans, and their studies of marine life, that they added to man's general store of knowledge of the sea.

In Homer the waters of the earth are divided into two parts, and it is doubtful if he regarded them as interconnected. The earth itself was thought of as a flat disc with slightly raised edges, like an oval dish. Around this flowed Oceanus, the ocean river, while in the centre was Thalassa, the modern Mediter-

* i.e. Rounding the Cape. – R.C.

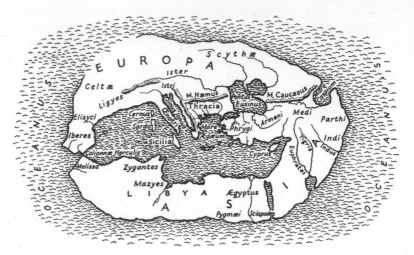

The world according to Hecataeus, 500 B.C.

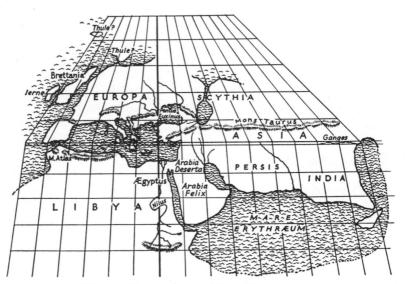

The world according to Hipparchus, 150 B.C.

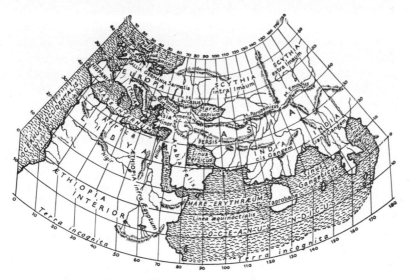

The world according to Ptolemaeus (Ptolemy), A.D. 150.

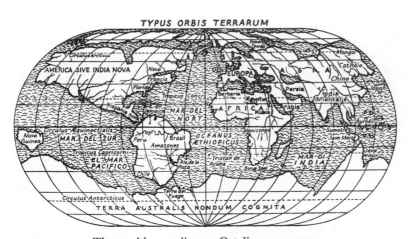

The world according to Ortelius, A.D. 1570.

ranean, with its extension, the Pontus Euxinus, or Black Sea. One of the distinctions between the internal 'sea' and the encircling 'ocean' was that the latter was regarded as flowing like a river, suggesting the strong tides and currents of the Atlantic and other open oceans, whereas the former was regarded as maintaining a consistent level like the almost tideless Mediterranean. Oceanus itself was the limit of the world, and its external borders were the support for the transparent vault of heaven. At this margin water and sky met in confusion and chaos, and in this mysterious region originated the gloom and dread which brooded over the ocean in men's imaginations right down to the time of Columbus.

The cosmological theories of the Greeks concerning the relationships of land and sea do not strictly concern us here, but before returning to our historical account of ocean exploration a word or two must be said about the first maps. In Homer's time there were no true maps, but only representations of the world which were little more than diagrams illustrating the voyages of the Argonauts. The first scientific attempt at map-making is attributed to Anaximander, an Ionian philosopher who lived from 611 until about 547 B.C. But this is no longer extant and the earliest map in existence is therefore that of the Greek historian Hecataeus of Miletus. It was a corrected and enlarged version of the map of Anaximander, and in general followed the Homeric concept of the world as a flat disc girdled by an all-encompassing ocean. Now, however, the ocean was regarded as having inlets which roughly corresponded with the present Red Sea and Persian Gulf. The existence of a connection between the ocean and the central sea at the Straits of Gibraltar was also clearly established for the first time.

The next step in map-making was made in the fifth century B.C. by Herodotus who, apart from his fame as an historian, can be bracketed with Hecataeus as one of the twin founders of physical geography. With Herodotus the concept of an encircling ocean was abandoned; land was now believed to stretch away indefinitely from the central sea to the north and east, while the continents of Europe, Libya and Asia were shown as being washed by three great oceans – the Mare Atlanticum to the west and the Mare Australis and Mare Erythraeum to the south. The shapes of the continents were still inaccurately drawn in peripheral regions, but the southern coast of Europe, despite many errors, had a quite recognizable outline, and the map as a whole looked far more 'modern' than that of Hecataeus.

Only three more names need be mentioned in connection with the geography of the oceans in the pre-Christian era. These are Dicaearchus (flourished c.320 B.C.), a pupil of the great Aristotle of Stagira; the Greek scientific writer Eratosthenes of Alexandria (c.276–c.194 B.C.); and Hipparchus (c.190 c.125 B.C.), the most celebrated astronomer of the ancient world. All these cartographers followed Aristotle in regarding the earth as a sphere, and the last-named introduced the concept of map projections, which revolutionized men's ideas concerning the distribution of land and sea. For the first time in history any point on the earth could be marked on a map with scientific precision. One of the most important results of this invention in the exploration of the oceans was that henceforward a navigator returning from a voyage through unknown seas could point out to others the exact course he had followed.

To carry the story of map-making from these early times to the present day would require a book in itself, and in any case such a study belongs more to the history of geography than to a survey of ocean exploration. The interested reader is referred to the admirable synoptic account given in the first supplementary volume to the *Report on the Scientific Results of the Exploring Voyage of H.M.S. Challenger* (1895). In the present context I shall return instead to the navigators themselves – the men whose adventurous spirits and painstaking observations enabled us to build up the almost complete map of the world ocean we possess today.

In the time of the great Alexandrian astronomer Claudius Ptolemaeus (flourished second century A.D.) the boundaries of the known world had scarcely been pushed beyond the limits shown three hundred years earlier on the map of Hipparchus. Neither the Greeks nor the Romans were of the temperament to follow up the maritime achievements of the Phoenicians, and such advances as were made in man's geographical knowledge were due less to ocean exploration than to the overland military expeditions of Xenophon, Alexander the Great, and Julius

Caesar. Apart from a few voyages by sailor traders to India, Malaya and southern China, the Romans contributed nothing to maritime exploration, and when the Empire collapsed many of the records of earlier discoveries were lost. At this time the only really active seafarers were the Vikings, but comparatively little is known of their achievements. From their homes on the inhospitable Norwegian coast they sailed westward to Britain, Iceland and Greenland, and even made a landfall on the eastern shores of North America. Whether they made settlements there has never been definitely established, but if they did it seems that these soon became extinct. By the time later explorers set foot on the soil of the New World this first landfall by the Vikings had been forgotten.

The great age of maritime exploration began in the time of Prince Henry the Navigator of Portugal (1394–1460), a grandson of John of Gaunt. In spite of his name, Prince Henry was no seaman, and never sailed further than the Straits of Gibraltar; he was, however, the first European statesman to realize that oceans were not barriers but great highways of commerce giving almost unassailable power to anyone who could dominate them. Inspired by this vision, the Prince embarked on the greatest programme of maritime expansion since the first Phoenician pioneers ventured forth from the Mediterranean Sea. The maritime achievements of Portugal are almost entirely due to the vision and energy of this remarkable man, and the new challenge his programme offered to other European nations was one of the main reasons why they also evolved ambitious plans for the exploration of the oceans.

The main achievement of the Portuguese in the fifteenth century was to circumnavigate Africa and open up the sea route to India. Until the time of Prince Henry, on the authority of the Ptolemaic maps, the Erythraean Sea, or Indian Ocean, was thought by many to be an enclosed expanse of water; it was assumed that a land mass, called Terra Incognita joined eastern Africa with southern China some 20° south of the equator. But fortunately the more progressive geographers did not accept the authority of Ptolemy without question. The report by Herodotus of a Phoenician circumnavigation of Africa was known to them, and the voyages of Arab traders on the east coast had already shown that the Erythraean Sea extended much further to the south than the Ptolemaic maps admitted. Prince Henry believed that it was in fact continuous with the Atlantic (the ancient Oceanus Occidentalis) and could be reached by sailing down the west coast of Africa until a southern cape was reached.

The early Portuguese expeditions sent to confirm this view were not particularly successful. At this time the waters lying beyond the fringes of the known world still inspired the same superstitious dread as they did in the days of the classical mariners. As a result the Portuguese navigators made no dare-devil dash towards the southern seas, but advanced cir cumspectly down the west coast of Africa, consolidating their discoveries with proper caution. The first Rubicon in their adventure was Cape Bojador, just to the south of the Canary Isles. Here a long ridge of rocks projects dangerously into the sea, and strong currents make coastal sailing full of hazards. As James Johnstone remarks, 'the vicinity acquired an evil reputation, and . . . became a sort of crucial point in the progress of navigation such that once it had been passed men became much more confident.'[58]

Beyond, however, still further terrors lay in store. Rumours of unknown dangers afflicted the souls of the superstitious mariners. The physical hazards were not limited to the normal seafaring risks of perilous seas and uncharted coasts. What strange and barbaric tribes might not inhabit these southern shores if a stricken ship were compelled to make a landfall? And could not the sea itself be the home of nightmare monsters inimical to man? The violence of tropical storms was an additional deterrent, and had not Hanno the Carthaginian spoken of the terrible burning heat and of rivers of fire running down to the sea?

When we consider the numberless dangers, real and imaginary, that the Portuguese sailors had to face before they could realize Prince Henry's dream we must be filled with the profoundest admiration. In spite of every adverse circumstance they pursued their quest and, after successive expeditions had explored the whole of the north-west coast of Africa, the navigator Diego Cano finally crossed the equator in 1484. The actual rounding of the southern tip of Africa took place in January 1488 when Bartholomew Diaz (with Bartholomew Columbus, the brother of Christopher, as a member of his crew) was the first man to enter the Indian Ocean from the west. At Angra Pequena in what is now South West Africa he set up a pillar to commemorate the progress of his voyage, and a fragment of this can still be seen at Cape Town. Thereafter adverse currents interrupted his plans and he was compelled to put well out into the South Atlantic. He sailed southward for thirteen days and then turned east, expecting to make a new landfall on the west African coast within a few days. But no land was sighted, so he shaped a northerly course until he reached a point on the southern coast of Africa some 220 miles east of the Cape of Good Hope. He landed at Mosselbaai on February 3rd 1488 and then, to confirm his suspicion that this was indeed the southern limit of Africa, he sailed eastward until the coast began to curve in a northerly direction just beyond the modern Port Elizabeth. The first part of Prince Henry's programme had been completed, and when Diaz returned to Lisbon in December of the same year he had every reason to congratulate himself on his success.

The second stage of the adventure was to attempt to reach India by the Cape route. This achievement was left to an even greater Portuguese navigator than Diaz, the famous Vasco da Gama, who lived from about 1460 until 1524 (Plate 24a). The voyage began on July 8th 1497 with da Gama in command of two ships of 120 tons each, a third smaller vessel of 50 tons, and a store ship of 200 tons.* Instead of hugging the coast he struck boldly across the Atlantic and, by what was for those days an amazing feat of navigation, made a successful landfall at St Helena Bay just north of Cape Town after a four months' voyage across the open ocean. He rounded the Cape in safety and then began a long voyage up the previously unexplored east coast of Africa until he reached the southernmost Arab ports. He found the first settlement at Mozambique, where he took two Arab pilots on board, and continued his northward voyage to Mombasa and Malindi. At Malindi the king, who was of Persian descent and favourably disposed to the adventurers, provided him with an excellent Hindu pilot, and on April 4th 1498 the expedition struck eastwards across the Indian Ocean. After twenty-three days out of sight of land the squadron

* To obtain the modern equivalent of these tonnages they should be doubled.
– R.C.

anchored off Calicut on the west coast of India. Not only had the sea route to India been found, but two of the world's great oceans had for the first time been successfully traversed by a European navigator.

The Portuguese were not slow to exploit da Gama's discoveries, and the boundaries of the Atlantic and Indian Oceans were soon being inked in on the map by a succession of commercial expeditions sent out in his train. In the present context it would be out of place to describe fully how these vast tracts of water were gradually charted in greater and greater detail, and I propose to turn instead to two other important aspects of the history of ocean exploration; the discovery of the Pacific and the first voyages into the circumpolar seas.

Already in classical times Phoenician sailor traders and Arab merchants had penetrated to the western Pacific by the Straits of Malacca, but they had no reason to voyage far from the coasts of Asia, and the full extent of this mighty ocean remained unrealized for over two thousand years. The discovery of the Pacific was a direct result of the discovery of America by the Genoese explorer Christopher Columbus (Plate 24c), who sailed from Europe in 1492 with the intention of finding a western sea route to India, but instead revealed the existence of a new world. Columbus and the other explorers of the time who made landfalls on the eastern coast of America firmly believed at first that they had reached the easternmost fringes of Asia, and it was not for some time that the existence of another ocean beyond the new continent was suggested by report and confirmed by observation. The first European to sight the Pacific Ocean was not 'stout Cortez', as Keats asserts in the famous sonnet, but the Spanish adventurer Vasco Núñez de Balboa. Little is known of Balboa's life until 1501, when he sailed with another Spanish explorer, Rodrigo de Bastidas, for Central America, arriving after numerous adventures in Darien, which corresponds with the region now known as the isthmus of Panama. Here his abilities soon enabled him to rise to a prominent position, and he established Spanish authority over many of the local Indian tribes. Early in 1513 he was told by a tribesman that southwards, beyond the dense jungles bordering the Chucunaque River, lay a great ocean and a land rich with gold (possibly this was the modern Peru). Accordingly he mounted an expedition to investigate, and after a twenty-five days' march, on September 25th 1513 obtained a distant view of the Pacific. Four days later, according to the traditional account, he arrived on the shore, and waded into the sea in full armour and with drawn sword to take symbolic possession of the ocean in the name of the king of Spain.

By this charmingly dramatic gesture the existence of the world's largest ocean was first established in the minds of European man, and soon seamen of all nations were questing along the eastern seaboard of America looking for a way to take their ships into the Great South Sea, as the Pacific was then called. It would be quite impossible in the space at my disposal even to outline the story of Pacific discovery, but a word must be said about the first man to venture into these as yet uncharted waters, and who succeeded in turning Columbus's dream of a western sea route to Asia into solid reality. This feat was achieved by the Portuguese explorer Ferdinand Magellan, who was born about 1480 at Sabrosa (Plate 24b). In his early years Magellan distinguished himself as a seaman in the service of the Portuguese navy, but a dispute with the King concerning some alleged irregularities in the distribution of booty after the Moroccan campaign of 1513 caused him to renounce his nationality and enter the service of King Charles of Castile and Aragon (later the Emperor Charles V). Intoxicated by dreams of finding a way to eastern Asia round the southern tip of South America he persuaded Charles to equip an elaborate expedition. In spite of violent political remonstrances from Portugal Charles held to his promise and on September 20th 1519 Magellan set sail from San Lucar in command of a squadron of five ships.

After numerous adventures and difficulties, including the suppression of an attempted mutiny, the navigator reached the straits lying between Patagonia and Tierra del Fuego which now bear his name. This historic event in the history of the exploration of the sea occurred on October 21st 1520. The straits run for 360 miles between inhospitable snow-capped peaks, and it took Magellan over a month to negotiate the narrow and tortuous channel. One of his ships had already been wrecked and now another, the *San Antonio*, deserted, so it was with only three vessels that, on November 28th 1520, he eventually rounded Cabo Deseado and sailed into the waters of Balboa's Great South Sea.

One might think that here Magellan could have legitimately rested on his laurels but, although supplies were running short and there was much sickness among the crews of his vessels, he could not bring himself to turn back. He would push on, he said, 'if they had to eat the leather of the rigging', and the three ships set out to the north-west across the Pacific. The sufferings of the explorers at this time were beyond belief. They indeed resorted to eating the leather of the rigging; ox-hide and sawdust became coveted delicacies, and even rats changed hands for pieces of gold. At last, after 98 days, they reached the Marianas, where they rested for three days (March 6th–9th 1521), before pushing on to the west. Seven days later they reached the Lazarus group of islands (now known as the Philippines) and here the greatest tragedy of all overtook the party. Magellan was killed in a fight with the natives of Mactan, and several other members of the expedition came to a violent end through the treachery of the King of Cebu. The survivors, under Juan Sebastian del Cano, eventually reached Spain on September 6th 1522 with only one serviceable ship, having crossed the Indian Ocean and rounded the Cape of Good Hope. Thus was completed the first circumnavigation of the world.

With the voyages of Vasco da Gama, Columbus, and Magellan the three great oceans of the world had at last been crossed, and for the first time in history the correct distribution of land and sea on the earth's surface began to be properly understood. The discoveries of the four decades before 1522 completely revolutionized man's geographical conceptions. The Ptolemaic view that the Indian Ocean was an enclosed sea was finally discredited, and the discovery of America and the Pacific Ocean added a new hemisphere to the map of the world. The existence of a southern temperate zone, which had been postulated by Aristotle, was now definitely established because it had been reached, while the spherical shape of the earth, previously denied by many people, had at last been recognized for the simple reason that del Cano had sailed round it in a ship. The extraordinary impression made on men's minds by these great events can be traced through all the profound intellectual and moral developments that characterized the Renaissance. As Sir John Murray writes: 'Columbus, Gama, Magellan; America, the route to India, the circumnavigation of the globe; three men and three facts opened gloriously a new era of history, of geography, and especially of oceanography.'[59]

As a result of the new knowledge of the extent and configuration of the oceans, sixteenth-century maps begin to approximate more closely to the maps we have today. An early attempt by the cosmographer Diego Ribero, published in 1529, well shows the relative position of the three great continents and oceans, although of course the coastlines remain vague and shadowy. Another, by the German geographer Abraham Ortelius, which appeared in his great *Theatrum Orbis Terrarum*, published in 1570, is considerably more complete, and includes the results of recent voyages on the western coast of America, previously unexplored. But this map also perpetuates the last great misconception made by man concerning the general outlines of world geography – that two great land masses lay at the northern and southern extremities of the earth immediately beyond the tips of the continents. To conclude this chapter we must briefly explain how this misconception was removed.

The idea of a great southern continent seems to have originated in the Terra Incognita of the Ptolemaic maps, which was formerly thought of as the southern boundary of the Indian Ocean. When Diaz and da Gama proved that Africa was not after all extended by a Terra Incognita, but was in fact surrounded at its southern tip by sea, men still seem to have been loth to give up the idea of a southern land mass. For no apparent reason, except the desire to cling to a long established tradition, the as yet undiscovered continent was believed to lie but a short way to the south of the Cape of Good Hope. It was assumed likewise to extend almost to the southern tip of America, and this view was regarded as having been triumphantly vindicated by Magellan, who believed that Tierra del Fuego, the southern shore of his straits, was part of the southern land mass.

The human desire for symmetry seems to have encouraged a corresponding belief in the existence of another continent in the region of the North Pole. This, it was believed, was separated from North America and northern Asia by narrow straits like the Straits of Magellan. The search to discover these entirely mythical straits, referred to respectively as the north-west and north-east passages, obsessed the navigators of northern countries throughout the whole of the seventeenth, eighteenth and early nineteenth centuries.

The gradual opening up of the polar regions which led to the discovery of the Arctic Ocean and the enormous southward extensions of the Indian, Pacific, and Atlantic Oceans to the shores of the comparatively small continent of Antarctica is a long and complicated story. Here it will only be possible to summarize its main outlines and mention a few of the outstanding polar explorers.

The Arctic was the first of the two polar regions to be investigated for the obvious reason that to find a route round the north of America or Asia to India would bring commercial advantage. Early explorations on behalf of England were made by the Venetian John Cabot, who discovered Newfoundland and Labrador in 1497, and by the Englishman Martin Frobisher who in 1576 made the first deliberate attempt to find the north-west passage. Frobisher was followed in 1585 by the west country seaman John Davis, who carried out a valuable reconnaissance up the west coast of Greenland and laid the foundations of all further discoveries in the region. Other great names in the early history of arctic exploration are Sir Hugh Willoughby, who led the way to the north-east passage in 1553, Henry Hudson who tried both the north-west and north-east routes between 1608 and 1611, and the Dutchman Barents, who discovered Spitzbergen in 1596.

In spite of the fact that so many men were sailing in search of the north-west and north-east passages the existence of a polar ocean instead of a polar continent was not generally regarded as probable until the late eighteenth century. Even then the question of proof remained, and this was not finally provided until 1893 when the Norwegian explorer Fridtjof Nansen purposely allowed his ship, the *Fram*, to become frozen into the ice and drift from one side of the polar ice-cap to the other. In these days when the shores bounding the Arctic Ocean have been almost completely surveyed, and when airlines run regular passenger flights over the North Pole itself, it is odd to think that the very existence of the Arctic Ocean was only established in such very recent times.

Turning now to Antarctica we find that the true vastness of the southern ocean was not even suspected for a century after Magellan's death. Sixteenth-century maps show the Terra Australis, as the southern continent was called, extending to within a mile or two of the coast of Patagonia and separated from Java and the Cape of Good Hope by at most 20° of latitude. We now know, of course, that, while an Antarctic continent exists, it is extremely small compared with the speculations of sixteenth-century geographers. Water covers by far the greater part of the southern hemisphere and, except in the region where Graham Land projects to within ten degrees of Cape Horn, Antarctica is separated from the northern land mass by several thousands of miles of sea.

The exploration of the southern ocean began in the early seventeenth century with the voyages of such explorers as Diego de Prado, Luis Vaez de Torres and Abel Tasman. But it was not until the second voyage of Captain James Cook (Plate 24d) that a true picture of the southern circumpolar seas really emerged and the old conception of a vast southern continent had to be finally abandoned. The voyage took place between 1772 and 1775, and consisted mainly of a circumnavigation of the globe in a high southern latitude. On a previous voyage between 1768 and 1771 Cook had explored the east coast of Australia and circumnavigated New Zealand. He had thus already proved that the southern continent did not lie where the Ptolemaic maps showed it to be and that New Zealand did not, as was once supposed, form part of it. He now aimed to complete the proof that it did not exist at all.

Cook sailed from Plymouth on July 13th 1772, with two ships, the *Resolution* and the *Adventure*, with a brief to voyage to the Cape of Good Hope and thence to seek for undiscovered land in the great unknown region to the south. Sailing southeast from the Cape he reached latitude 60° 22' S. on January 17th 1773, thus making the first crossing of the Antarctic circle in the history of mankind. Land was not sighted, however, and Cook pressed on to the eastward until on March 26th he reached New Zealand. Here he turned south again, working in a series of loops across the South Pacific in search of land. On the first loop he reached 67° 31' S. and on the second 71° 10', man's nearest approach yet to the South Pole. Here he was halted by the pack ice, which extended east and west as far as he could see.[60] Being thus thwarted in any further advances to the south, the navigator turned towards Easter Island, where the explorers were delighted by the now famous statues.[61] He returned to England via Cape Horn and the South Atlantic with visits to the Cape of Good Hope, St Helena, Ascension, Fernando, Noronha and the Azores. The existence of a Terra Australis of the size previously claimed was shown to be a myth; but it is interesting to note that Cook himself still expressed the belief that a smaller Antarctic continent might lie beyond the barrier of the ice.[62]

It was not until the second decade of the nineteenth century that exploration in the region was resumed. The work was pioneered by a Russian expedition under Admiral Thaddeus Bellingshausen in 1819 and was continued by explorers of many nationalities, notably British, French and American. This is not the place to discuss the discovery of the Antarctic continent in detail, and the interested reader is referred to the admirable books by Hugh Mill and L. P. Kirwan listed in the bibliography at the end of this volume. It must suffice to say that through the work of a multitude of explorers from many lands the outlines of Antarctica, and therefore of the limits of the great southern ocean, were gradually built up throughout the nineteenth and early twentieth centuries. Thus the dreams of the medieval geographers gave place at last to an ordered scientific scheme, and the final phase in the discovery of the oceans was triumphantly concluded.

Chapter Eighteen

THE GROWTH OF SEA SCIENCE

I N the previous chapter we dealt mainly with the sea as a geographical feature of our planet; here we shall consider how men have gradually acquired knowledge of its physical composition and behaviour and of the plants and animals inhabiting it.

The first ocean explorers, as we have seen, were mainly motivated by the prospect of commercial gain allied to the lure of adventure; they attached little importance to observation as an end in itself, or to the purely intellectual satisfaction of discovering new facts in nature. Only gradually did men begin to comprehend the intrinsic wonder and interest of the sea and attempt to discover more about the laws that governed it. Even then the purely scientific aspects of marine research were largely subordinated to the practical results that might be achieved.

The Greeks, with their intense intellectual curiosity concerning all aspects of nature, were the first to point the way to the future development of the science of oceanography. But they lacked a sufficient body of well-attested facts to form a solid basis for induction, and many of their theories concerning the oceans and marine life were the result more of their imaginative daring than the discipline of a highly evolved scientific method. Nevertheless the Greek contribution to oceanography was far from being negligible. By their constant probing of the principles governing the natural world, Greek philosophers revealed the scope of many of the problems involved even when they failed to find a convincing solution.

Sometimes by a mixture of intelligent speculation and something very like inspired guesswork a Greek thinker arrived at an explanation of some oceanographic phenomenon that has stood the test of time. For example, according to Plutarch, the Greek geographer Pytheas of Massilia (the modern Marseilles) was responsible for the idea that the movement of the tides is due to the influence of the moon. He was thus the discoverer

216

of a perfectly valid scientific fact which was not, however, generally accepted until the time of Newton.

The great Aristotle of Stagira (384–322 B.C.) made numerous contributions to the science of oceanography, his views concerning the general configuration of continents and oceans and his studies in the field of marine biology being particularly important. He named and described, often in considerable detail, some hundred and eighty species of animals inhabiting the Aegean Sea, including 116 fish, and over 60 invertebrates. His observations of marine animals were often extraordinarily acute, and he has left fascinating accounts of their breeding habits, methods of feeding, and other aspects of their behaviour, as well as their taxonomy, anatomy and physiology.

The study of oceanography continued in a somewhat desultory way until the end of the pre-Christian era, mainly as the result of isolated work by individual enthusiasts. Such observations as were made usually formed part of some other investigation, and there was no attempt to build up a co-ordinated body of oceanographical knowledge. Among the workers of this time we must particularly mention the Stoic philosopher Posidonius, who voyaged to Spain in the first century B.C. to determine for himself the truth of the popular rumour that when the sun set in the Atlantic it made a hissing noise, as when a red hot body is plunged into water. While pursuing this object he also carried out some measurements of the Atlantic tides, and remarked that the depth of the sea near the coast of Sardinia was a 1,000 fathoms. This is the earliest reference to a deep-sea sounding in the history of oceanography, but unfortunately the methods by which it was made are unknown.

As we have already seen, the Romans had no tradition of seafaring, and their voyages were mainly restricted to the coasts and to crossing the Mediterranean and the English Channel to their overseas dominions. They made no attempt to explore the open oceans like the Phoenicians, nor did they contribute much to the science of the sea, even by philosophical speculation. Seneca and Pliny may be regarded by some as exceptions to this statement, but the former's contribution was mainly restricted to observations on the geological action of marine water and the latter was an inspired synthesist rather than an original thinker. The most important work carried out in oceanography in Roman times was therefore that of the Greek scientist Strabo, who was born about 60 B.C. Strabo must be numbered among the greatest of all the classical geographers, and in the field of oceanography he had much of value to say concerning the relief of the sea floor, the changing outlines of continents and oceans, and the behaviour of breaking waves. Oddly enough he makes no mention of currents, although he must have had frequent occasion to observe these and speculate on their causes.

After the appearance of the map of Claudius Ptolemaeus little of importance occurred in oceanography until the resurgence of interest in maritime exploration inspired by Prince Henry of Portugal. During the so-called Dark Ages the Arabs were mainly responsible for keeping oceanographical speculation alive. Their long voyages enabled them to make valuable contributions to the science of navigation, and we probably owe to them the introduction of the mariner's compass from China. This remarkable instrument seems to have been treated with great suspicion at first by western navigators, and for some time no master mariner was prepared to use it, fearing that he would be accused of entrusting his ship to an invention of the devil.

In physical oceanography the Arabs made contributions on many levels. At their best they anticipated the scientific methods of later times, and Mas'ūdī, an Arabian geographer and naturalist of the tenth century, has left some admirably intelligent comments on the possible causes of evaporation, the formation of rain, the aerial circulation of water, and the causes of the sea's salinity. The exposition of these ideas no doubt lacks precision and contains many errors, but, as Murray writes, 'the principles expressed are true, and prove the relative state of advancement of Arabian philosophy'.[63]

But we must remember that in spite of such valuable speculations the general level of knowledge remained low, and many quaint beliefs persisted. One was that sea water was composed of the accumulated secretions of the earth which had run down into the ocean basins as the result of the scorching heat of the sun – a kind of terrestial sweat. Another, recorded by Mas'ūdī himself, is surely the most charming theory ever put forward to explain the behaviour of the tides. Mas'ūdī writes:

'The angel to whose care the seas are confided immerges the heel of his foot into the sea at the extremity of China, and, as the sea is swelled, the flow takes place. Then he raises his foot from the sea, and the water returns into its former place, and this is the ebb. They demonstrate this by an example: If a vessel is only half full of water, and you put your hand or foot into it, the water will fill the whole vessel, and, when you take out the hand, the water will be as before. Some think that the angel puts only the great toe of his right foot into the water, and that this is the cause of the tide'.[64]

During the great age of maritime discovery scientific research continued alongside the actual work of exploration. An example is Magellan's attempt to sound the Pacific, already referred to in the first chapter of this book (p. 9). Other voyages were made with an exclusively scientific object in view – for instance, the voyage of the Astronomer Royal, Edmond Halley, in 1699 which was mainly concerned with studying techniques for determining the exact positions of vessels at sea. Some especially important scientific observations were made by Captain Cook, who brought back a mass of data which formed quite as valuable a contribution to knowledge as the discoveries themselves.

The progress of oceanography after the death of Cook in 1779 shows an increasing emphasis on the importance of scientific investigation as an end in itself. From 1779 until 1872, when the famous *Challenger* expedition introduced the modern era of sea science, two men were outstanding in the field: the Manx naturalist Edward Forbes (1815–54) and the American naval officer Matthew Fontaine Maury (1806–73). The title 'founder of oceanography' is given sometimes to one and sometimes to the other of these two men and, ridiculous as such titles always are, there is one sense in which both Forbes and Maury may be specially said to deserve it. As we have seen, workers before their time had discovered much of interest in various departments of sea science, and their observations and discoveries certainly played an important part in the foundation of modern oceanographic research. But it was Forbes and Maury who first thought of the sea as a single dynamic entity. They were the most important among the pioneers who, in Coker's phrase, 'engaged in comprehensive studies of the sea as a whole, or of some substantial part of it, with the purpose of integrating oceanic observations and attempting generalizations respecting the oceans'.[65]

Forbes (Plate 25a) had an early passion for natural science and at the age of seven had already collected and arranged a museum of natural objects and appointed a younger sister as assistant curator. There is a story that his grandmother saw him grubbing for snails in a hedge, and cried despairingly in her native Manx: 'Ta mee credjah naugh vod slane Ellan Vannin sauail yn guilley shoh veich cheet dy ve ommydan', meaning 'I believe the whole Isle of Man cannot save this boy from being a fool.'[66] In the event this foolish boy turned out to be one of the most brilliant and witty of all the scientists of the first half of the nineteenth century.

Edward Forbes brought humour as well as scientific brilliance to his work. Above is one of his own illustrations to his classic *History of British Starfishes* (1841).

Forbes made contributions to many sciences, including geology, botany, palaeontology and zoology, as well as oceanography. Apart from his contributions to marine biology, especially the biology of the invertebrates, he pioneered the use of the dredge as an aid to scientific studies in shallow waters, and was among the first to divide the world ocean into natural zones on scientific grounds. Although many of his propositions have not been borne out by the facts – for instance he believed the deep sea to be entirely without life – his breadth of outlook gave his fellow workers a new perspective on the problems involved, and was a powerful stimulus to later researches.

In contrast to Forbes, who was primarily a naturalist, Maury (Plate 25b) was more concerned with the physical and mechanical aspects of sea science. He was an officer in the United States Navy and his extensive voyages included a circumnavigation of the globe. In 1839 he was rendered permanently lame by an accident, and thereafter began to concern himself with collecting data from the logs of ships about winds, currents, temperature, and so on. As a result of his researches, which led to the publication of a famous series of charts, an international conference was called in 1853 to investigate the future possibilities of such work. This conference really marks the starting point of physical oceanography, and Maury's work *The Physical Geography of the Sea*, published in 1855, can be regarded as the first textbook of the new science.

The next landmark in the history of sea science occurred in December 1872. It was then that the famous *Challenger* Deep Sea Exploring Expedition left Portsmouth on the most comprehensive voyage of scientific exploration ever undertaken by man. The *Challenger* (Plate 26a), a wooden corvette of 2,306 tons, circumnavigated the globe by way of the Atlantic, the Cape of Good Hope, the Indian and Pacific Oceans, and the Straits of Magellan. She visited numerous Atlantic islands, including Robinson Crusoe's island of Juan Fernandez, as well as Tristan da Cunha, of which she made the first comprehensive survey; she called at the remote Kerguelen Island, a mass of desolate rock in the southern Indian Ocean; she sailed south to be the first steamship to cross the Antarctic circle; and she ranged far and wide in the Pacific, travelling by way of Melbourne to New Zealand, Fiji, Hong Kong, Yokohama, Honolulu, Tahiti and Valparaiso, returning eventually to Sheerness in May 1876 after a voyage of three and a half years. The scientific staff was headed by the Scottish naturalist Sir Charles Wyville Thomson, and the results, which were investigated by a team of workers under the great oceanographer Sir John Murray (Plate 25d), were published by the British Government in fifty thick quarto volumes over a period of sixteen years (1880–95). These covered a multitude of subjects, ranging from records of deep sea soundings to the classification of organic oozes, and from the behaviour of currents to the anatomy of the strange creatures of the abyss. With the 69,000 mile voyage of H.M.S. *Challenger* the era of modern oceanography had begun.

Since the voyage of the *Challenger*, advances in oceanography have been due more to dedicated teamwork than the inspiration of individual pioneers. The cult of great men died with Queen Victoria, and scientists have very properly assumed a becoming anonymity. But before briefly reviewing a few of the scientific voyages of the past fifty years a word or two must be said about the Swiss-American scientist Alexander Agassiz, who is the last representative of what we may call the classic period of the history of oceanography.

Agassiz (Plate 25c) lived from 1835 until 1910 and was thus approximately contemporary with Wyville Thomson and Murray. In fact he was a member of the *Challenger* team, and contributed a two volume *Review of the Echini* to the reports. He is not a particularly spectacular figure, and his personality has never captured the public imagination like that of his famous father Louis Agassiz, a world authority on living and fossil fish. Yet Alexander Agassiz made many notable contributions to the study of the oceans. He was the first to use steel cables for deep sea dredging; his soundings, especially in the Caribbean, Indian Ocean and tropical Pacific, were probably more extensive than those made by any other expedition before or since; and he invented several ingenious pieces of oceanographical equipment, such as the 'Agassiz' trawl and a new type of towing net for collecting plankton from different levels. Sir John Murray even went so far as to say that the advanced state of oceanography at that time probably owed more to the work and inspiration of Alexander Agassiz than to any other man.

Since the time of Agassiz numerous scientific expeditions have conducted researches in all the oceans of the world. Many different nationalities have contributed to the work, notably the French, the Germans, the Americans, the Dutch, the Norwegians, the Danes, the Russians, the Belgians, the Italians and the British. A particularly important contribution was made by Prince Albert I of Monaco (1848–1922) who about the turn of the century was dispatching a series of expeditions to the Atlantic and Mediterranean in the yachts *Hirondelle* and *Princesse Alice*. In more recent times much of value has been done by the Danes on the *Galathea* expedition of 1950–52 and by Commandant Cousteau of the Musée Oceanographique in Monaco, whose research ships the *Calypso* and *Winaretta-Singer* have been seen at work by an exceptionally wide public through the cinema and television. Another famous modern research ship, regarded by some as the finest in the world, is Russia's *Mikhail Lomonosov*.

To continue with an account of modern oceanographical research would be to turn this chapter into a tedious recital of the names and dates of expeditions, facts which can be easily obtained by reference to the specialist libraries of the various scientific institutions connected with the sea.* I therefore propose to pass on now to some of the techniques by which the work is carried out.

Oceanographical research is of two kinds, the chemico-physical and the biological. The first deals with such things as the depth of the sea bed at any given point, the speed and direction of currents, the salinity and temperature of the water, and the laws governing the behaviour of waves. The second deals with the living world beneath the surface and those other organisms, principally sea birds and sea mammals, which play a part in the general ecology of the oceans. Such subjects as sounding, current measurement and testing salinity, have already been touched upon (pp. 9–10, 31–2, 44), so I propose to restrict myself here to some of the representative techniques used in biological investigation.

One of the basic requirements of this type of research is that organisms should be removed from the sea for study in the laboratory. For this purpose the most important instrument always has been, and doubtless always will be, the net. But the net used by oceanographers is by no means the simple affair you and I remember as children when we went shrimping on the seashore. It is a generic term for a wide range of specialized equipment having roughly the same function – that is, to allow living organisms, small or large, to be drawn to the surface while the water containing them passes through a meshed framework and is left behind.

The smallest and largest organisms naturally provide the greatest problems in this respect. In fact to catch the largest in a

* e.g. the National Institute of Oceanography at Wormley and the Marine Biological Association of the United Kingdom at Plymouth.

net is seldom attempted (one has only to consider how one would net a blue whale to understand the difficulties), but there are now several efficient devices for obtaining samples of the small organisms of the plankton. The most commonly used is the plankton tow net, which was apparently introduced by the great German biologist Johannes Müller in 1846. As its name suggests, this device is towed behind the research ship. It consists of a conical sack of finely meshed material, the broad, open end being supported by a metal ring, the cod or tail end leading into a detachable strainer which receives the concentrated tow. The filtering material is so fine that thirty-six or more holes may be present in an area one millimetre square; it usually consists of silk bolting cloth of the kind used for sifting flour. A particularly important point is that the strands must be so woven that the aperture size remains constant. This is achieved by criss-crossing every alternate strand in one direction so as to stabilize the whole fabric of the net.

To catch the larger swimming or floating animals, nets of the kind used by fishermen are normally employed. The most important of these are the trawl, the drift net, and the seine, all of which work on different principles. The trawl is a net of flattened conical shape which is towed behind the ship. The lower edge is weighted by a heavy foot-rope which stirs up the fish from the bed of the sea and causes them to swim upward into the advancing mouth of the net. At the rear of the trawl there is a chamber known as the cod-end or purse in which the fish collect; once there they are prevented from swimming forward by valve-like devices known as flappers and pockets. The purse is eventually closed by pulling on a rope known as the cod-line, after which the entire catch can be safely pulled to the surface.

The drift net is more commonly used in commercial fishing than scientific research, but nevertheless merits description. Unlike the trawl, which is used for catching fish living on or near the sea bed, the drift net is intended to deal with the shoals of the upper waters, especially herring and mackerel. It has no chamber intended to retain the catch while the water passes through, and is thus an exception to the generic description of nets given above; it is designed instead to ensure that the fish actually become entangled in the mesh itself. The holes in this are of such size that once the head of a herring or a mackerel has passed through one of them it cannot be withdrawn, for the twine of the mesh catches in the gill covers. The fish must therefore remain there helplessly until the net is pulled up.

Drift nets are normally used at night when the fish they are designed to catch are swimming nearest to the surface. They are strung together across the tide in walls which may be as much as three miles long, the upper edge being buoyed with corks, the lower weighted with lead. The fish presumably cannot see the nets in the dark and swim straight into them; in this way many thousands may be caught in a single night.

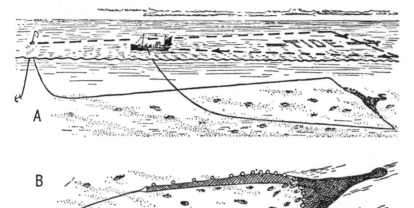

A seiner at work. A: Laying the net. B: The net is towed like a trawl. *From Hardy* (1959), *p.* 159.
Reproduced by permission of Messrs. Wm. Collins Sons & Co., Ltd.

The seine net, now to be described, may perhaps be the ancestor of the trawl, although opinions differ concerning this. It has in any case been used for many years by continental nations, and has recently undergone a revival in the commercial fisheries of the North Sea. In appearance the seine is like a very wide trawl with wing-like extensions of its side walls, to each of which is attached a length of cable. The seiner begins by putting out a buoy with a flag on it, to which is attached the cable leading to one side of the mouth of the seine. She then sets out 'down-tide' of the buoy and travels for about a hundred yards at an angle of 30° from the tide's line of flow, paying out the cable as she goes. She next turns sharply across the tide and travels for a further sixty yards, dropping the seine net in the middle of this leg of her journey. Continuing to pay out the cable attached to the other side of the seine's mouth, she then returns to her starting point having completed an isosceles triangle of which she now lies at the apex with the seine lying on the sea bed at the middle of the base. All that then remains to be done is to heave on the two cables at the same time, thus gradually drawing the seine towards the ship. The upper edge of the mouth is supported by floats, and as the net moves across the sea bed its wings gradually come closer together, guiding the fish towards the meshed chamber, which finally encloses them. Fish caught by this method are usually in much better condition than those caught by trawls, and it is therefore more highly favoured by many scientific workers.

The methods so far described have been mainly used for capturing the drifting organisms of the plankton or the larger free-swimming creatures of the nekton. To obtain samples of the bottom-dwelling benthos two pieces of equipment are normally employed, the dredge and the grab. There are many types of dredge, but the apparatus consists essentially of a rectangular or triangular frame of heavy metal, usually wrought iron, to which is attached a bag-like net of cotton or wire mesh. The size of the dredge may vary from one to five feet across the frame, and it is dragged slowly along the bottom by a rope or wire cable according to its dimensions and weight. The frame itself has sharply bevelled edges (some models are equipped with knives) which bite into the sand and gravel and scrape off animals that are tightly fastened to rocks. An astonishing number of organisms can be collected in quite a small naturalist's dredge in a very short time.

The dredge is a highly satisfactory piece of equipment when the main object is to collect a large number of organisms from a particular region of the ocean floor. It is not, however, useful for quantitative surveys, for the catch is concentrated, and there is no way of determining the distribution or relative abundance of the different organisms on any given spot. For the latter purpose it is necessary to use a bottom sampler, or grab, of the type developed by the Danish marine biologist C. G. J. Petersen in the first decade of this century. This acts on the same principle as the grab used by road workers and coal heavers for moving masses of material from one place to another. It consists essentially of two hinged jaws which are lowered on a cable until they strike the bed of the sea. The apparatus is very heavy so that the jaws, which during the descent are held in the open position by a locking device, bite deeply into the sea bed. The impact releases the lock, so that when the cable is drawn in, the jaws are pulled together by their own weight and the grab retains a solid sample of the sea floor. Later, in the laboratory, the organisms are sieved out from the bottom material, classified and counted, so that a picture of the animal population in a particular area of the ocean bed can be obtained.

Apart from the removal of organisms from the sea by the methods just described, reference must be made to another method of marine biological research which is beginning to assume increasing importance. This is the study of the living animals and plants by observers who actually descend beneath the surface of the sea. This work was pioneered between the wars by the American William Beebe, who was among the first to make purely scientific observations by the use of diving equipment; it has been continued in the 'skin-diving' era by such workers as Jacques-Yves Cousteau and Hans and Lotte Hass. The results of such researches have been covered more than adequately in a number of recent books by these and other writers, so I propose to restrict myself here to a third method of underwater exploration which has received less general attention. This is the use of specially constructed metal chambers, known as bathyspheres and bathyscaphs, which have enabled man to penetrate to far greater depths than would be possible by any other means.

The idea of exploring the sea by such methods is not a modern development. According to the ancient manuscript known as the pseudo-Calisthenes, Alexander the Great on at least one occasion took time off from his military adventures to descend to the sea bed in a diving bell made from transparent material and asses skins. The most remarkable feature of this descent, which perhaps throws some doubt on its credibility, was that Alexander saw a fish so vast that it took three days and three nights to pass his observation point. Nevertheless the tale suggests that the use of diving chambers had been seriously considered at this time, and that descents may even have been made in them.

Several proto-bathyspheres were constructed between the sixteenth and nineteenth centuries, the outstanding example being the diving bell designed by the astronomer Halley in 1716. This was a wooden structure, open at the bottom, which could be lowered to a depth of nine or ten fathoms. Five people could be accommodated in the bell, and breathing was made possible by sending down alternately two barrels of air from the surface, their contents being transferred to the bell through a leather hose. The foul air was released through a cock at the top. The bell was unquestionably successful, and it was even possible for a single diver with a leather helmet to work outside it, drawing air from the bell through a second hose.

The disadvantage of the diving bell is, of course, that it cannot be used at great depths. The pressure of the water becomes greater as the descent is made, and the air in the bell soon becomes so compressed that life can no longer be supported. To overcome this limitation it was obviously necessary to devise some kind of exceptionally tough-walled chamber in which air could be retained at normal atmospheric pressure throughout the dive. The result was the bathysphere invented by William Beebe, Otis Barton and John Butler in 1929.

This revolutionary piece of equipment consisted of a spherical steel chamber 4 feet 9 inches in diameter, with walls $1\frac{1}{4}$ inches thick and weighing 5,400 lbs. There were three circular windows of fused quartz 8 inches across and 3 inches thick and a circular man-hole, politely termed the 'door', only 14 inches in diameter. Air was manufactured inside the sphere itself with the aid of oxygen cylinders and chemicals for absorbing moisture and carbon dioxide. A searchlight was provided for illuminating the dark waters below the lowest limit of natural light, and there was a telephone for reporting back data to the surface. The whole apparatus was designed to be lowered from a winch by a single, non-twisting steel cable.

Between 1930 and 1934 Beebe and Barton made numerous successful descents in the bathysphere, and brought back the earliest first-hand accounts of a region never previously explored by man. In their deepest dive, made in 1934, they reached a record depth of 3,028 feet in the open ocean off Bermuda, and Beebe has given a fascinating account of this in his book *Half Mile Down* (1934). Finally, in the summer of 1949 in a bathysphere of somewhat different design, Barton descended alone to a depth of 4,500 feet off the coast of California, thus setting up a new record for this kind of oceanographical equipment.

Great as were the achievements of Beebe and Barton in deep sea exploration they have been greatly exceeded in recent years as the result of an entirely new invention. This is the bathyscaph, the first free-ranging vessel to be designed to explore the ocean depths without any physical connection by cable or even telephone wire with its parent ship. It was the brain child of the Swiss physicist Professor Auguste Piccard, who first captured the public imagination by his record-breaking ascents into the stratosphere by balloon. His inventive brain proved to be as capable of designing apparatus for penetrating the ocean depths as for ascending to the outermost regions of the atmosphere, and by the early 1950s two prototypes of the bathyscaph had already been constructed. These were the French Navy's F.N.R.S.-3, and the famous *Trieste*, first operated by Piccard's son Jacques, and later by Robert S. Dietz of the United States Office of Naval Research (Plate 26b).

Like the bathysphere, the bathyscaph is beautifully simple in concept. It may be compared to a kind of underwater airship, with a pressure-resistant 'gondola' attached to the belly of a buoyant envelope, or float. But instead of being filled with helium as in an airship, the float contains about 25,000 gallons of petrol which, being about 30% lighter than water, provides the lifting power. The vessel is carried to the required depth by a maximum ballast of 10 tons of iron pellets, which are then jettisoned by the operators in large or small quantities according to the desired speed of ascent. A limited degree of horizontal movement can be achieved at any level by the use of two propellers powered by battery-driven electric motors.

The gondola – or, more correctly, the diving chamber – of

the bathyscaph is quite roomy, that of the *Trieste* measuring 6 feet 7 inches in diameter. Two men can therefore be carried in comparative comfort instead of being curled up like twin embryos in an egg. The float is just under 50 feet long, and does not need to be pressure resistant, as water is allowed free access through openings on the underside. This does not, of course, mix with the petrol which, being lighter, is held in the upper part of the float. Mercury vapour floodlamps are suspended from the float so that the underwater scene can be brilliantly illuminated.

Compared with an ordinary submarine, or even the bathysphere, the bathyscaph can reach astonishing depths. The $3\frac{1}{2}$ inch walls of the diving chamber enable it to withstand pressures encountered at a depth of 20,000 feet with a very wide safety margin. Recently even greater depths have been achieved. While the first draft of this book was in the press the *Trieste*, manned by Jacques Piccard and Lieutenant Don Walsh of the U.S. Navy, made a record-breaking descent of 37,800 feet to the bottom of the Marianas Trench off the Pacific Island of Guam. This was 2,000 feet deeper than the 35,800 feet previously given by the Scripps Institution of Oceanography as the greatest depth in the area.[67]

The bathyscaph has many obvious advantages over all previous methods of deep sea research. Perhaps the most important is that it provides a means of direct visual inspection of the ocean floor and the creatures of the abyss. This is obviously much more satisfactory than lowering cameras to great depths and then taking photographs at random, which was previously the only technique available. Further developments of the bathyscaph will also certainly make it possible within a short time to take samples of the deepest water and sediments under direct visual control, thereby adding greatly to our knowledge of the ocean floor. These and other possibilities make the bathyscaph quite as remarkable a piece of equipment in its own field as are rockets and satellites in the more obviously spectacular field of interplanetary research. It worthily represents the contribution of the mid-twentieth century to the growth of sea science.

Chapter Nineteen

THE HARVEST OF THE SEA

FROM the earliest times man has attempted to turn the sea and its products to his own use. The first act of one of our ancestors on walking down the beach to the ocean was probably either to plunge into it to cleanse and refresh his body or to take up a handful of the water and drink it. One experience would have been found to be pleasurable, the other not, and so the earliest discriminating judgement would have been made concerning the sea's potential value to man. As time went on, more sophisticated uses for the sea were investigated. It was found to contain many different kinds of organisms which either made good eating or provided valuable by-products, such as pelts, oils, or chemical substances of benefit to man. Then, as we have seen, the invention of ships enabled men to use the sea as a highway of commerce, so that goods could be exchanged between peoples at opposite ends of the world. Finally the growth of chemistry and physics allowed valuable substances to be extracted from sea water itself, and showed that even the mechanical force of waves, currents and tides could be turned to human advantage. To follow up all these aspects of the exploitation of the sea would be of great interest, but for reasons of space we must limit ourselves here to some of the uses that have been found for the marine population of plants and animals and for the chemical substances extracted from sea water.

Since our ancestors first cast their nets in the prehistoric seas of the Pleistocene epoch some twenty or more thousand years ago, the world's sea fisheries have grown into a vast and highly organized industry. The fishing grounds mainly lie within the 200 fathom line, and the most important are concentrated in a few well-defined areas. The oldest and most highly developed occur in the North Atlantic, especially around the British Isles, off the coasts of Norway, Russia and Newfoundland, and in the vicinity of Iceland and the Faroes. The second in importance lie off the coast of Japan, where more than two million people derive their livelihood from this industry alone. Well-established fisheries also exist off Malaya and South Africa, and others which have come into existence more recently round the shores of Australia and off the south-east coast of South America are gradually increasing in importance.

The fisheries are of two kinds, pelagic and demersal. The meaning of the word pelagic we have already explained; the pelagic fisheries include all the creatures of the upper, open waters, especially herring, mackerel and sprats. Demersal simply means 'living near the sea bottom' (from the Latin *demersus*, meaning 'plunged under'), and in this context can be said to include the true benthic organisms of the bottom itself. The most important creatures of the demersal fisheries are cod, haddock, whiting, hake, and the various forms of flatfish, such as plaice and sole.

The main gear used in fishing is the same as that used for scientific work, and was described in the last chapter. But apart from trawls, drift nets and seines, the line is still used to a limited extent in commercial fishing. A typical line consists of a thick piece of rope well over half a mile long to which hooks are attached at intervals by shorter and thinner lines. Forty such lines, with a total of more than five thousand hooks, may be used by a single line-fishing vessel. The lines are usually baited with herring, mackerel or pieces of squid, and are mainly used to fish for cod, halibut, skate and other large fish.

When sea fishing was confined to a few enterprising individuals sailing out from the coasts to supply the needs of a comparatively small community there were few problems to be solved. But with the growth of the world's population and the vast expansion of the fishing industry it has become increasingly necessary to deal with the development of fisheries on scientific lines. To improve fishing methods and to guard against the dangers resulting from the rapid expansion of the fisheries, numerous research stations have been set up in some twenty or more countries. At least nine international stations have also been created to deal with the many complex problems involved.

The greatest danger resulting from the expansion of the sea fisheries at the present time is that of over-fishing. The effects of over-fishing were already becoming apparent before the

First World War, when the plaice trawled up in the North Sea became gradually smaller and smaller in successive years because the larger fish were being pulled in more quickly than the small ones could grow to replace them. The respite of the war years allowed the fish population to increase enormously, with the result that in 1919 the proportion of large fish was back to what it had been at the beginning of the century. But the story repeated itself during the twenties and thirties, until the six years of the Second World War once again gave the fish a breathing space and allowed the stock to recover. We are now seeing a declining curve for the third time in two generations, and without the dubious dispensation of yet a third world war the problem will again reach serious proportions.

At various times during the last thirty years suggestions were made to close various areas to fishing for specified periods to give the stock time to recuperate. Unfortunately in most cases a misguided emphasis on short-term self-interest prevented agreement, but at last it seems that a more co-operative spirit is beginning to prevail. One of the most important methods of preventing over-fishing is to use nets of sufficiently wide mesh to allow the small and commercially valueless fish to escape. After much heated argument even those who feared they might lose a certain amount of immediate profit were compelled to see the sense of this argument, and international agreement was reached. Another method of tackling the problem is to restock the off-shore waters with larvae produced in a number of scientifically controlled coastal hatcheries. The possibility of farming sea fish in this way has been seriously studied in recent years and some important experiments have already been made, especially with plaice, at the Fisheries Laboratory at Lowestoft and elsewhere.[68] But such efforts are only a beginning, and much more drastic action will have to be taken before the future of the sea fisheries is assured.

The main products of the British fisheries are cod, haddock, hake, whiting and plaice among demersal fishes, and herring among pelagic fishes. There is also a small but flourishing shell-fish industry, dealing both with true molluscs such as oysters, mussels and whelks, and crustacean 'shellfish' such as lobsters and crabs. The fisheries of the United States, like those of Britain, produce vast numbers of cod, haddock and herring;

there is also an exceptionally well-developed shellfish industry. The Japanese fisheries have gone from strength to strength since the war, and now account for between 15 and 18% of the world's total fish production. In spite of a marked decline in the catches of herring and pilchard, the anchovy harvest has increased by 40% in five years, and there has likewise been an increase in the catches of salmon, mackerel, pike and whales. The decreasing catches of herring in Japanese waters, as elsewhere, can probably be attributed to a progressive exhaustion of resources and thus forms part of the world over-fishing problem.

Apart from direct fishing for food there are several fisheries which are concerned principally with the by-products of the animals caught, or with their use for industrial and commercial purposes. These include particularly the sponge and pearl fisheries, and the hunting of marine mammals such as whales and seals and marine reptiles such as turtles. Sponges, as we have seen earlier, are not aquatic plants as some people still believe, but a primitive phylum of marine* invertebrates. About seven or eight species are of commercial importance, and these are found mainly in the comparatively warm waters of the Mediterranean and the Gulf of Mexico. Sponges can be trawled, but this method has the disadvantage of tearing both young and mature individuals from the sea bed, thus depleting the fishing grounds. The customary method of sponge fishing is therefore still by the descent of naked divers or, less frequently, by divers using the conventional heavy diving suit.

The Mediterranean sponge fishery is traditionally, and almost exclusively, Greek. Its centre is in the Dodecanese, especially the island of Kalymnos, where there is a huge receiving, sorting and processing centre from which sponges are dispatched all over the world. The finest commercial sponges come from the coasts of Libya and Egypt, where they are fished from anything between 50 yards and several miles off shore according to the depth of the water. The sponges are found attached to the sea bottom between 5 and 55 fathoms down, but those at the lower levels are of course not accessible to skin divers without special equipment.

There are still a number of Greek divers in the Mediterranean who operate from a small boat as a single family team,

* Only about 200 of the world's 20,000 species of sponges live in fresh water.

but the fishery is now mostly in the hands of large organizations which operate with a number of boats working from a parent ship. The comparatively recent development of the mask and cannister apparatus to supplement the resources of the lungs has done much to increase the efficiency of those who cannot afford heavy diving equipment. The diver descends to the sponge bed and tears as many of the animals as he can from their anchorage with his bare hands; a knife is never used, as this damages the sponge. The sponges remain alive until brought on board the ship, where their outer skin, or ectosome, is peeled off and the milky coating of their skeletons removed under pressure in a special machine. The soft parts must be removed at once in this way or they congeal on the skeleton and the sponge is spoiled. The skeletons are then strung from the masts to dry in the sun until the ship returns to the processing factory. The last stage is to pass the sponge through successive baths of weak sulphuric acid, permanganate of potash, and other chemicals until it is sufficiently disinfected, softened and bleached to tempt the customer at the chemist's shop.*

The pearl fisheries are another way in which man has learnt to exploit one of the creatures of the sea for his own gain. Pearls, as everyone knows, are produced in the bodies of oysters, and rank in value with the small group of precious metals and stones that includes gold, platinum, rubies, emeralds, sapphires and diamonds. From the earliest times they have been used for physical adornment, and were particularly prized by the Romans, who were prepared to pay vast sums for exceptionally fine specimens.

The means by which pearls are formed has for long been a matter for speculation. The ancient Hindus believed that they were caused by the action of the sun's rays on dewdrops that fell in the opened shell of the oyster. Another ancient theory was that they were the result of the action of lightning. In more recent times the explanations have become more sophisticated, but are still controversial. The most likely is that they are due to a reaction by certain cells in the animal to an intrusive substance or organism. In an attempt to seal off the foreign body the oyster coats it with a pearly substance similar to the nacre,

* I am indebted to much of this information on sponge fishing and processing to Mr Gregory Theodorou, the well-known London merchant.

or 'mother of pearl', which forms the inner lining of its shell. The pearl is then gradually built up by the addition of successive layers to the central intrusive nucleus.

The various kinds of pearl-bearing oysters are quite different from the edible oysters, and are in fact more closely allied to the common mussel. The best-known species is *Pteria margaritifera*, which measures some three inches across and is the source of the world's finest pearls. A larger species is *Pteria maxima*, which may measure a foot across and weigh up to twelve pounds; but the pearls of this oyster are less lustrous than those of its smaller relation and its principal value lies in the mother of pearl of its shell. Although now somewhat unfashionable, this has been widely used in the past in the manufacture of *objets d'art* and as an inlay for furniture.

Pearl fisheries are found in many parts of the world, and fine specimens are produced in the waters bordering such widely separated places as Tahiti, Borneo, California, Venezuela, New Guinea and Mexico. The most famous of all the fisheries lies in the Persian Gulf, which is the world source of the finest so-called 'oriental' pearls from *Pteria margaritifera*. Between May and September several hundred Arab dhows work the oyster beds of the Bahrein archipelago. A few divers are now beginning to avail themselves of a mask and cannister for prolonged descents, but the majority still dive only with nose-clips, leather sheaths to protect their fingers and toes from the sharp shells, and a bag round their necks to collect the oysters wrenched from the ocean floor. The beds lie between 10 and 15 fathoms below the surface and the average length of each dive is about $1\frac{1}{2}$ minutes. The diver is carried down by a weight attached to a rope, and he can be rapidly pulled to the surface by a second rope in case of emergency. The work is extremely exhausting, and about thirty dives constitutes a day's work for the average diver.

Whaling is one of the oldest methods of exploiting the sea, and porpoises, pilot whales, killer whales and possibly other species may have been actively hunted by Stone Age man.[69] In historic times the pursuit of the whale was pioneered by the Indians, Eskimos, Japanese and Norsemen, while right whales were being systematically hunted by the Basques in the Bay of Biscay well before the twelfth century A.D. In these early days whaling was an extremely hazardous occupation, for the animal was followed in small boats and the harpoons had to be driven in by hand. Nowadays the harpoon, with an explosive charge mounted in its nose, is fired from a gun mounted on the deck of a large ship, and much of the old thrill has gone.

The reader interested in the history and techniques of whaling is referred to the recent book by Budker listed in the bibliography. Here I shall only have space to mention a few of the products which whales provide. Apart from meat (and most of us had the doubtful privilege of sampling whale steaks during the war), the main products of the whale are oil, ambergris, bone flour, meat meal, and whalebone, or baleen. Originally in great demand as a fuel for lamps, whale oil is now mainly used in the manufacture of soap, and certain kinds of margarine. The oil of the sperm whale is of particular value as a lubricant, and a waxy substance in the head, known as spermacetti, is in demand for medical purposes and in the manufacture of cosmetics. Ambergris is a concretion which may be extracted from the intestine of the dead whale, but is also found floating in the sea or cast up on the shore. It is extremely valuable, and is used as a fixative for high-quality perfumes. The whalebone of the whalebone whales (see Chapter 16) was formerly one of the main products of the industry and fetched as much as £2,250 a ton. Apart from its use in the manufacture of fishing rods, brushes and frames for portmanteaux, it once provided the indispensable stiffening in women's corsets and brassières. It has now been largely replaced by light steel and plastics for these purposes, and its value has therefore declined.

The seal is another marine mammal of great value to man both for its blubber and its hide. The most important commercial species are the fur-seals, which provide the hides for the manufacture of high-quality sealskin coats, jackets, and caps, and trimmings for women's dresses. Although sealing is practised in a number of regions the world centre of the industry is the North Pacific, particularly the Pribylov and Commander Islands in the Behring Sea.

After much indiscriminate sealing in the nineteenth century, which led to a catastrophic depletion of stocks, the industry has now settled down to a more balanced policy under scientific control. Today the hunting of seals in the open sea is forbidden by law, and killing is restricted to the period when the animals come ashore to breed. Fortunately the habits of the seal on land make selective killing a fairly easy matter. The young males, or bachelor seals, usually haul out to rest and sleep on beaches near to, but distinct from, the breeding beaches where the old bulls congregate with their harems. Here the bachelors are surrounded by the sealers, and driven inland in parties two or three thousand strong to the killing grounds. The big droves are then broken up into small units, or 'pods', between thirty and forty strong, and the three-year-old bulls killed with clubs while the rest are allowed to escape. It is a cold-blooded business, but at least this selective method of killing has called a halt to the decline in the world's population of fur-seals which once threatened the animals' existence.

Another marine animal that has been much exploited for its fur is the sea-otter. The intensive pursuit of the animal for this purpose began some two hundred years ago, but long before this it had been hunted by the Chinese and west coast American Indians. Soon the sea-otter was brought to the verge of extinction, and the slaughter has only been stopped in comparatively recent times by the introduction of strict protective legislation. The fur is extremely beautiful, with a fine, soft undercoat about $\frac{3}{4}$ inch long with a sparse overlay of long guard hairs; white or silvery near the roots, it darkens progressively towards the outer tips. A good sea-otter pelt is one of the most valuable commodities in the world, and has been known to fetch up to two or three pounds per square inch.[70]

Among other sea mammals the polar bear is not without a certain commercial importance. The larger pelts are in much demand by American business men as rugs or wall hangings, and many fetch up to three or four hundred pounds. The Eskimos, more practically, use them as bed coverings. They also regard the meat of the animal as a valuable food, and make necklaces from its teeth and claws.

The only marine reptiles to be exploited on a large scale for human use are the turtles. Two genera have been particularly persecuted: the hawksbills (*Eretmochelys*) and the green turtles (*Chelonia*), both inhabiting the Atlantic, Pacific and Indian Oceans. The former is the source of the valuable 'tortoise-shell' of commerce (incidentally tortoises, which are land animals, do not produce tortoise-shell); the latter the meat which is turned into the much-prized turtle soup. The hawksbills are normally caught when the females come ashore to breed, and the practice, once widely followed, of taking them before they had laid their eggs led to a serious reduction in their numbers. In spite of the fact that the best shell comes from the oldest turtles, it is to be feared that young breeding females are still sometimes taken by irresponsible individuals. Green turtles are often captured under water in a device known as a bullen. This consists of a net attached to a heavy ring which is dropped over the turtle as it is taking its meal of eel-grass on the ocean floor. The turtle rises in alarm and becomes entangled in the net, when it can be quickly hauled to the surface.

One remarkable method of capturing turtles still practised in some areas takes advantage of the behaviour of another marine animal, the sucking-fish, or remora. This creature, as its name suggests, is equipped with a powerful sucker with which it fastens itself to the bodies of other animals, particularly sharks; by this means it is carried around from place to place and can share the prey captured by its host. The natives of the Torres Straits and Mozambique tie a light line to the tail of a captured remora and throw it in the direction of a turtle. The remora then firmly attaches itself to the underside of the turtle's shell. It will rather have its body torn in half than let go its grip, so if the turtle is a small one it can be hauled into the boat by the line. If, on the other hand, a large turtle has been seized, a native dives down and secures it with a rope.

Man's exploitation of marine life is not necessarily limited to the comparatively large creatures of the benthos and nekton. In recent years some interesting experiments have been made with plankton as human food. Professor Sir Alister Hardy has found that the planktonic organism *Euchaeta* can be made into a table delicacy of the highest order by lightly boiling it in sea water, frying it in butter, and serving it on toast. He has also used *Calanus* in the preparation of an appetizing shrimp paste. Experiments have shown that another use for plankton could be in the preparation of protein-rich meals for poultry and other livestock. But unfortunately the amount of water that has to be filtered to procure a worth-while yield is so enormous that it seems impractical to follow this up on a commercial basis. As Hardy remarks, plankton may help to supplement the diet of shipwrecked mariners, and may become an ingredient in certain luxury foods, but it is unlikely ever to be harvested on any large scale for the benefit of man.[71]

So far we have dealt only with the exploitation of marine animals, but we should remember that certain marine plants, particularly seaweeds, also produce valuable commodities. Several species, such as *Chondrus crispus* and *Porphyra laciniata* can be eaten boiled with vinegar, but the main commercial value of seaweeds is in the chemicals that can be extracted from them. Thus the wrack that is swept up on beaches in Scotland and elsewhere can be burnt in kilns to produce iodine, bromine and potash. Seaweeds also produce alginic acid, which is used to thicken blancmanges and custards; if collected in heaps and allowed to rot, they make a useful manure, containing up to 1% of nitrogen and some potash.

To conclude this chapter let us briefly consider a few of the commodities that can be obtained from sea water itself. The most obvious of these, of course, is salt. For many hundreds of years men have extracted salt from the sea by allowing it to evaporate in special pans under the sun's rays. The Romans, the Greeks, and the ancient Egyptians all obtained salt by this means, and solar extraction still continues today on the shores of the Persian Gulf, in the Far East, and on the western seaboard of North America – anywhere, in fact, where sun and wind are strong enough to produce rapid evaporation.

Another substance that can be extracted from the sea is magnesium. It has been calculated that every cubic mile of sea water contains some 4 million tons of magnesium, and part of this can now be isolated by a direct extraction process. The rapid production of aircraft in the United States during the Second World War was partly due to increased supplies of magnesium obtained from sea water. Magnesium is also used to make such wartime products as incendiary bombs, star shells and tracer bullets, while in time of peace it plays a part in the manufacture of printing ink, toothpastes and certain medicines. Perhaps the oddest use for sea water is that announced in *The Times* of December 11th 1959. It was there stated that a joint Israel-American company had been formed to turn sea water

25a–d Four great pioneers of oceanography: Edward Forbes
(*top left*); Matthew Fontaine Maury (*top right*); Alexander
Agassiz (*bottom left*); and Sir John Murray (*bottom right*)

26a The famous research ship H.M.S. *Challenger*

26b The U.S. Navy's bathyscaph *Trieste*

27*a* Pilot whales stranded on a sandy bar

27*b* Pilot whales travelling at speed off the
South American coast (*below*).

28*a* The south sea whale fishery in the last century

28*b* Processing a fin whale at Grytviken, South Georgia

29a Baleen, the characteristic 'whalebone' of the Mysticeti

29b Foetus of a blue whale

30*a* Deep sea trawling: hauling in the nets

30*b* The harvest of the sea

31a A French fishing boat, mainly used for catching
sardines and tunny in the Bay of Biscay

31b Flare-fishing in Tonga

32a 'The Hollow of the Deep-sea Wave off Kanagawa'. A Japanese colour print by Hokusai (1760–1849) in the Oriental Print Room of the British Museum

32b 'Ships in a Storm', by W. Van de Velde

into fresh water for irrigation and drinking purposes. This scheme, if successful, would provide arid areas of the Middle East with fresh water as cheap as, or cheaper than, in the United States.

The beds of ancient seas can be exploited for human use just as satisfactorily as the modern ocean itself. In the past, as we have seen (Chapter 3), the dispositions of land and sea were very different from what they are now, and their boundaries have fluctuated throughout geological time. Where, perhaps many millions of years ago, ancient seas transgressed over the land and then withdrew, they laid down chemicals which are now available for our use. These beds of 'fossil salt water', as Rachel Carson has aptly termed them,[72] now form part of the sedimentary rock strata, and their chemical and mineral resources can be drawn upon with comparative ease. Gypsum, potassium and magnesium sulphate, borax, bromine, lithium and potassium chloride are all substances that are now extracted from marine strata of this kind.

But the most important of all the legacies of the primeval ocean is undoubtedly petroleum. Even today no one can say exactly how petroleum came to exist in the earth's crust, but it may well have originated in the decomposing bodies of marine animals and plants which became buried under the sediments of early seas. Whatever the truth of this hypothesis, it is certainly a fact that all the world's great oilfields are related to past or present oceans. The connection can be traced in North America, where vast oilfields were laid down under the seas that invaded that continent in Palaeozoic times; in the Middle East, where the famous oilfields of Saudi Arabia, Iran and Iraq once lay beneath the ancient sea known as Tethys; and even now in the lands bordering the Arctic Ocean, where seepages have suggested to scientists that more great oilfields may lie concealed. It is interesting to reflect that when we start our motor car each morning we are using a substance that is quite as surely, if less obviously, a product of the sea as the kipper we have just eaten for breakfast.

Chapter Twenty

THE SEA AND THE
SPIRIT OF MAN

SINCE the dawn of human consciousness the sea has aroused the intellectual curiosity of man; but perhaps even more remarkable has been its effect on that part of him which, for want of a better word, we term his spirit. The wonder that has been aroused by this most inaccessible and challenging of natural environments, and the varied emotional responses that the oceans and their inmates have prompted in the human heart are as much a part of the story of the sea as physical and biological facts. In this final chapter, therefore, I propose to abandon the record of intellectual enquiry and consider the influence of the sea on the human imagination.

In prehistoric times, long before the first written records, it is certain that legends and superstitions connected with the sea were part of the magical equipment of every littoral tribe, and especially of those peoples who first ventured upon the ocean's surface. The vastness and mystery of the sea, the dangers associated with its varying moods, its immense power, and even perhaps its beauty, would have greatly influenced the primitive mind. Awe, reverence, terror, and a consuming wonder: it was emotions such as these that inspired the earliest myths and legends of the sea.

Confronted with an element so powerful and mysterious one of man's first acts would have been to worship it. This he did not do directly, but in the form of personalized marine deities which were more comprehensible to his mind than an abstract, all-pervading spirit. These deities were undoubtedly worshipped in Stone Age times, as their counterparts are by primitive tribes today, but we do not gain a clear idea of their nature until the growth of the first settled civilizations. In ancient Babylon there was already a famous sea god named Oannes, human in shape but wearing a fish's head as a cap. At a later stage he became associated with another Babylonian sea god named Ea, or Hea, 'the deity of the abyss'. This god was half man and half fish, and had temples dedicated to him at Ur and other Mesopotamian cities. There were sea goddesses too, the best known being the glamorous Atargatis, who was shaped like the typical mermaid of tradition. Another famous sea goddess was the eastern Aphrodite, forerunner of the Greek goddess of love and beauty, and the Roman Venus, who, it is alleged, sprang directly from the ocean's foam.

The ancient Egyptians, as we have seen, had a fear and loathing of the sea, and therefore had no deities restricted entirely to that element. But their great moon goddess Isis, wife and sister of Osiris, was also patroness of navigation, and when her cult was borrowed by the Romans her feast day on March 5th became the chief festival of navigators. In contrast to the Egyptians, the Phoenicians had a wide range of sea deities. Some of these resembled the sea gods and goddesses of ancient Babylon in being half human and half fish, while others, known as the Cabiri, had their carved images placed as figureheads on ships.[73]

The most famous sea gods of antiquity were those of the Greek pantheon. The chief was Poseidon, corresponding to the Roman Neptune, whose home was reputed to be a golden palace in the depths of the Mediterranean. According to Herodotus,[74] he was of North African origin, but this view has been questioned by later authorities.[75] In any case he is traditionally depicted with a trident, with which he lashed the sea to fury whenever provoked. Another function of the trident was to produce rivers and, still more surprisingly, horses, by striking it on rocky cliffs. All occupations connected with the sea were under Poseidon's protection, and mariners often claimed to be directly descended from him. As ruler of the waters he was believed to be in constant dispute with the land deities over coastline problems and other matters. He was quick to anger, and if thwarted would think nothing of getting his own way by shaking his rival's territory with earthquakes. The outlines of continents and oceans were constantly being altered by these tantrums, which the god seemed unable to control.

In many works of art Poseidon is depicted alongside an altogether more glamorous and attractive personality: his wife, Amphitrite. The god is reputed to have seen her first dancing at Naxos and, with that shameless and self-confident egocentricity so characteristic of Greek divinities, he forthwith carried her off without so much as a by your leave. Perhaps as a result of these high-handed methods Amphitrite never really seems to have settled down with him. She is as often depicted riding some sea animal with detached and melancholy grace as sitting dutifully in her husband's chariot, and her connection with Poseidon in worship is entirely restricted to formal maritime affairs. On one occasion, it is alleged, she even flew from him to the furthermost ends of the ocean; but her tyrannical husband recaptured her with the aid of his own private dolphin, who was rewarded afterwards by being placed among the stars.

Poseidon and Amphitrite were both gods of the sea – that is, of Thalassa, or the Mediterranean. In classical times, as we have seen (pp. 203–4), this was regarded as being quite distinct from the ocean river which flowed around the world. The principal god of these encircling waters was Oceanus himself, who dwelt with his consort Tethys in a palace far to the westward, towards the setting sun. They were a prolific couple – or perhaps it would be more correct to say that Oceanus was a productive father; he is alleged to have sired three thousand streams and four thousand ocean nymphs, so it seems that at least some of these must have been born out of wedlock. He himself was the son of Uranus and Ge, the god and goddess respectively of heaven and earth. Following this genealogy the ocean of the Greeks must be regarded as a secondary production, not the origin of all things. But the position is reversed in Homer, where Oceanus is the father of every other phenomenon, even the gods, and can claim equal status with everyone except Zeus himself. (By now I hope the reader will have begun to understand how refreshing it is for an author to allow himself an incursion into mythology after nineteen chapters of submission to the disciplines of science.)

Around these principal gods of ocean and sea, classical mythology recognized a vast concourse of lesser divinities, as well as water nymphs and other marine personalities. To name but a few, there were the Tritons, ancestral mermans who attended Poseidon's chariot; there were the four thousand daughters of Oceanus, already mentioned, who were known as the Oceanids (and incidentally inspired an early tone poem by

Sibelius); there were the Nereids, half women, half fish, who attended the major divinities and had altars on the seashore where sacrifices were made to them; and there were such minor gods as Proteus and Nereus himself, the father of the Nereids, who ruled over the deepest waters of the abyss as the kind of benthic equivalents of the nektonic Poseidon. The list could be multiplied almost indefinitely, and the reader interested in the natural, or unnatural, history of such personages is confidently referred to the classical writers, where even the most prurient minded oceanographer will find bedside reading to his taste.

A Triton. *From Gesner* (1558), *Book* 4, *p.* 1197.

Outside the Mediterranean region gods and goddesses of the sea occurred in equal diversity, many of them being simple equivalents of the classical divinities under different names. In northern countries the difference between 'sea' and 'ocean' in the Greek sense was of course not recognized, and a single composite god normally existed in place of the classical Poseidon and Oceanus. In Scandinavia he was known as Niörd, and in Germany Nerthus. The other gods likewise had their counterparts. Thus Oegur, a benthic deity, corresponded to Proteus and Nereus, with the additional quality that he could stir up huge storms by boiling his kettle. Britain also had her sea gods, the best known being Nav, while Man-a-nan and Avaron were the Irish and Welsh sea deities respectively.[76]

In the East and among primitive tribes living near the coast sea divinities are equally popular. Even today nearly every Chinese junk has a shrine to the goddess Tien-how, who is the tutelary deity of seamen. An inscription over her image reads 'When on the wide waste of waters, fail not, O goddess, to show us thy favour', or alternatively (for the Chinese are a practical people) 'Enable us by trading to acquire wealth.'[77] In Africa, many tribes have their sea gods to whom human sacrifices were made as recently as a hundred years ago, while the Polynesians have almost as many sea gods as there are islands. A particularly famous god of the South Pacific is Vatea, 'lord of the ocean'. His anatomy shows a startling variation from the bilateral symmetry usually displayed by vertebrates, for he has one human eye, ear, hand and foot, while the corresponding organs and appendages on the other side are those of a shark.

The need to placate the gods and goddesses of the ocean, or to encourage them to perform benevolent acts, has led to many quaint and sinister practices. Sir James Frazer tells in *The Golden Bough* how the Leucadians used to hurl a criminal each year into the sea from a white cliff somewhat ironically known as Lover's Leap. According to a common interpretation of such acts, which were widely practised in classical times, they were supposed to discharge the debt owed to the sea god for permitting safe navigation. The Leucadians, however, seem to have fulfilled their obligations with a certain amount of humanity; a small flotilla of boats used to stand by the scene of the sacrifice to rescue the criminal and escort him to neighbouring territory.[78]

Less violent oblations were also made than the foregoing, such as throwing pieces of bread into the sea to placate the local deity, or smearing rocks with oatmeal and butter so that the sea might enjoy the taste, and not dash a ship to pieces. One particularly charming example of such an offering comes from Norway where it was once the custom to offer the sea deities and water sprites a cake on Christmas day. According to a popular legend a fisherman arrived on the shore with his offering one Christmas morning to find that the sea was frozen over. Being unwilling to leave his gift on the ice (perhaps for fear that one of his less scrupulous colleagues might steal it) he decided to make a hole and drop it through. But the ice was thick, and after much hard work the hole was still not big enough to receive the cake. Suddenly to his delight a tiny white hand emerged from the hole, folded the cake in two, and withdrew it. In this memorable event, it is said, originated an old Norwegian compliment to a beautiful woman: 'your hand is like a water sprite's.[79]

The fear of the sea has not only inspired the widespread use of sacrifices and oblations, but has caused people with special powers over it to be held in high esteem. Unfortunately, as Canute's experience with the element clearly proved, such powers are likely to be more imaginary than real, and those to whom they are attributed are seldom available to give a practical demonstration. The Bible is, of course, one of the main sources to which we can turn for accounts of sea miracles. The most spectacular example is the passage of the Red Sea by the Jews, and the remarkable effect of faith on meteorology, fisheries and the physical properties of sea water can be studied in the New Testament. During the first part of the Christian era a number of ambitious saints are said to have achieved results as remarkable as any reported in the Bible itself. For example, walking on the sea was a common practice, and St Scothinus habitually crossed the Irish Channel by this means. St Aidan, it is alleged, went even further and took his horses onto the sea, the waves becoming solid under their feet as they progressed.[80]

From classical times right down until the eighteenth century, and even later, one of the most famous myths of the sea was connected with the so-called 'lost continent' of Atlantis. This was first mentioned by Plato in the *Timaeus*, where certain Egyptian priests in a conversation with the Athenian lawgiver Solon, speak of a huge island in the Atlantic lying beyond the Pillars of Hercules. The legend was transmitted by Arab geographers to medieval writers, who built up an alluring picture of Atlantis as an earthly paradise lying beyond the western horizon of the sea. Attempts to find it were unsuccessful, however, and disappointed romantics were compelled to accept the rationalist identification of Atlantis with the Azores, the Canaries, or even Ireland or Scandinavia. Any serious possibility that Atlantis might really exist has now been abandoned for at least 150 years, but we have, of course, a worthy substitute for this land of heart's desire in the United States of America. Sky-scrapers, juke boxes, and high-powered automobiles for all must surely represent a more advanced standard of civilization than anything ever dreamed of by Plato, and even those who might dissent from this view must at least admit that American has not yet foundered beneath the waves.

I should like to pursue the mythological aspects of the sea at greater length, but for reasons of space I must turn now to another aspect of my subject: the legends of sea animals. These include legends of entirely mythical creatures such as mermaids, hydras, krakens, and the like (of which many nevertheless may be based on some misinterpretation of phenomena actually observed), and beliefs that have grown up about the habits and behaviour of real sea animals and about their various magical properties and powers. I have dealt with the first class at length in my book *Mermaids and Mastodons*, to which the interested reader is referred, but both the mermaid legend and the problem of the Great Sea Serpent are of such universal interest to students of the sea that I must also make a brief reference to them here.

The mermaid is the classic example of man's romantic vision of the sea. These mysterious sea maidens with their high, rounded breasts, flowing hair and seductive songs, have haunted generations of mariners in all the oceans of the world. Half woman, half fish, yet of surpassing beauty, they were enough to gladden the eye of the most jaundiced sailor, especially after a voyage of many months without the company of women. In such circumstances even the mermaid's unusual posterior anatomy would scarcely have deterred him, and there are tales of mariners who have plunged from the safety of their ships into the dark waters in the hopes of holding some imagined mermaid in their arms.

The mermaid legend, like many others, is based on a substratum of fact. It sprang from a compound of the generally accepted idea of the early sea goddesses such as Atargatis with observations of real animals that could be transformed into mermaids by the expectant attention of superstitious and love-starved seamen. What these animals were has not been definitely agreed, but it seems probable that in northern waters they were seals, and in warmer regions manatees or dugongs. In fact, as we have seen, the last two animals are generally known to zoologists either as sea-cows or as sirens. The choice

An unusual, and rather unromantic, species of mermaid with vestigial hind limbs as well as a tail. *From Gesner* (1558), *Book* 4, *p.* 522.

between the two terms is a matter for the individual zoologist, and perhaps depends on the view he takes of the female of his own species; but at least the very quality of the names suggests that the association of the animals with the mermaid legend is backed by scientific authority.

Sea serpents have already been briefly mentioned in Chapter 14 (pp. 166–70), where I described some of the real reptiles actually known to live in the sea. But apart from these scientifically recognized creatures there have been persistent reports for over two thousand years of a gigantic marine animal that appears from time to time at the surface to frighten mariners and delight the hearts of journalists working for the sensational press. A proper consideration of these reports is not possible here, and it must suffice to say that the existence of the traditional 'sea serpent' remains an open question. Many of the accounts have been disproved, and others are too irresponsible and unscientific even to be considered. But at the end a small body of evidence remains which is difficult to explain away. For example, there is the episode which took place in the

Atlantic on August 6th 1848, when a huge serpent-like animal was sighted from Her Majesty's corvette *Daedalus* and watched for fifteen minutes or more by at least seven members of the crew. At one time it was only a few yards from the ship's stern so that every detail of its head and features could be made out. Even the great anatomist Professor Sir Richard Owen was unable to give a convincing explanation of what this animal might have been. Again, there was the still more remarkable animal sighted from the yacht *Valhalla* on December 7th 1905. This creature had a long neck, small head and a sail-like frill or fin on its back; from its description, it was undoubtedly a species quite unknown to science. The authenticity of this report is increased by the fact that the yacht was on a scientific research cruise, and the two eye-witnesses were both trained zoologists.

Such reports show that the Great Sea Serpent, or the Great Unknown of the Seas as it was romantically named by the naturalist Philip Gosse, may not be simply a figment of the imagination. The appearance of the allegedly extinct coelacanth off South Africa in 1938 shows that it is never safe to be dogmatic in these matters. But at present it is safer to suspend judgement until some one has produced a clear cinematograph film of a sea serpent or, better still, caught one and installed it in a museum or zoo.

So much for the legendary or semi-legendary creatures that the human spirit has conjured from the chaos of the sea. Let us now turn to man's superstitious beliefs concerning some real marine animals whose existence is so little in doubt that they are firmly docketed in the pages of the *Nomenclator Zoologicus*.

Some of the most ancient legends relate to the behaviour of dolphins, which were regarded as humorous and kindly creatures, with a deep affection for mankind. The classical sea gods either rode on dolphins, or had a tumbling troupe of the animals in attendance, while mariners of all ages have regarded their presence near a ship as a symbol of good luck and a guarantee of a successful voyage. Dolphins were believed to be particularly partial to music, especially, according to Pliny, 'the water instrument', whatever that may have been, and to the sound of the human voice. Their own voices were less musical, and have been compared to the moaning of a man in distress, for which reason they liked to be called by the name *Simo*, an onomatapoeic representation of the sound they were supposed to make. Their affection for children was one of their most attractive traits, and on at least one occasion a dolphin was prepared to act as a kind of water taxi. In Philemon Holland's translation of Pliny's *Natural History* (1601) we read:

'In the daies of Augustus Cæsar the Emperour, there was a Dolphin entred the gulfe or poole Lucrinus, which loved wonderous well a certain boy, a poore mans sonne: who using to go every day to schoole from Baianum to Puteoli, was woont also about noone-tide to stay at the water side, and to call unto the Dolphin, *Simo*, *Simo*, and many times would give him fragments of bread, which of purpose hee ever brought with him, and by this meane allured the Dolphin to come ordinarily unto him at his call. . . . Well, in processe of time, at what houre soever of the day, this boy lured for him and called *Simo*, were the Dolphin never so close hidden in any secret and blind corner, out he would and come abroad, yea and skud amaine to this lad: and taking bread and other victuals at his hand, would gently offer him his backe to mount upon, and then downe went the sharpe pointed prickes of his finnes, which he would put up as it were within a sheath for fear of hurting the boy. Thus when he had him once on his back, he would carrie him over the broad arme of the sea as farre as Puteoli to schoole; and in like manner convey him backe againe home: and thus he continued for many yeeres together, so long as the child lived. But when the boy was falne sicke and dead, yet the Dolphin gave not over his haunt, but usually came to the woonted place, & missing the lad, seemed to be heavie and mourne again, untill for verie griefe and sorrow (as it is doubtles to be presumed) he also was found dead upon the shore.'[81]

No one who has studied dolphins in one of the American Marinelands, and has appreciated their extraordinary charm and intelligence, will blame Pliny for giving credence to a tale by which only the slightest stretch of the imagination, could almost be true.

Among other cetaceans, whales have naturally had a strong effect on the human imagination by their size and spectacular appearance alone. Olaus Magnus, the sixteenth-century

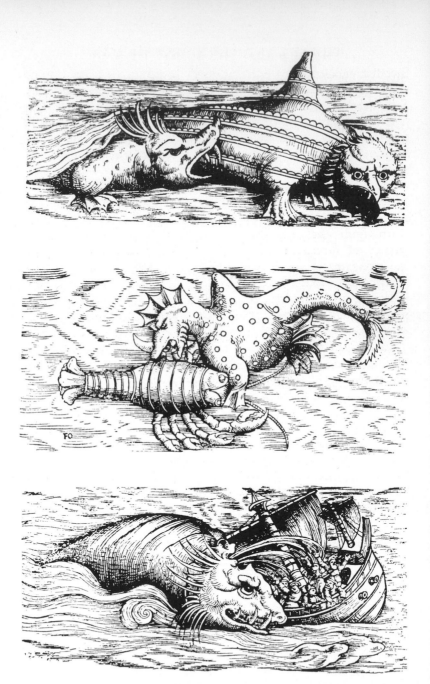

The whale of Renaissance natural history. *From Gesner* (1558), *Book* 4, *pp.* 138, 248 *and* 249.

Swedish ecclesiastic and natural historian, records some startling facts about the size of whales in his *Historia de Gentibus Septentrionalibus*, translated into English in 1658 as *A Compendious History of the Goths*. In his chapter 'Of the many kinds of Whales' he records that 'some are hairy, and of four Acres in bigness', while others have eyes 'so large, that 15 men may sit in the room of each of them, and sometimes 20 or more.'[82] Similar statements are to be found in the writings of Ulyssis Aldrovandi, director of the botanical gardens at Bologna in the sixteenth century, and other Renaissance naturalists. Both Aldrovandi and the Swiss naturalist Conrad Gesner depict whales of monstrous proportions devouring ships, spouting huge streams of water from the tops of their heads, and performing other extravagant acts.

Northern countries particularly have been the source of many odd ideas concerning whales. For example, in Iceland it was once thought that good whales always spouted high, protecting men from bad whales, which produced only mean, staccato spouts. A particularly bad whale was the red-maned whale, whose lust for human blood could only be assuaged by the destruction of seven brothers. Other whales were reputed to be shaped like oxen, or to have heather growing on their backs.[83]

One particularly charming, if inconsequential, legend, which belongs to the Micmac Indians tells how a hero named Glooskap was carried across the sea on the back of a huge female whale named Bootup. As Bootup and her passenger reached shallow water a song was heard coming from the clams as they lay under the sand. These clams were deadly enemies of Glooskap, and were appealing to the whale to throw him off her back and drown him. But fortunately Bootup did not understand the clam language and continued on her way. Shortly afterwards there was a new crisis, for Bootup ran high and dry on the beach. She appealed to Glooskap to help her, and with a hefty shove he managed to push her out into deep water. By this time, however, the whale was not unnaturally a little flustered, and to soothe her shattered nerves she asked Glooskap if he happened by chance to have an old pipe and some tobacco. This he gave her gladly, and a light into the bargain. The last he saw of her was swimming away towards the horizon, smoking happily as she went, and leaving a long low cloud on the surface of the sea.[84]

Quite apart from Jonah's classic excursion, there have been many other human ventures to the interior of whales. Thus, an Italian folk-tale recounts how a little girl was received in the belly of an enchanted whale, where she found many people and a palace surrounded by a beautiful garden. In a Russian story a whale swallows up a whole fleet and a forest grows out of its back. The North American Indians have many similar tales, including one that is remarkably like the legend of Glooskap and Bootup. In this a hero named Boin is carried to paradise in the belly of a whale, giving tobacco as the price of his passage. The spouting of the whales off the coast of Nova Scotia is still traditionally believed to be due to the smoke of Boin's tobacco.[85]

So far we have only described legends relating to sea mammals, but fish have likewise been the subject of many superstitious beliefs. Even today every fishing village is a mine of fish lore, and it seems that certain species have always been singled out for special attention. Of the better-known marine fish the hake, cod, salmon, haddock, flounder, herring, halibut and turbot, among others, all have several picturesque legends and beliefs attached to them. For instance, in Finland the white side of the flounder is believed to have been produced by the Virgin Mary laying her hand on it. In the Shetland Islands turbot and halibut are both regarded as holy fish, and even to pronounce the name of the turbot is thought by some fishermen to bring ill luck. Some fish are also thought to have therapeutic powers, and in the remoter parts of Europe as recently as the last century they were still being applied to various parts of the body as magical remedies for afflictions ranging from rabies to worms.[86]

Among less familiar fish the remora, or sucking fish, already referred to in connection with catching turtles, is reputed to have had other habits less advantageous to man. Pliny, who knew the fish by its Greek name of echeneis, wrote:

'There is a very little fish, keeping ordinarily about rockes named Echeneis. It is thought that if it settle and sticke to the Keele of a ship under water, it goeth the slower by that meanes.'[87]

These characteristics, attributed by Pliny to the remora, are simply those accepted by generations of seamen as belonging to the barnacle (if present in sufficient numbers on a ship's bottom) but other writers have made more extravagant claims on the creature's behalf. According to Phil Robinson 'antiquity believed it had the power of arresting a ship under full sail by attaching its tail-end to a rock, and its head-end to the keel of a passing vessel.'[88] This habit of the remora's is referred to by Plutarch, Oppian, Ovid, Lucan and other classical writers, and in Elizabethan times by Ben Jonson in *The Magnetic Lady*. In the ninth stanza of *Visions of the World's Vanity* Edmund Spenser described how the fish held up 'a goodly ship' in full career:

> 'All sodainely there clove unto her keele
> A little fish that men call *Remora*,
> Which stopt her course, and held her by the heele,
> That winde nor tide could move her thence away.
> Straunge thing me seemeth, that so small a thing
> Should able be so great a one to wring.'

And here again is the eighteenth-century poet Samuel Martins invoking suckers in an apt couplet:

> 'Remora! anchor of the watery main,
> The rooted barks thy finny strength proclaim.'

These glimpses of the remora at its mischievous work must conclude my examples of fish legends, for the others are far too long and numerous to quote. Turning next to marine invertebrates we find that one of the most celebrated of all sea superstitions has to do with that familiar animal the barnacle. In medieval and renaissance times it was believed by many writers that certain species of wild geese, and particularly the goose still called the barnacle goose (*Branta leucopsis*), were hatched not from eggs like other birds but from the shells of barnacles. Although this magical idea was derided by such eminent thinkers as Albertus Magnus, Pierre Belon, Roger Bacon and John Ray, among others, it also had a wide following. Ecclesiastics particularly seem to have favoured it, perhaps because by stretching a point it allowed barnacle geese to be classified as fish and eaten on Fridays. It was also supported by several reputable naturalists, and even by Sir Robert Moray, a vice-president of the Royal Society, who claimed that he had opened innumerable shells and found the bird embryos inside. [89] The explanation of the belief probably lies in the feather-like cilia that protrude from the shells of several species of barnacle. It could also have been strengthened by the fact that barnacle geese are only winter visitors to Britain, and therefore ignorant persons, not finding their nests or eggs, thought up fanciful theories to account for their presence.[90]

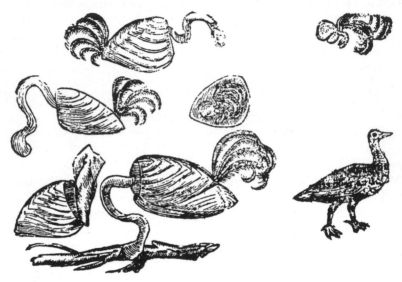

The origin of the barnacle goose. *From Aldrovandi* (1642), *p.* 544.

Sea birds, particularly albatrosses, petrels, and seagulls, have inspired men to a variety of curious beliefs. Some ancient superstitions concerning the first two were touched upon in Chapter 15, while even today a tradition persists that gulls are possessed by the spirits of dead seamen. If we are to believe a newspaper report (not always a prudent thing to do) a woman who broke the two minutes silence at the Cenotaph in 1954 by singing a song in memory of her drowned sailor son subscribed to this belief, and was much moved by the spectacle of the gulls flying overhead. I have myself heard this modern version of the theory of transmigration of souls supported in several British fishing villages, while according to that scholarly ornithologist

Edward Armstrong it is applied not only to gulls, but also sometimes to gannets.[91]

We must turn now from the legends and superstitions concerning marine animals to another aspect of the sea's influence on the human spirit. This is the inspiration it has given to those men and women who, for want of a more precise word, we know collectively as artists. And by 'artists' in this context I do not simply mean those who practise the visual arts of drawing or painting, but also novelists, poets, musicians and, in fact, all those who use formal arrangements of line, colour, words, or sounds to interpret the non-material aspects of the universe for our edification and delight.

The appeal of the sea to such specially insighted persons has been universal and profound. There are good reasons for this, for the sea offers a manifold inspiration which can be translated into the various media of expression at many different levels. First, as a physical entity, it has a dynamic potential which quite outweighs the aesthetic appeal of any purely static phenomenon, an appeal which is exceeded only by the majestic movements of the celestial bodies themselves. Second, it is a vast theatre of life, the element in which all living things originated, and the stage on which they have acted out the greater part of the evolutionary drama. Third, its close association with purely human activities as a hostile or benevolent force has caused it to be accepted as a background which will throw into the highest possible relief the more fundamental problems and conflicts of men and women. This epic quality of the sea as a background to human hopes and fears has long been recognized by those artists who have sought to elucidate the more fundamental problems with which we are all confronted. More than the solid earth, which is too close, or the stars, which are too remote, it has been for artists a kind of touchstone of reality. It has given a greater significance to those profounder aspects of human life such as love, duty, honour, courage, and pity, with which they are mainly concerned.

The effect of the sea on the human spirit as a physical entity and as a theatre of life has not been dealt with to any extent by artists (although we may hope that scientists, who seem destined to become the poets of the future, will eventually rise to this challenge); but in its third role, as a background to human activities, it has been a source of great inspiration. This has been particularly true in literature, and it would be impossible to think of some works, from the Odyssey to *Youth* and *Moby Dick* ever having existed without it. The thunder of the ocean breakers is as much a part of the creations of Homer, Conrad and Melville as it is of the seaboard itself.

On a lower level of inspiration many other admirable works exist – so many, in fact, that it would be quite impossible to name them. In this category of sea writing the author is not directly concerned with the ultimate emotions, and no voyage into prophecy is attempted; but the works usually satisfy by the appeal of the simple manly qualities: courage, humour, comradeship, loyalty, and so on. The novels of Marryat and Michael Scott and the sea poems of Kipling and Masefield may be cited as examples of the kind. Jules Verne's *Twenty Thousand Leagues under the Sea* is in a different class, but it contains some entertaining observations on scientific questions ranging from ocean currents and the birth of volcanic islands to the habits of manatees and the existence of giant squids.

The sea has always attracted painters, partly because of its immense visual beauty and partly because of the technical challenge it offers to the artist in its varying moods. Painters such as Turner and Van de Velde (Plate 32*b*) have specialized in seascapes, and have succeeded admirably in capturing the patterns created by cloud, wind and wave. Eastern artists have also been seduced by the beauty of the sea, but usually impart to it the decorative quality so characteristic of their style. Thus, the tempestuous sea depicted in the Japanese print by Hokusai reproduced on Plate 32*a* is as pleasingly stylized and unfrightening as a wooden dragon in a pantomime.

Sea animals have inspired both artists and illustrators, and the old natural histories are full of quaint drawings of real and imaginary creatures. In the other visual arts both primitive and civilized peoples have carved models of sea animals, or made vases and other objects in the shape of fish. Decorative sea creatures such as dolphins and sea-horses (not to mention mermaids) make numerous appearances in the work of goldsmiths and silversmiths, potters, engravers, and other craftsmen, and are a reliable standby for jaded interior decorators and designers of plastic curtains for bathrooms. The reader will need no further examples to underline the important part the sea and its inhabitants have played in giving pleasure to the human eye.

The impact of the sea on music has been less obvious than on literature or the visual arts, but it has nevertheless been a powerful one. Music is the most abstract of the arts, and the interplay of harmony and melody in the dynamic evolution of a great symphony has a beauty as subtle, sensual and majestic as the movement of the sea itself. Yet, as in the sea, the disciplines of form and law lie behind the external manifestation, and are in fact essential to the effect. Thus in a sense the emotions produced by the sea and by great music are the same, and this may be the reason why direct representations of the sea in music are rare. The identity, or at least the parallelism, is so apparent that it becomes pointless to represent one in terms of the other. Nevertheless musical works directly based on the inspiration of the sea exist, such as Vaughan Williams's *Sea Symphony*, Debussy's *La Mer* and *Sirènes*, and Mendelssohn's overture *The Hebrides*, to name only a few obvious examples. And it is strange how effective a musical interpretation, conscious or unconscious, of sea sounds can sometimes be: for example, the clarinet theme which Elgar borrowed from Mendelssohn in the thirteenth *Enigma* variation, and which immediately brings before us a vision of a great liner on a calm, glittering sea; the picture of Sinbad's doomed ship in the first and fourth movements of Rimsky-Korsakov's *Scheherezade*; and the two mighty breakers that thunder up the shore towards the close of Mahler's First Symphony.

And here, in the sounds of great music, where the influence of the sea on the spirit of man perhaps reaches its ultimate limit, we reach also the end of our theme. I began this book by imagining a traveller from the outer universe approaching our planet and seeing the complex pattern of the oceans spread across the face of the world. Since then the reader and I have made a long voyage together, tracing the evolution of this great natural phenomenon through time, examining some of the physical principles by which it is governed, and looking at some of the strange animals and plants that depend on it for their existence. We came at last to the influence it has had upon ourselves – our own history and our own souls. We saw how our ancestors, in their growing consciousness of themselves and the world around them, first became aware of the sea, conquering their terror of its vast impersonality by the creation of strange and powerful gods; we watched them venture for the first time upon its surface and gradually spread across the waters to the furthermost ends of the earth. We saw how the lure of material gain was slowly supplemented by the quest for knowledge as an end in itself, and how fear gave place first to curiosity and then to a new awe as science revealed more and more of the wonders of the all-encompassing ocean. And in the end we considered how men were moved by this wonder and channelled it to create new means of artistic expression.

If our space traveller had been able to land on earth and join us in our exploration I hope he too might have felt something of the beauty and the glamour of the sea. In the world beyond the stars from which perhaps he came there may be greater wonders, and perhaps one day we also may be privileged to penetrate them. Meanwhile the most I can hope to have done in this brief Biography of the Sea is to describe some of the marvels of our own planet, which are open for all of us to study, to be moved by, and if possible to understand.

KEY TO BIBLIOGRAPHICAL
REFERENCES IN THE TEXT

1. Ommanney (1949), p. 16.
2. Lake (1952), p. 154.
3. Coker (1947), p. 78, Note 1.
4. Ommanney (1949), p. 15.
5. Coker (1947), p. 85.
6. Sverdrup, Johnson and Fleming (1942), p. 912.
7. Coker (1947), p. 85.
8. Johnstone (1923), p. 146.
9. Lake (1952), p. 199.
10. Russell, R. C. H., and Macmillan (1952), p. 32.
11. Ommanney (1949), p. 27.
12. Coker (1947), p. 142.
13. Johnson, D. W. (1919), p. 40.
14. Haldane (1954), p. 12.
15. Carrington (1956), pp. 51–6.
16. *The Observer*, London, January 20th 1957.
17. Herdman (1923), p. 160.
18. Herdman (1923), p. 161.
19. Hardy (1956), p. 248.
20. Russell, F. S., and Yonge (1928), p. 117.
21. Murray and Hjort (1912), p. 68.
22. Darwin (1839), pp. 190–1.
23. Coker (1947), p. 211.
24. Hardy (1956), p. 172.
25. Sverdrup, Johnson and Fleming (1942), p. 805.
26. Ekman (1953), pp. 286–310; p. 373.
27. Yonge (1949), p. 110.
28. Ommanney (1949), p. 106.
29. MacGinitie and MacGinitie (1949), pp. 293–9.
30. Schmidt (1957).
31. Norman (1931), pp. 174–5.
32. MacGinitie and MacGinitie (1949), p. 414.
33. McCoy (1883), pp. 20–1.
34. Norman and Fraser (1937), p. 31.
35. Romer (1941), p. 40.
36. Norman (1931), pp. 220–1.
37. Marshall (1954), p. 221.
38. Carrington (1957b), p. 85.
39. Harvey (1952), p. 513.
40. Dunbar (1952), pp. 123–6.
41. Pope (1956), p. 109.
42. Bruun, Greve, Mielche and Spärck (1956), p. 90.
43. Bruun, Greve, Mielche and Spärck (1956), pp. 90–1.

44. Carrington (1957a), pp. 20–46.
45. Gilliard (1958), p. 50.
46. Linnaeus (1806), Vol. 1, p. 38.
47. Darling (1950), p. 4.
48. Cahalane (1947), p. 206.
49. Cahalane (1947), p. 207.
50. Norman and Fraser (1937), p. xxi.
51. Matthews (1952), pp. 313–17.
52. Norman and Fraser (1937), p. 293.
53. Dakin (1934), pp. 140–5.
54. Colbert (1955), p. 303.
55. Humboldt (1836), Vol. 3, p. 91.
56. Herodotus (1910), Vol. 1, pp. 302–3.
57. Encyc. Brit., 13th ed., Vol. 3, p. 63 and Avienus (1922).
58. Johnstone (1926), p. 68.
59. Murray (1895), p. 46.
60. Cook (1777), Vol. 1, pp. 267–8.
61. Cook (1777), Vol. 1, pp. 294–6.
62. Sykes (1950), p. 179.
63. Murray (1895), p. 36.
64. Mas'ūdī (1841), pp. 294–5.
65. Coker (1947), p. 19.
66. Herdman (1923), p. 14.
67. Dietz (1958), and *Sunday Times*, London, January 24th 1960.
68. Shelbourne (1959).
69. Clark (1947), p. 98.
70. Jennison (1927), p. 117.
71. Hardy (1956), p. 164.
72. Carson (1951), p. 194.
73. Bassett (1892), pp. 57–8.
74. Herodotus (1910), Vol. 1, p. 139.
75. Bassett (1892), p. 58.
76. Bassett (1892), pp. 67–9.
77. Jones (1880), pp. 44–5.
78. Frazer (1933), p. 579.
79. Jones (1880), pp. 62–3.
80. Jones (1880), p. 56.
81. Plinius Secundus (1601), Vol. 1, p. 239.
82. Magnus (1658), p. 226.
83. Bassett (1892), p. 234.
84. Leland (1884), pp. 31–5.
85. Bassett (1892), p. 238.
86. Bassett (1892), p. 252.
87. Plinius Secundus (1601), Vol. 1, p. 248.
88. Robinson (1883), p. 25.
89. Moray (1678).
90. Lee (1884a), pp. 315–17.
91. Armstrong (1958), pp. 211–13.

SELECTED BIBLIOGRAPHY

Note. The literature of the sea is so vast that to compile a fully representative bibliography would be impossible in the space available. The following list therefore represents only those books and papers actually consulted by the author in preparing his manuscript. It is nevertheless hoped that all the standard works on the sea in the English language are included, together with a number of other contributions that may be less familiar. Excellent bibliographies of a more specialized kind are contained in Hardy (1956), Hardy (1959), Popovici and Angelescu (1954), and Sverdrup, Johnson and Fleming (1942). *A Bibliography of Fishes*, published between 1916 and 1923 by the American Museum of Natural History is also indispensable.

R.C.

ADAMS, WILLIAM HENRY DAVENPORT. See LANDRIN, ARMAND (1875).

ALDROVANDI, ULYSSIS (1638a): De Cetis. Bologna.

ALDROVANDI, ULYSSIS (1638b): De Piscibus. Bologna.

ALDROVANDI, ULYSSIS (1642): Animalibus Exanguibus. Bologna.

ALEXANDER, WILFRID BACKHOUSE (1954): Birds of the Ocean. Putnam, New York.

ALLEN, EDGAR JOHNSON. See FOWLER, GEORGE HERBERT.

ANGELESCU, VICTOR. See POPOVICI, ZAHARIA.

APPLEBY, R. M. (1959): The origins of the ichthyosaurs. *New Scientist*, Vol. 6, No. 153, pp. 758–60. London.

ARBER, AGNES (1920): Water Plants: a study of aquatic angiosperms. University Press, Cambridge.

ARISTOTLE (1862): Aristotle's History of Animals. Translated by Richard Cresswell. London.

ARMSTRONG, EDWARD ALLWORTHY (1958): The Folklore of Birds: an enquiry into the origin and distribution of some magico-religious traditions. The New Naturalist. Collins, London.

ARMSTRONG, EDWARD FRANKLAND, and MIALL, LAURENCE MACKENZIE (1946): Raw Materials from the Sea. Constructive Publications, Leicester.

AVIENUS, RUFIUS FESTUS (1922): Avieni Ora Maritima. Edited by A. Schulten. Barcelona and Berlin.

BASSETT, FLETCHER STEWART (1892): Sea Phantoms: or legends and superstititions of the sea and of sailors in all lands and at all times. Chicago.

BEAGLEHOLE, JOHN CAWTE (1947): The Exploration of the Pacific. Second edition. Black, London.

BEEBE, CHARLES WILLIAM (1926): The Arcturus Adventure: an account of the New York Zoological Society's first oceanographic expedition. G. P. Putnam's Sons (The Knickerbocker Press), New York and London.

BEEBE, CHARLES WILLIAM (1928): Galápagos: world's end. Published under the auspices of the New York Zoological Society. G. P. Putnam's Sons; New York and London.

BEEBE, CHARLES WILLIAM (1934): Half Mile Down. Published under the auspices of the New York Zoological Society. Harcourt, Brace and Co., New York; John Lane, The Bodley Head, London.

BELLAIRS, ANGUS D'ALBINI (1957): Reptiles. Hutchinson's University Library. Hutchinson, London.

BELON, PIERRE (1551): L'Histoire Naturelle des Estranges Poissons Marins, avec la vraie peincture et description du daulphin, & de plusieurs autres de son espece. Paris.

BELON, PIERRE (1555): La Nature et Diversité des Poissons, avec leurs pourtraicts, representez au plus pres du naturel. Paris.

BIGELOW, HENRY BRYANT (1931): Oceanography: its scope, problems and economic importance. Houghton Mifflin Company, Boston: Chapman and Hall, London.

BOULENGER, EDWARD GEORGE (1935): A Natural History of the Seas. Duckworth, London.

BOULENGER, GEORGE ALBERT. See LYDEKKER, RICHARD.

BOWDER, K. F. (1959): The oceanic tides. *New Scientist*, Vol. 6, No. 146, pp. 348–51. London.

BROOKS, CHARLES ERNEST PELHAM (1925): The Evolution of Climate. Second edition. London.

BROOKS, CHARLES ERNEST PELHAM (1949): Climate Through the Ages: a study of the climatic factors and their variations. Revised edition. Benn, London.

BRUUN, ANTON FREDERIK (1956): The abyssal fauna: its ecology, distribution and origin. *Nature*, Vol. 177, No. 4520, pp. 1105–8. London.

BRUUN, ANTON FREDERIK; GREVE, SVEND BERNHARD VILHELM JOHANNES; MIELCHE, HAKON; and SPÄRCK, HAKON RAGNAR GISIKO (1956): The Galathea Deep Sea Expedition, 1950–1952. Translated from the Danish by Reginald Spink. Allen and Unwin, London.

BUCHSBAUM, RALPH (1948): Animals without Backbones: an introduction to the invertebrates. Revised edition. University of Chicago Press, Chicago.

BUDKER, PAUL (1958): Whales and Whaling. Harrap, London.

BUDKER, PAUL. See also LE DANOIS, EDOUARD JULES (1957).

BULJAN, MILJENKO (1955): Deep submarine volcanisms and the chemistry of the ocean. *Bulletin Volcanologique*, Series 2, Vol. 17, pp. 41–56. Naples.

BUNBURY, EDWARD HERBERT (1879): A History of Ancient Geography among the Greeks and Romans, from the earliest ages till the fall of the Roman Empire. 2 vols. London.

CAHALANE, VICTOR H. (1947): Mammals of North America. Macmillan Company, New York.

CAMOENS, LUIS VAZ DE (1952): The Lusiads. Translated by William C. Atkinson. Penguin Books, Harmondsworth.

CARR, ARCHIE (1952): Handbook of Turtles: the turtles of the United States, Canada and Baja California. Comstock Publishing Associates, Cornell University Press, Ithaca.

SELECTED BIBLIOGRAPHY

CARRINGTON, RICHARD (1956): A Guide to Earth History. Chatto and Windus, London.

CARRINGTON, RICHARD (1957a): Mermaids and Mastodons: a book of natural and unnatural history. Chatto and Windus, London.

CARRINGTON, RICHARD (1957b): East from Tunis: a record of travels on the northern coast of Africa. Chatto and Windus, London.

CARSON, RACHEL LOUISE (1951): The Sea Around Us. Staples Press, London.

CARSON, RACHEL LOUISE (1955): The Edge of the Sea. Staples Press, London.

CHADWICK, HERBERT CLIFTON. See JOHNSTONE, JAMES.

CHALLENGER REPORTS. See REPORT ON THE SCIENTIFIC RESULTS OF THE EXPLORING VOYAGE OF H.M.S. CHALLENGER, etc.

CHAPMAN, VALENTINE (1950): Seaweeds and their Uses. Methuen, London.

CLARK, GRAHAME (1947): Whales as an economic factor in prehistoric Europe. *Antiquity*, Vol. 21, pp. 84–104. Gloucester.

COKER, ROBERT IRWIN (1947): This Great and Wide Sea. University of North Carolina Press, Chapel Hill.

COLBERT, EDWIN HARRIS (1955): Evolution of the Vertebrates: a history of the backboned animals through time. Wiley, New York; Chapman and Hall, London.

CONTINENTAL DRIFT. See SYMPOSIUM ON THE THEORY OF CONTINENTAL DRIFT.

CONWAY, MONCURE DANIEL (1879): Demonology and Devil-Lore. 2 vols. Chatto and Windus, London.

COOK, JAMES (1777): A Voyage towards the South Pole, and Round the World, performed in His Majesty's ships the *Resolution* and *Adventure* in the years 1772, 1773, 1774 and 1775. 2 vols. London.

CORNISH, VAUGHAN (1934): Ocean Waves, and kindred geophysical phenomena. With additional notes by Harold Jeffreys. University Press, Cambridge.

CORREA, GASPAR (1869): The Three Voyages of Vasco da Gama, and his Vice-royalty. Translated from the Portuguese, with notes and an introduction, by the Hon. Henry E. J. Stanley. Hakluyt Society, London.

COX, ROLAND A. (1959): The chemistry of seawater. *New Scientist*, Vol. 6, No. 149, pp. 518–21. London.

CUNNINGHAM, JOSEPH THOMAS. See LYDEKKER, RICHARD.

CURRIE, RONALD (1953): Food resources of the sea: methods of production and harvesting. *Times Science Review*, No. 10, pp. 10–13. London.

CURRIE, RONALD (1959): Organic production in the sea. *New Scientist*, Vol. 6, No. 150, pp. 584–7. London.

DAKIN, WILLIAM JOHN (1934): Whalemen Adventurers: the story of whaling in Australian waters and other southern seas related thereto, from the days of sails to modern times. Angus and Robertson, Sydney.

DALY, REGINALD ALDWORTH (1926): Our Mobile Earth. Charles Scribner's Sons, New York and London.

DALY, REGINALD ALDWORTH (1934): The Changing World of the Ice Age. Yale University Press, New Haven; Humphrey Milford, London.

DALY, REGINALD ALDWORTH (1942): The Floor of the Ocean: new light on old mysteries. The Page Barbour lectures at the University of Virginia, 1941. University of North Carolina Press, Chapel Hill.

DANOIS, EDOUARD JULES LE. See LE DANOIS.

DARBYSHIRE, JACK (1959): Recent research on sea waves. *New Scientist*, Vol. 6, No. 137, pp. 26-9. London.

DARLING, FRANK FRASER (1950): Seals of the World. *Zoo Life*, Vol. 5, pp. 2-7. London.

DARWIN, CHARLES ROBERT (1839): Journal of Researches into the Geology and Natural History of the Various Countries visited by H.M.S. Beagle, under the command of Captain Fitzroy R.N. from 1832 to 1836. London.

DEACON, GEORGE EDWARD RAVEN (1957): Deep ocean currents. *Discovery*, Vol. 18, No. 9, pp. 386-7. Norwich.

DEACON, GEORGE EDWARD RAVEN (1958a): British Studies in Oceanography. *Impulse*, No. 4, March 1958, pp. 30-3. London.

DEACON, GEORGE EDWARD RAVEN (1958b): The use of oceanography. *Impact of Science on Society*, Vol. 9, No. 2, pp. 79-92. United Nations Educational Scientific and Cultural Organization, Paris.

DEACON, GEORGE EDWARD RAVEN (1958c): Ocean waves. *Endeavour*, Vol. 17, No. 67, pp. 134-9. London.

DEACON, GEORGE EDWARD RAVEN (1959): The increasing influence of marine science. *New Scientist*, Vol. 6, No. 143, pp. 178-9. London.

DECKERT, KURT. See GÜNTHER, KLAUS.

DIETZ, ROBERT SINCLAIR (1957): Deep sea diving by bathyscaph. *Times Science Review*, No. 26, pp. 5-6. London.

DIETZ, ROBERT SINCLAIR (1958): Deep sea research in the bathyscaph 'Trieste'. *New Scientist*, Vol. 3, No. 74, pp. 30-2. London.

DISCOVERY REPORTS, issued by the National Institute of Oceanography (1929-). University Press, Cambridge. (Work in progress.)

DIXON, JOSEPH SCATTERWOOD. See GRINNELL, JOSEPH.

DOUKAN, GILBERT (1957): The World Beneath the Waves. Translated from the French by A. and R. M. Case. Allen and Unwin, London.

DUNBAR, CARL OWEN (1952): Historical Geology. Wiley, New York; Chapman and Hall, London.

DU TOIT, ALEXANDER LOGIE (1957): Our Wandering Continents: an hypothesis of continental drifting. Oliver and Boyd, Edinburgh and London.

EKMAN, SVEN PETRUS (1953): Zoogeography of the Sea. Translated from the Swedish by Elizabeth Palmer. Sidgwick and Jackson. London.

ENCYLOPAEDIA BRITANNICA, 13th Edition (1926): Otto Krümmel and Henry Robert Mill: Ocean and oceanography. Vol. 19, pp. 967-87. Encyclopaedia Britannica Company, London and New York.

FISHER, JAMES MAXWELL MCCONNELL (1956): Adventure of the Sea. Rathbone Books, London.

FISHER, JAMES MAXWELL MCCONNELL, and LOCKLEY, RONALD

MATHIAS (1954): Sea-Birds: an introduction to the natural history of the sea-birds of the North Atlantic. The New Naturalist. Collins, London.

FLATTELY, FREDERIC WILLIAM, and WALTON, CHARLES LIVESEY (1946): The Biology of the Sea-Shore. Second impression. Sidgwick and Jackson, London.

FLEMING, RICHARD HOWELL. See SVERDRUP, HARALD ULRIK.

FORBES, EDWARD (1841): A History of British Starfishes, and other animals of the class Echinodermata. London.

FORBES, EDWARD (1859): The Natural History of the European Seas. Edited and continued by R. Godwin-Austen. Outlines of the Natural History of Europe. London.

FOWLER, GEORGE HERBERT, and ALLEN, EDGAR JOHNSON, Editors (1928): Science of the Sea: an elementary handbook of practical oceanography for travellers, sailors, and yachtsmen. Originally edited by G. H. Fowler; second edition edited by E. J. Allen. Clarendon Press, Oxford.

FRASER, FRANCIS CHARLES (1955): 'Whale: whaling' in Chambers's Encyclopaedia, Vol. 14, p. 557. Newnes, London.

FRASER, FREDERICK CHARLES. See also NORMAN, JOHN ROXBOROUGH.

FRAZER, JAMES GEORGE (1933): The Golden Bough: a study in magic and religion. Abridged edition. Macmillan, London.

FURON, RAYMOND (1941): La Paléogéographie: essai sur l'évolution des continents et des océans. Payot, Paris.

GALATHEA DEEP SEA EXPEDITION. See BRUUN, GREVE, MIELCHE and SPÄRCK (1956).

GAMOW, GEORGE (1941): Biography of the Earth: its past, present and future. Viking Press, New York.

GARDINER, JOHN STANLEY (1931): Coral Reefs and Atolls: being a course of lectures delivered at the Lowell Institute at Boston, February, 1930. Macmillan, London.

GEIKIE, ARCHIBALD. See WILSON, GEORGE.

GESNER, CONRAD (1558): Historiae Animalium: Liber IIII, qui est de piscium & aquatilium animantium natura. Zurich.

GIBSON-HILL, CARL ALEXANDER (1947): British Sea Birds. Witherby, London.

GIBSON-HILL, CARL ALEXANDER (1949): Birds of the Coast. Witherby, London.

GILLIARD, ERNEST THOMAS (1958): Living Birds of the World. Hamish Hamilton, London.

GODWIN-AUSTEN, ROBERT ALFRED CLOYNE. See FORBES, EDWARD (1859).

GOSSE, PHILIP HENRY (1846): The Ocean. Society for Promoting Christian Knowledge. London.

GREELY, ADOLPHUS WASHINGTON (1910): Handbook of Polar Discoveries. Fourth edition, revised and enlarged. London, and Cambridge, Mass.

GREELY, ADOLPHUS WASHINGTON (1929): The Polar Regions in the Twentieth Century: their discovery and industrial evolution. Harrap, London.

SELECTED BIBLIOGRAPHY

GREENWAY, JAMES COWAN (1958): Extinct and Vanishing Birds of the World. Special publication No. 13. American Committee for International Wild Life Protection, New York.

GREVE, SVEND BERNHARD VILHELM JOHANNES. See BRUUN, ANTON FREDERIK.

GRINNELL, JOSEPH; DIXON, JOSEPH SCATTERWOOD; and LINSDALE, JEAN MYRON (1937): Fur-bearing Mammals of California: their natural history, systematic status, and relations to man. 2 vols. University of California Press, Berkeley.

GUILLEMARD, FRANCIS HENRY HILL. See MARKHAM, CLEMENTS ROBERT (1921).

GÜNTHER, KLAUS, and DECKERT, KURT (1956): Creatures of the Deep Sea. Translated from the German by E. W. Dickes. Allen and Unwin, London.

HALDANE, JOHN BURDON SANDERSON (1954): The origins of life. *New Biology*, Vol. 16, pp. 12–27. Penguin Books, London.

HARDY, ALISTER CLAVERING (1956): The Open Sea: its natural history. [Part 1:] The World of Plankton. The New Naturalist. Collins, London.

HARDY, ALISTER CLAVERING (1959): The Open Sea: its natural history. Part 2: Fish and Fisheries; with chapters on whales, turtles and animals of the sea shore. The New Naturalist. Collins, London.

HARVEY, EDMUND NEWTON (1920): The Nature of Animal Light. J. B. Lippincott Company, Philadelphia and London.

HARVEY, EDMUND NEWTON (1940): Living Light. University Press, Princeton.

HARVEY, EDMUND NEWTON (1952): Bioluminescence. Academic Press, New York.

HARVEY, HILDEBRAND WOLFE (1928): Biological Chemistry and Physics of Sea Water. University Press, Cambridge.

HARVEY, HILDEBRAND WOLFE (1945): Recent Advances in the Chemistry and Biology of Sea Water. University Press, Cambridge.

HARVEY, HILDEBRAND WOLFE (1957): The Chemistry and Fertility of Sea Waters. Second edition. University Press, Cambridge.

HASS, HANS (1952): Diving to Adventure: harpoon and camera under the sea. Jarrolds, London.

HAWKINS, THOMAS (1840): The Book of the Great Sea-Dragons: Ichthyosauri and Plesiosauri . . . , extinct monsters of the ancient earth. London.

HAYES, JAMES GORDON (1932): Conquest of the South Pole: Antarctic exploration, 1906–1931. Butterworth, London.

HEDGPETH, JOEL WALKER (1957): Treatise on Marine Ecology and Palaeoecology: Vol. 1: Ecology. Memoir 67. Geological Society of America, New York.

HEILMANN, GERHARD (1926): The Origin of Birds. Witherby, London.

HEPBURN, IAN (1954): Flowers of the Seaside. The Country Naturalist. Collins, London.

HERDMAN, WILLIAM ABBOTT (1923): Founders of Oceanography and their work: an introduction to the science of the sea. Arnold, London.

SELECTED BIBLIOGRAPHY

HERODOTUS (1910): The History of Herodotus. Translated by George Rawlinson, 2 vols. Everyman Library. Dent, London.

HILL, CARL ALEXANDER GIBSON. See GIBSON-HILL.

HOBBS, WILLIAM HERBERT (1921): Earth Evolution and its Facial Expression. Macmillan Company, New York.

HOUOT, GEORGES S. (1958): Four years of diving to the bottom of the sea. *National Geographic Magazine*, Vol. 113, pp. 715–31. Washington.

HUMBOLDT, FRIEDRICH HEINRICH ALEXANDER VON (1836–9): Examen Critique de l'Histoire de la Géographie du Nouveau Continent et de Progrès de l'Astronomie Nautique au 15me et 16me Siècles. 5 vols. Paris.

HUSSEY, RUSSELL CLAUDIUS (1947): Historical Geology: the geologic history of North America. Second edition. McGraw-Hill, New York and London.

HUTCHINSON, HENRY NEVILLE (1910): Extinct Monsters and Creatures of Other Days: a popular account of some of the larger forms of ancient animal life. New and enlarged edition. London.

INGLE, ROBERT M., and SMITH, F. G. WALTON (1949): Sea Turtles and the Turtle Industry of the West Indies, Florida and the Gulf of Mexico, with annotated bibliography. A special publication of the Marine Laboratory, University of Miami, in cooperation with the Caribbean Research Council. University Press, Miami.

IRVING, WASHINGTON (1850): The Life and Voyages of Christopher Columbus; together with the voyages of his companions. 2 vols. London.

JAYNE, KINGSLEY GARLAND (1910): Vasco da Gama and his Successors, 1460–1580. London.

JENNISON, GEORGE (1927): Natural History: Animals: an illustrated Who's Who of the animal world. Black, London.

JOHNSON, DOUGLAS WILSON (1919): Shore Processes and Shoreline Development. Wiley, New York; Chapman and Hall, London.

JOHNSON, MARTIN WIGGO. See SVERDRUP, HARALD ULRIK.

JOHNSTONE, JAMES (1911): Life in the Sea. Cambridge Manuals of Science and Literature. University Press, Cambridge.

JOHNSTONE, JAMES (1923): An Introduction to Oceanography, with special reference to geography and geophysics. Second edition, revised. University Press, Liverpool; Hodder and Stoughton, London.

JOHNSTONE, JAMES (1926): A Study of the Oceans. Arnold, London.

JOHNSTONE, JAMES; SCOTT, ANDREW; and CHADWICK, HERBERT CLIFTON (1924): The Marine Plankton, with special reference to investigations made at Port Erin, Isle of Man, during 1907–1914: a handbook for students and amateur workers. University Press, Liverpool; Hodder and Stoughton, London.

JOLEAUD, LÉONCE (1939): Atlas de Paléobiogéographie. Lechavalier, Paris.

JONES, J. W. (1959): The spawning behaviour of the salmon. *New Scientist*, Vol. 6, No. 141, pp. 122–3. London.

JONES, WILLIAM (1880): Credulities Past and Present, including the sea and seamen, miners' amulets and talismans, *etc.* Chatto and Windus, London. Chapter 1, pp. 1–119: The Sea and Seamen.

SELECTED BIBLIOGRAPHY

KELLOGG, REMINGTON (1940): Whales, Giants of the Sea. *National Geographic Magazine*, Vol. 77, pp. 35–90. National Geographic Society, Washington.

KIRWAN, LAURENCE PATRICK: (1959): The White Road: a survey of polar exploration. Hollis and Carter, London.

KRÜMMEL, OTTO. See ENCYCLOPAEDIA BRITANNICA, 13th Edition (1926).

KUENEN, PHILIP HENRY (1950): Marine Geology. Wiley, New York; Chapman and Hall, London.

KUENEN, PHILIP HENRY (1955): Realms of Water: some aspects of its cycle in nature. Cleaver-Hume Press, London.

KYLE, HARRY M. (1926): The Biology of Fishes. Sidgwick and Jackson, London.

LADD, HARRY STEPHEN (1957): Treatise on Marine Ecology and Palaeoecology: Vol. 2; Palaeoecology. Memoir 67, Geological Society of America, New York.

LAKE, PHILIP (1952): Physical Geography. Third edition. Revised and enlarged by J. A. Steers, G. Manley and W. V. Lewis. University Press, Cambridge.

LAMBRECHT, KÁLMAN (1933): Handbuch der Palaeornithologie. Berlin.

LANDRIN, ARMAND (1867): Les Monstres Marins. Paris.

LANDRIN, ARMAND (1875): The Monsters of the Deep; and Curiosities of Ocean Life. A book of anecdotes, traditions and legends. Founded on Landrin (1867) with additions by W.H.D.A. (i.e. W. H. Davenport Adams). London.

LAUGHTON, A. S. (1957): Exploring the deep ocean floor. *Journal of the Royal Society of Arts*, Vol. 106, pp. 39–56. London.

LAUGHTON, A. S. (1959): The sea floor. *New Scientist*, Vol. 6, No. 144, pp. 237–40. London.

LE DANOIS, EDOUARD JULES (1957): Fishes of the World. With the collaboration of Jacques Millot, Théodore Monod, and Paul Budker. Harrap, London.

LE DANOIS, EDOUARD JULES (1958): Marine Life of Coastal Waters. Translated and adapted by N. A. Holme. Harrap, London.

LEE, HENRY (1884a): Sea Fables Explained. The Fisheries Exhibition Literature, Vol. 3, pp. 178–317. London.

LEE, HENRY (1884b): Sea Monsters Unmasked. The Fisheries Exhibition Literature, Vol. 3, pp. 318–440. London.

LEGENDRE, RENÉ (1948): La Découverte des Mers. Presses Universitaires de France, Paris.

LEITHÄUSER, JOACHIM GUSTAVE (1956): Worlds Beyond the Horizon Translated from the German by Hugh Merrick. Allen and Unwin, London.

LELAND, CHARLES GODFREY (1884): The Algonquin Legends of New England, or myths and folklore of the Micmac, Passamaquoddy, and Penobscot tribes. Boston.

LEMON, JAMES MCWILLIAMS. See TRESSLER, DONALD KITELEY.

LEWIS, WILLIAM VAUGHAN. See LAKE, PHILIP.

SELECTED BIBLIOGRAPHY

LINNAEUS, CARL (1806): A General System of Nature through the three grand kingdoms of animals, vegetables, and minerals, systematically divided into their several classes, orders, genera, species and varieties, with their habitations, manners, economy, structure and peculiarities. Translated by William Turton. 7 vols. London.

LINSDALE, JEAN MYRON. See GRINNELL, JOSEPH.

LOCKLEY, RONALD MATHIAS. See FISHER, JAMES MAXWELL MC-CONNELL.

LYDEKKER, RICHARD; CUNNINGHAM, JOSEPH THOMAS; BOULENGER, GEORGE ALBERT; and THOMSON, JOHN ARTHUR (1912): Reptiles, Amphibia, Fishes, and Lower Chordata. London.

MCCOY, FREDERICK (1883): Natural History of Victoria: Prodromus of the Zoology of Victoria, etc. Decade 8. Melbourne.

MACGINITIE, GEORGE EBER, and MACGINITIE, NETTIE (1949): Natural History of Marine Animals. McGraw-Hill, New York, London and Toronto.

MACMILLAN, D. H. See RUSSELL, ROBERT CHRISTOPHER HAMLYN.

MAGNUS, OLAUS (1555): Historia de Gentibus Septentrionalibus, earumque diversis statibus, conditionibus, moribus, etc. Rome.

MAGNUS, OLAUS (1658): A Compendious History of the Goths, Swedes, and Vandals, and other Northern Nations. London. (Being an English translation of the 'Historia de Gentibus Septentrionalibus, etc.')

MANLEY, GORDON. See LAKE, PHILIP.

MARKHAM, CLEMENTS ROBERT (1892): Life of Christopher Columbus. The World's Great Explorers. London.

MARKHAM, CLEMENTS ROBERT (1912): The Conquest of New Granada. London.

MARKHAM, CLEMENTS ROBERT (1921): The Lands of Silence. A history of Arctic and Antarctic exploration. Completed and revised by F. H. H. Guillemard. University Press, Cambridge.

MARR, JAMES WILLIAM SLESSOR (1956): Euphausia superba and the Antarctic surface currents: an advance note on the distribution of the whale food. Norwegian Whaling Gazette (Norsk Hvalfangst-Tidende), Vol. 45, No. 3, pp. 127–34. Sandefjord.

MARSHALL, NORMAN BERTRAM (1954): Aspects of Deep Sea Biology. Hutchinson's Scientific and Technical Publications, London.

MAS'ŪDĪ (1841): El Mas'ūdī's Historical Encyclopaedia entitled: 'Meadows of Gold and Mines of Gems'. Translated by Aloys Sprenger. Vol. 1. London.

MAS'ŪDĪ (1861–77): Les Prairies d'Or. Texte et traduction par C. Barbier de Meynard et Pavet de Courteille. 9 vols. Paris.

MATTHEWS, LEONARD HARRISON (1929): The natural history of the elephant seal, with notes on other seals found at South Georgia. Discovery Reports, Vol. 1, pp. 235–55. University Press, Cambridge.

MATTHEWS, LEONARD HARRISON (1952): British Mammals. The New Naturalist. Collins, London. Ch. 11, pp. 305–40: Whales in general. Ch. 12, pp. 341–63: Whales of British seas.

MAURY, MATTHEW FONTAINE (1860): The Physical Geography of the

Sea, and its Meteorology. Being a reconstruction and enlargement of the eighth edition of Maury's 'The Physical Geography of the Sea' (1855). London.

MEEK, ALEXANDER (1916): The Migrations of Fish. Arnold, London.

MEUNIER, STANISLAS (1917): Histoire Géologique de la Mer. Bibliothèque de Philosophie Scientifique. Paris.

MIALL, LAURENCE MACKENZIE. See ARMSTRONG, EDWARD FRANKLAND.

MIELCHE, HAKON. See BRUUN, ANTON FREDERIK.

MILL, HENRY ROBERT. See ENCYCLOPAEDIA BRITANNICA, 13th Edition (1926).

MILL, HUGH ROBERT (1903): The Siege of the South Pole: the story of Antarctic exploration. London.

MILLOT, JACQUES. See LE DANOIS, EDOUARD JULES (1957).

MONOD, THÉODORE. See LE DANOIS, EDOUARD JULES (1957).

MOORE, HILARY BROOKE (1958): Marine Ecology. Wiley, New York.

MORAY, ROBERT (1678): On barnacles. *Philosophical Transactions of the Royal Society*, Vol. 12, No. 137, p. 925. London.

MURPHY, ROBERT CUSHMAN (1936): The Oceanic Birds of South America. 2 vols. American Museum of Natural History, New York.

MURRAY, JOHN (1895): A Summary of the Scientific Results obtained at the Sounding, Dredging and Trawling Stations of H.M.S. Challenger. Vol. 1, pp. 1–106E: Historical introduction [to the science of oceanography]. London. Part of the first Supplementary Volume to the 'Report on the Scientific Results of the Exploring Voyage of H.M.S. Challenger,' etc.' (*q.v.*).

MURRAY, JOHN, and HJORT, JOHAN (1912): The Depths of the Ocean: a general account of the modern science of oceanography based largely on the scientific researches of the Norwegian steamer Michael Sars in the North Atlantic. London.

NORMAN, JOHN ROXBOROUGH (1931): A History of Fishes. Benn, London.

NORMAN, JOHN ROXBOROUGH, and FRASER, FRANCIS CHARLES (1937): Giant Fishes, Whales and Dolphins. Putnam, London.

OAKLEY, KENNETH PAGE, and MUIR-WOOD, HELEN MARGUERITE (1959): The Succession of Life through Geological Time. Fourth and revised edition. Trustees of the British Museum, London.

OLIVER, JAMES ARTHUR (1955): The Natural History of North American Amphibians and Reptiles. D. Van Nostrand Company; Princeton, Toronto, London, and New York.

OMMANNEY, FRANCIS DOWNES (1949): The Ocean. Home University Library. Geoffrey Cumberlege, Oxford University Press; London, New York, and Toronto.

ORKIN, P. A. (1959): The eel and the salmon: modern views on fish migration. *Times Science Review*, No. 32, pp. 10–12. London.

ORTELIUS, ABRAHAM (1570): Theatrum Orbis Terrarum. Antwerp.

PARKER, GEORGE HOWARD (1948): Animal Colour Changes and their Neurohumours: a survey of investigations, 1910–1943. University Press, Cambridge.

SELECTED BIBLIOGRAPHY

PETTERSSON, HANS (1954): The Ocean Floor. Being the Silliman lectures for 1952. Yale University Press, New Haven; Geoffrey Cumberlege, Oxford University Press, London.

PICCARD, AUGUSTE (1956): In Balloon and Bathyscaphe. Translated by Christina Stead. Cassell, London.

PIGAFETTA, ANTONIO (1874): The First Voyage Round the World, by Magellan: translated from the accounts of Pigafetta, and other contemporary writers. Accompanied by original documents, with notes and an introduction by Lord Stanley of Alderley. Hakluyt Society, London, 1874.

PINCHER, CHAPMAN (1948): A Study of Fishes. Jenkins, London.

PLINIUS SECUNDUS, CAIUS (1601): The Historie of the World, commonly called the Naturall Historie of C. Plinius Secundus. Translated into English by Philemon Holland. 2 vols. London.

POPE, CLIFFORD HILLHOUSE (1956): The Reptile World: a natural history of the snakes, lizards, turtles and crocodilians. Knopf, New York; Routledge and Kegan Paul, London.

POPOVICI, ZAHARIA, and ANGELESCU, VICTOR (1954): La Economia del Mar, y sus relaciones con la alimentacion de la humanidad. 2 vols. Y. Casa Editora, Buenos Aires.

RAY, CARLETON, and CIAMPI, ELGIN (1958): The Underwater Guide to Marine Life. Kaye, London.

RAYMOND, PERCY E. (1935): Pre-Cambrian life. *Bulletin of the Geological Society of America*, Vol. 46, pp. 375–92. New York.

REID, HUGH ALISTAIR (1959): Sea-snake bite and poisoning. *The Practitioner*, Vol. 183, pp. 530–4. London.

RENAULT, GILBERT (1959): The Caravels of Christ. Translated by Richmond Hill. Allen and Unwin, London.

REPORT ON THE SCIENTIFIC RESULTS OF THE EXPLORING VOYAGE OF H.M.S. CHALLENGER DURING THE YEARS 1873–76 (1880–95): Prepared under the superintendence of . . . C. Wyville Thomson and John Murray. Vols. 1–32; with an additional unnumbered volume on Deep-Sea Deposits, and two Supplementary Volumes containing a Summary of the Scientific Results. London.

ROBINSON, PHIL (1883): Fishes of Fancy. The Fisheries Exhibition Literature, Vol. 3, pp. 1–97. London.

ROMER, ALFRED SHERWOOD (1941): Man and the Vertebrates. University of Chicago Press, Chicago.

ROMER, ALFRED SHERWOOD (1945): Vertebrate Paleontology. Second edition. University of Chicago Press, Chicago.

ROMER, ALFRED SHERWOOD (1959): The Vertebrate Story. University of Chicago Press, Chicago.

RONDELET, GUILLAUME (1554–55): Libri de Piscibus Marinis, in quibus veræ piscium effigies expressæ sunt, *etc.* 2 parts. Lyon. (The title of Part 2 reads Universæ Aquatilium Historiæ pars altera, *etc.*)

ROSE, JOHN HOLLAND (1935): Man and the Sea: stages in maritime and human progress. Heffer, Cambridge.

RUSSELL, FREDERICK STRATTEN, and YONGE, CHARLES MAURICE

(1928): The Seas: our knowledge of life in the sea and how it is gained. Warne; London and New York.

RUSSELL, ROBERT CHRISTOPHER HAMLYN, and MACMILLAN, D. H. (1952): Waves and Tides. Hutchinson's Scientific and Technical Publications; London, New York, Melbourne, Sidney and Cape Town.

SCAMMON, CHARLES MELVILLE (1874): The Marine Mammals of the North-western Coast of North America, described and illustrated; together with an account of the American Whale-Fishery. San Francisco and New York.

SCHEFFER, VICTOR BLANCHARD (1958): Seals, Sea Lions and Walruses: a review of the Pinnipedia. Stanford University Press, Stanford; Oxford University Press, London.

SCHMIDT, KARL PATTERSON (1957): Amphibians. Part of annotated bibliography to Hedgpeth (1957). Memoir 67, Vol. 1, pp. 1211–12. Geological Society of America, New York.

SCOTT, ANDREW. See JOHNSTONE, JAMES.

SÉBILLOT, PAUL (1901): Le Folk-lore des Pêcheurs. Being Vol. 43 of Les Littératures Populaires de Toutes les Nations. Paris.

SENECA, LUCIUS ANNAEUS (1614): Of Naturall Questions. Printed between pp. 755 and 903 of The Workes of L. A. Seneca both Morall and Naturall. Translated by T. Lodge. London.

SHELBOURNE, J. E. (1959): Could sea fish be farmed? *New Scientist*, Vol. 5, No. 118, pp. 413–15. London.

SHEPARD, FRANCIS PARKER (1948): Submarine Geology. Harper, New York.

SIMPSON, GEORGE GAYLORD (1953): Life of the Past: an introduction to paleontology. Yale University Press, New Haven.

SINGER, CHARLES JOSEPH (1950): A History of Biology: a general introduction to the study of living things. Revised edition. Schuman, New York.

SMITH, F. G. WALTON. See INGLE, ROBERT M.

SPÄRCK, HAKON RAGNAR GISIKO. See BRUUN, ANTON FREDERIK.

STANLEY, HENRY EDWARD JOHN (LORD STANLEY OF ALDERLEY). See CORREA, GASPAR, and PIGAFETTA, ANTONIO.

STEERS, JAMES ALFRED (1932): The Unstable Earth: some recent views in geomorphology. Methuen, London.

STEERS, JAMES ALFRED (1953): The Sea Coast. The New Naturalist. Collins, London.

STEERS, JAMES ALFRED. See also LAKE, PHILIP.

STRABO (1917–32): The Geography of Strabo, with an English translation by Horace Leonard Jones. Based in part on the unfinished version of J. R. S. Sterrett. 8 vols. Loeb Classical Library. Heinemann, London; G. P. Putnam's Sons, New York.

SVERDRUP, HARALD ULRIK (1945): Oceanography for Meteorologists. Allen and Unwin, London.

SVERDRUP, HARALD ULRIK; JOHNSON, MARTIN WIGGO; and FLEMING, RICHARD HOWELL (1942): The Oceans: their physics, chemistry and general biology. Prentice-Hall, New York.

SWALLOW, J. C. (1957): Eight thousand feet under the sea. *Listener*, Vol. 57, No. 1473, pp. 997–8. London.

SWINTON, WILLIAM ELGIN (1954): Fossil Amphibians and Reptiles. Trustees of the British Museum (Natural History), London.

SWINTON, WILLIAM ELGIN (1958): Fossil Birds. Trustees of the British Museum, London.

SYKES, PERCY MOLESWORTH (1950): A History of Exploration from the earliest times to the present day. Third edition, with appendix. Routledge and Kegan Paul, London. (The date 1949 shown on the verso of the title page is incorrect.)

SYMPOSIUM ON THE THEORY OF CONTINENTAL DRIFT (1951): *The Advancement of Science*, Vol. 8, No. 29, pp. 67–88. British Association for the Advancement of Science. London.

TCHERNAVIN, VLADIMIR VYACHESLAVOVICH (1953): The Feeding Mechanisms of a Deep Sea Fish, *Chauliodus sloani* Schnieder. Trustees of the British Museum, London.

THOMSON, CHARLES WYVILLE (1873): The Depths of the Sea: an account of the general results of the dredging cruises of H.M.SS. *Porcupine* and *Lightning* during the Summers of 1868, 1869, and 1870, under the scientific direction of Dr Carpenter, F.R.S., J. Gwyn Jeffreys, F.R.S., and Dr Wyville Thomson, F.R.S. London.

THOMSON, CHARLES WYVILLE (1877): The Voyage of the 'Challenger': The Atlantic: a preliminary account of the general results of the exploring voyage of H.M.S. 'Challenger' during the year 1873 and the early part of the year 1876. 2 vols. London.

THOMSON, JOHN ARTHUR. See LYDEKKER, RICHARD.

THORNBURY, WILLIAM DAVID (1954): Principles of Geomorphology. Wiley, New York; Chapman and Hall, London.

TOIT, ALEXANDER LOGIE DU. See DU TOIT.

TRESSLER, DONALD KITELEY, and LEMON, JAMES MCWILLIAMS (1951): Marine Products of Commerce. Reinhold Publishing Corporation, New York.

TUCKER, M. J. (1959): The study of sea waves. *New Scientist*, Vol. 6, No. 145, pp. 275–7. London.

VERNE, JULES (1876): Twenty Thousand Leagues under the Sea. Complete edition. Translated by H. Frith. 2 vols. London.

VEVERS, HENRY GWYNNE (1954): The British Seashore. Routledge and Kegan Paul, London.

WALFORD, LIONEL A. (1958): Living Resources of the Sea: opportunities for research and expansion. A Conservation Foundation Study. The Ronald Press Company, New York.

WALLACE, ALFRED RUSSEL (1892): Island Life; or, the phenomena and causes of insular faunas and floras, including a revision and attempted solution of the problem of geological climates. Second and revised edition. London.

WALTON, CHARLES LIVESEY. See FLATTELY, FREDERIC WILLIAM.

WEGENER, ALFRED LOTHAR (1924): The Origin of Continents and

Oceans. Translated from the third German edition by J. G. A. Skerl. Methuen, London.

WILLISTON, SAMUEL WENDELL (1914): Water Reptiles of the Past and Present. Chicago.

WILSON, GEORGE, and GEIKIE, ARCHIBALD (1861): Memoir of Edward Forbes. Cambridge and London.

WOOD, HERBERT JOHN (1951): Exploration and Discovery. Hutchinson's University Library. Hutchinson, London.

WORCESTER, PHILIP GEORGE (1939): A Textbook of Geomorphology. Chapman and Hall, London.

YONGE, CHARLES MAURICE (1949): The Sea Shore. The New Naturalist. Collins, London.

YONGE, CHARLES MAURICE. See also RUSSELL, FREDERICK STRATTEN.

ZOBELL, CLAUDE E. (1953): The occurrence of bacteria in the deep sea and their significance for animal life. Abstract from the colloquium 'On the Distribution and Origin of the Deep Sea Bottom Fauna', International Union of Biological Sciences, Series B, No. 16, pp. 20–6, 1954. Secrétariat général de l'U.I.S.B., Naples.

ZWEIG, STEFAN (1948): Magellan: pioneer of the Pacific. Second edition. Translated by Eden and Cedar Paul. Cassell, London.

INDEX

Entries in heavy type refer to figures, maps and charts in the text

277

INDEX